Break Their Haughty Power
Joe Murphy in the Heyday of the Wobblies

A biographical novel
by Eugene Nelson

ism

press

San Francisco

Library of Congress Cataloging–in–Publication Data

Nelson, Eugene, date.
    Break their haughty power : Joe Murphy in the heyday of the
Wobblies : a biographical novel / by Eugene Nelson.
        p.   cm.
    Includes index.
    ISBN 0-910383-31-6 (pbk. : alk. paper) : $16.00
    1. Murphy, Joe, 1905-1987—Fiction. 2. Industrial Workers of the
World—History—Fiction. 3. Labor movement—United States—
History—Fiction. I. Title.
PS3564.E4616.B74   1993
813'.54—dc20   93-16106
                                                                CIP

ism press, inc.
P.O. Box 12447
San Francisco, CA 94112

*Cover oil painting
by Liz Penniman*

TABLE OF CONTENTS

LIST OF PHOTOS

Joe Murphy at age 27,
in the spring of 1933

PREFACE

I met Joe Murphy in 1970; a fellow Wobbly introduced me. Joe lived in Occidental, about seventy miles north of San Francisco, with his wife Doris. I was living in Forestville, about twelve miles away. For the next ten years I visited him about once a week. He told me many stories of his fantastic career traveling all over the world as an organizer and fundraiser for the IWW, meeting Big Bill Haywood, Helen Keller, Vincent St. John, Upton Sinclair, Emma Goldman, Sylvia Beach, Eugene Debs and Charlie Chaplin. And of taking part in some of the most important strikes in the dramatic history of the IWW. And of his later career as head of the Laborers Union in San Francisco and later that union's representative for eleven western states.

In the mid–1970s Joe asked me to record his life story. I later taped around four hours of his memoirs for the labor history archives at the University of California at Berkeley. Unfortunately I was unable to collect enough verbatim material for a full–length nonfiction book by the time Joe died at age eighty–one on May 18, 1987 (the 59th anniversary of Bill Haywood's death in Moscow).

A few months after Joe died, another friend of his, Henry Anderson, asked me to collaborate on a semi–fictional book about Joe dramatizing the outstanding events of his life as a Wobbly. Later I decided to write my own book.

The vast majority of the scenes are based upon events Joe participated in; a few are purely fictional. Joe Murphy's memory was much better than that of the average person, but not perfect. For example, he could not remember the exact year he met Helen Keller in Chicago, or the dates of some of the lesser–known events he described. But I have attempted to make these events as historically accurate as possible.

Here it is.

Eugene Nelson, Oakland, March 21, 1992

ACKNOWLEDGMENTS

Next to the late Joe Murphy, who spent hundreds of hours telling me of his experiences in the IWW, I am indebted, first of all, to Henry P. Anderson of Oakland, California. One of the chief promoters of the unionization of farmworkers in California, Henry contributed to me, gratis, valuable research material for an earlier novel of mine, *Bracero*, and sent me to see César Chávez, with whose farmworker union I worked for two years, the most satisfying years of my life. Without Henry's urging me to write this book, collaboration on its early stages, and inspiration and help with the research, the book would not have been written.

To Doris Murphy, wife and companion of a great man.

To Willa Baum, head of the Regional Oral History Office of the University of California at Berkeley, who urged me to tape-record Joe Murphy's memoirs.

To Judy Eda, for her excellent job of proofreading.

To Liz Penniman, for her enthusiastic interest in the book and her superb painting for its cover. To Marisha Swart, for her creative and painstaking work on the cover design.

To the late Herb Edwards (born Edvartsen) of Kvalösater, Norway and Seattle, Washington, whose own fine book about IWW organizing in the Northwest, *Slowly We Learn*, provided much valuable background information and inspiration.

To the following persons, for reading the manuscript and/or giving me valuable suggestions:

My daughter, Tamar Juana Nelson, RN; Jake Kenney, Charles Pusey, Carlos Cortez, Steve Lehmann, Larry Skoog, George Underwood, Barbara Atchison, and Mike Moriarty.

To Tommy Zee, for much valuable background information on the merchant marine.

To the staff of the IWW at its former headquarters in Chicago.

To Thomas Featherstone, archivist at the Walter P. Reuther Library at Wayne State University in Detroit, for his friendly help providing historical photos for reproduction. To Edward C. Weber, head of the Labadie Collection of the University Library at the University of Michigan, for providing the photo of Elizabeth Gurley Flynn. To the researchers at the Bettmann Archive in New York, who supplied several photos of historical figures and settings reproduced here. Thanks also to the *New York Times* for permission to reproduce headlines and articles from their coverage of the 1922 national railway strike; and to University Microfilms International in Ann Arbor, Michigan, for supplying photocopies of several of those articles.

And to the wonderful librarians of the public libraries in Springfield and Kansas City, Missouri; Pueblo, Colorado; the University of California at Berkeley; the library of the Historical Society of Oregon (in Portland); the Nevada State Museum and Historical Society (in Las Vegas); and the historical museum in Telluride, Colorado.

GLOSSARY

AFL—American Federation of Labor
amscray—scram
ARU—American Railway Union

balloon—bedroll, bindle
batter on the drag—to beg, panhandle
beanmaster—cook
bindle—bedroll in which a hobo wrapped his possessions
blind pig—illegal bar during Prohibition
bloke—guy
blue streak—very fast, "in a flash"
'bo—hobo
boomer—construction worker traveling from job to job
bos'n—boatswain: petty officer on a merchant ship
bozo—clown, fool
BS—bullshit
bucko mate—bully
bull—policeman
burg—town

calaboose—jail
can—jail
cat—worker engaged in a specific occupation; sabotage cat
  let the cat loose—launch sabotage
  sab cat—sabotage cat, the black cat symbolizing sabotage
Centralists—faction, popularly called the "Four Treyers," headed by farmworker union leaders Tom Doyle and Joe Fisher at the IWW convention. They favored centralized control of the IWW's constituent industrial unions.

Glossary

chinwhisker—pertaining to a farmer
coffee an'—coffee and a doughnut
coldcock—to deck someone

dehorn—bootleg whiskey of inferior quality
dehorn squad—Wobbly team that would close bars during a strike
drygulch—to ambush with intent to kill or maul
duds—clothing

El, the—elevated inner-city train (in Chicago)
EP—Emergency Program, name of faction headed by lumber union leader James Rowan at the 1924 IWW convention. They favored decentralization and autonomy for industrial unions within the IWW.
EP'er—member of the EP, or decentralist faction of the IWW

flivver—car
flop—shelter, place to sleep
foc's'le—forecastle (of a ship)
frogskin—dollar bill

galoot—silly, awkward person
gam—leg (especially a female's)
gandy dancer—person who maintains or lays railroad track
gazabo—sly person, sharpie; fellow
GEB—General Executive Board
glom the guts of a rattler—hop aboard a freight train
goon—thug
greasy spoon—cheap cafe/restaurant
gunsel—criminal armed with a gun

hasher—cook
hayrick—haystack
highball—fast
hijack—holdup; holdup man
hog, on the—broke, out of money

hoosegow—jail
hoosier—farmer or country bumpkin; incompetent person
hoosier up—to pretend innocence, act incompetent

IWW—Industrial Workers of the World, or "Wobblies"

java—coffee
Jerusalem Slim—Jesus of Nazareth, a kind of secular folk hero among Wobblies.
Jim Hill's goat—Great Northern railroad
jungle—hobos' encampment, usually near a railroad junction

kazoo—buttocks, anus

lizzie, tin—Model T or a cheap car

Mick—Irishman
muckamuck—important person, likely to be haughty
mucker—worker who shovels away debris that miners blast loose
mug—face

nose bag—lunch pail
  put on the nose bag—to eat

OBU—One Big Union, an IWW concept and goal
on the hog—broke, out of money

peckerwood—poor rural white, a term often used disparagingly in the South
pendejo—pubis; fool; coward
piecard—a labor union official who sits "on the gravy" or "on the pie," instead of doing real work to serve the rank and file.
plug–ugly—goon, thug
plutes—plutocrats, bosses
  plute press—mainstream, capitalist newspapers
prole—proletarian, wageworker

rattler—freight train

glom the guts of a rattler—hop aboard a freight train

rockpile—jail

rods—drawrods beneath a freight train

rotgut—cheap liquor

roustabout—unskilled laborer

rube—country bumpkin

sab cat—black cat, IWW symbol for sabotage

Saint, the—Vincent St. John

scab—strikebreaker

scissorbill—a selfish worker, lacking in class consciousness

scratch—secretary

shack—brakeman on a train

shyster—lawyer (often used in a friendly non-pejorative way
   when Wobblies speak of their own attorneys)

silent agitator—IWW sticker, mini-poster

singlet—man's undershirt or jersey

sinker—doughnut

skid road—district where migrants gather in a town

skypilot—preacher, especially one who urges workers to suffer
   humbly so as to earn "pie in the sky when you die"

slave market—employment agency, especially one where
   recruiters demand hefty fees/bribes from job-seekers

slum—food, grub

smilo joint—tavern selling bootleg liquor

speakeasy—illegal bar during Prohibition

stamps—IWW dues stamps, which members pasted into their
   IWW booklets to show their payment of dues

stamp up—to collect dues from (an IWW member)

stoolie—stoolpigeon, informer

tinhorn—petty gambler

tin lizzie—Model T or a cheap car

vittles—victuals, food supplies

Wob, Wobbly—IWW member

1

BILL HAYWOOD'S BOY

We stood under the bare light-bulb on the little back porch. I remember my mother's last words to me: "Your hair's so beautiful, Joe—just like a hayrick shot through with sunlight."

I was trembling. "I love you, Ma," I said. "I'll write—as soon as I get to Harper."

"Write but don't put your name on the envelope."

"I won't, Ma."

"And give my love to your brother Emmett."

"I will, Ma."

She was crying now. We were both crying. I gave her one last hug and was gone off through the darkness. "Be good to folks, Joe" —the wind flung her words after me.

I went through the shadows across the low undulating fields, threading my way among little frame houses, wary of arousing dogs, taking a different route than usual far west of town to avoid the police. Off to the east I could see a scattering of late-night lights floating off toward downtown Springfield like fireflies with insomnia. I hefted my pack and went on through the darkness, starting at every sudden shadow, feeling my pulse race.

The events of earlier in the evening were still screaming in my mind. I had been carrying dinner to my dad at the railyards. I was always wary because of the beatings I had gotten from the Catholic-baiting gangs.

This time they caught me unawares, springing out into the darkness from behind an abandoned shed.

"There he is! Let's get the dirty Mick!"

"Hey, pope-bugger!"

"Let's kill 'im this time!"

"Let's cut off his pecker!"

"Nigger–lovin' Cath'ic bas'ard!"

I had already almost reached my full six foot four at age thirteen—but they were big too. They were all over me before I could turn and run. One of them ripped open the lunch pail and smashed my dad's dinner against my face. I was too scared to speak, or even to see who they were. Probably some of the KKK kids who had been tormenting me for years. I finally wrenched loose and tried to run up a little bank, but the damp grass was slippery and I slid back down toward them.

They began beating me with their fists, all over my head and body. I squirmed loose again. I saw one of them pick up a big rock. I was terrified. I can't quite remember exactly what went through my mind or how it happened, but suddenly my pocket-knife was in my hand and its blade flipped open.

"Kill 'im, Josh!" I heard one yell. And suddenly one of them seemed to be pushed or fell against me. I heard him gasp and realized my knife had gone into his stomach. He slumped to the ground at my feet like a sack of spuds.

"Jesus," someone said.

I didn't wait to see what the others might do next. Some ambiguous force seemed to propel me off through the darkness. I was so scared I couldn't even feel my feet and legs—I just seemed to be a disembodied head and beating heart rushing into the shadows.

Now I seemed to see them again, rushing at me from behind every shadowy bush or tree. I was running hard through the low steamy woods now, for I'd heard the distant whistle of a perhaps already departing freight train back in the yards in Springfield a mile or two to the east. My bindle jostled against my back, and several times I stumbled and almost fell.

I heard the gradually approaching roar of the train now and rushed faster. I knew from experience how even the longest trains can pick up speed with amazing rapidity. I had ridden freights the summer before with a neighbor kid to work in the strawberry

harvest down in Arkansas. I knew that by the time the train
reached me it might be going fifteen, twenty miles an hour.

I fell once, picked myself up, and climbed through some bushes
up to the track bed. Now I saw the blinding glare of the engine's
light and ducked back into the shadows. I was lucky: The long line
of cars seemed to be doing only about ten per. I waited, out of
breath, praying for an empty boxcar. There should be plenty of
empties headed out to the grain harvest in Kansas.

I could barely make out the names on the sides of the cars in
the darkness: B & O, Great Northern, Rock Island Line. And I
remembered how as a little boy I had loved to sit by the tracks
reading in wonder the different names on the train cars, excited
and envious at the thought of what far part of the sprawling
continent they'd come from and were going to, burning to see
those far-off places.

Now that the light of the engine was past, I edged closer to the
track, the rhythmical clack-clack of the rolling cars deafening in
my ears. I saw what looked like an empty, started to run and
reach up—then saw faces peering out and backed off. The damn
shebang was going faster now. Another empty came along. I ran
alongside it, grabbed the bottom of the open door and pulled
myself up.

I plopped down breathless on the straw-strewn floor of the car,
my backpack flying loose. Faces peered at me in the darkness.
"You got the red ducat, Pard?"

"What?"

Bump! I was suddenly in a clump of bushes beside the tracks.
And that was the end of that ride. It all happened so fast I was
hardly aware of how it had happened. It was as if a powerful gust
of wind had ejected me from the moving boxcar with a hundred
invisible hands.

I pulled myself up out of the bushes and watched the caboose
swoosh past with an empty feeling. Then, about fifty yards down
the track, I saw my bindle come sailing out of the boxcar and roll
down into a clump of bushes. Now what kind of crazy pecker-
woods would practically kill me and then return my bindle? I
stood up creakily and rubbed my butt. Now the freight I'd hoped
would save me from jail was just a memory.

Then it struck me: Wobblies! A phrase came back to me: *the
thousand-mile picket line*. To keep non-union men out of the harvest
belt. My older brother Emmett, working in the harvest near

Harper, Kansas, had sent me the IWW papers from time to time, and I had read every word. Throwing un–class-conscious stiffs who'd work for lower wages off the freights was the only way they could get anything even near decent pay.

But that was little consolation now. I stood looking down the long long tracks that stretched deserted to the west. I knew that at any time a posse might be coming for me. I dashed back into the bushes, feeling more empty and lonely than I had ever felt in my life. Then when I saw no one coming, I edged my way slowly through the bushes, down to where my pack lay. Fortunately it wasn't damaged.

I went back into the deeper woods and sat panting, my hands and my whole body trembling. My mind was a chaotic jumble of thoughts. I hardly knew what I was thinking. Five or six different thought patterns and feelings seemed to be overlaid on top of one another in my brain, moving back and forth and repeating and interrupting one another nightmarishly. Strongest of all seemed to be my fervent hope my attacker did not die. Superimposed on this was my mother's face as I had last seen it, and then the faces of my dad and my brothers and sisters sliding back and forth on the screen of my mind as if a drunken movie projectionist was flashing a dozen different projectors off and on indiscriminately.

I had the dismals bad. I thought of the shame to myself and my family. Suddenly I saw an image of myself lying dead across the railroad tracks and felt sick at my stomach and felt an urge to throw myself across the tracks and wait for the next train to end my misery. At the same time I began to feel a wavering thrill of excitement and freedom and adventure, the fugitive thought of shooting off into the great world on my own for the first time, of joining my older brother Emmett, of getting to know more about the great and mysterious IWW.

It got cold. I took my two blankets out of my backpack and wrapped them about me. I was too keyed up and frightened to sleep. I was too sick with fear to want to eat the sandwiches my mother had put in my pack. I sat trying to calm myself, going over and over in my mind what I would do if I heard someone approaching. Every time I heard the faintest sound made by some small animal I jumped, prepared to run off through the woods. I felt in my jacket pocket the hot chili powder I'd brought along in case they sent dogs after me, and wished I'd thought to sprinkle some of it along my route farther back. Once I almost dozed off, but I jostled myself awake and forced myself to keep listening intently, praying another train would come along soon.

But a train didn't come, and the cold night seemed to go on forever. God, I thought, if dawn comes and I'm still here I'll be a goner. I wondered if I would be executed or only spend the rest of my life in prison. But dawn finally came, and the sun was a big splotch of red in the east, like a big red patch on a pair of blue overalls.

With the growing light my fear increased. I packed my blankets back into my bindle with trembling hands. Then, moving a little, I realized with a start that I could see down into a little hollow nearby among the trees where blue smoke rose from sleepy cabins. I moved my head quickly behind a bush and sat watching through its leaves.

In the faint morning breeze the smoke curled in a gauzy blue haze from chimney to chimney, as if the cabins were all connected to one another and the people in the different cabins were talking to one another like Indians by means of the smoke. As if all the people themselves were connected in one big happy family, I thought, and I wondered why the whole world couldn't be like that. Because that was the way the whole world should be, my dad had often said: one big happy family. No more squabbling and fighting, everybody working for the common good. But I knew the world was not like that, I knew it now more than ever.

The wind began to rise and the patches of smoke blew apart. Then I heard it again: the far-off whistle of a train. This time, I knew, I *had* to make it, I had to. If I didn't glom this one I was done for, for sure. Seeing no one down the tracks, I carefully began to creep closer to town through the bushes to be sure I nailed this one before it was going too fast.

Then it hove into view, puffing slowly toward me, slowly gaining speed. With a shock I saw the faces of the engineer and fireman in the big black locomotive, hoping they wouldn't see me in the bushes. It was another long one, and I saw three or four boxcars with men in them pass, then several closed cars, and then another open boxcar with men in it, and finally an empty in which I could see no one.

I rushed out of the bushes and up the bank to the gravelly roadbed, hoping no bull or brakeman was watching. I ran along beside the long car, my bindle shaking, grabbed the open door and pulled myself up. Too late, I saw several men sitting back in one end of the car. I lay panting for a moment, then sat up to face them. They didn't look such a mean lot in the dim light, and one older man in overalls had a sort of kindly face that reminded me a little of my father's.

The boxcar bumped and rattled along. "You got a moniker, son?" the older man asked. "You got a handle?"

The long train creaked along, picking up speed. Out of the side of my vision I glimpsed the last outskirts of Springfield passing by, each second taking me farther away from arrest and prison. And at the same time I realized with growing panic that the faster the train was going, the more I risked death if I was booted out again. I looked in desperation into the eyes of my interlocutor.

"Joe," I said. "Joe Murphy." I noticed that the six or eight men in their clean but ragged work clothes had a small fire going in the front end of the car.

The big man looked at me, rubbing his whiskers. "Well, Joe, I don't suppose you have a red card—a working stiff's ticket to ride this here elegant side-door Pullman?"

I felt fear rise inside me. A jolt of the train threw me against the boxcar's wall and I put out a steadying hand. "I know about the IWW," I said rapidly. "I plan to join as soon as I make a few bucks in the harvest."

Another man spoke, a small wiry guy with a scar across his forehead. "'Plan to join,'" he mimicked. "We've heard that line before, 'Bo."

I felt myself tense up, prepared to be facing forward so I could run to try to keep from falling if they threw me out.

The older man spoke again. "We don't mean to be unfriendly, Joe," he said. "But this is serious business. I'm afraid if you ain't got a red card we'll have to ask you to hit the grit, son, the next time this contraption slows down a mite."

"Look," I pleaded. "My brother's a Wobbly. My dad, Big Bill's a Wobbly," naming the most famous Wobbly of all. "You musta heard of him. I promise I'll join my first payday."

The men in the end of the car seemed to perk up. A guffaw went up.

"Big Bill!" someone chortled. "And I'm Molly Maguire. And what would this Big Bill's last name happen to be?"

I looked levelly at the eight men. "William Dudley Haywood," I managed to get out without batting an eye.

The men facing me in the jolting boxcar looked dumbfounded. Except for the older man, who seemed to have a gleam of appreciation in his eye. After a moment one of the men said: "Now wait a minute, hotshot. Big Bill's only kid was a little girl — I read all about it in *Industrial Solidarity.*"

I hung my head. "That's why I don't usually mention it," I muttered. "I'm strictly illegit. My dad met my mom in Chi just before the IWW's founding convention in 1905. I guess they weren't together long. Pop went back to Denver after that…"

"Well, he knows *somepin* about it, at least," said one of the men.

One of the others scooted closer to me. "All right, kid," he said. "If you know so much about the IWW, what's the first line of the Preamble?"

Some of the men laughed. "We've got the young know–it–all now," I heard a man at the back mutter.

I looked at their dim shadows dancing on the wall of the boxcar from the small fire. I thanked Saint John for my near photographic memory. I looked at the eight men steadily.

"'The working class and the employing class have nothing in common,'" I began. I felt a sharp stab of pride at the surprise on their faces. "'There can be no peace so long as hunger and want are found among millions of working people and the few, who make up the employing class, have all the good things of life. Between these two classes a struggle must go on until the workers of the world organize as a class, take possession of the earth and the machinery of production, and abolish the wage system…'"

The train rocked on. The jaws of my listeners seemed locked open, as if witnessing some minor religious miracle. The words I'd never before uttered aloud sounded good to me, burning hot and spicy on my tongue. I finished up with a flourish:

"'…It is the historic mission of the working class to do away with capitalism. The army of production must be organized, not only for the everyday struggle with capitalists, but also to carry on production when capitalism shall have been overthrown. By organizing industrially we are forming the new society within the shell of the old.'"

A round of applause greeted my performance.

"I'll be damned," one man said.

"By god, maybe the kid's the real goods after all," said another.

The older man patted my arm. "Well, I don't know if you're Bill Haywood's son," he grinned through rotting teeth, "but you're good enough for me, kid." He turned to the others. "Whatayou say, fellow workers—shall we give the kid a break?" An outpouring of assent went up from the others. "Okay, kid, you can tag along with us and pay for your red card when you get your first payday. Put 'er there—they call me Mac."

"Here, kid—come up and have a cup of java," said a voice from the front of the car.

I went up and sat by the fire flaming from a large can by the front wall of the car. I smiled and shook hands with the men. The coffee came in a tin can, but it tasted better than any cup I'd ever had. Some of the others were drinking too, and one of my new companions lifted his tin cup in salute: "Here's for putting the parasites of the master class to work!"

"Hear, hear!" piped a squinty-eyed little Englishman, and we all touched our cans together and drank.

The train rolled on west. I was feeling better and better among my new friends—Wobblies all. The nightmare of last night began to seem like something that had happened to someone else, in another land. Presently one of the men began to fry some meat in a big skillet over the fire. When it was sizzling brown he gave the first piece to me. "'One for all and all for one'—that's our motto," he said with a big toothy grin. "We gotta feed you well, Joe—we need a big guy like you to defend us from the bulls."

After we had eaten, one of the men pulled out a tattered red booklet and we all began to sing. My brother Emmett had left a copy of the *Little Red Songbook* with me once, and I'd learned several of the songs, but I didn't know most of the tunes. One of the men handed me another copy of the songbook, and soon I was singing along at the top of my lungs with the others. We sang Joe Hill's "Where the Fraser River Flows" and "Dump the Bosses Off Your Back" and "Fifty Thousand Lumberjacks"—and ended up with Ralph Chaplin's "Commonwealth of Toil":

> ...For we have a glowing dream
> Of how fair the world will seem
> When all men can live their lives secure and free...

By the time we'd finished, I felt like I'd gone through some intense and joyous religious experience and had entered an exciting new world where people actually loved and respected one another. It was just like my brother Emmett had said: The IWW was the greatest thing on earth, and to be a member was the proudest thing any person could ever hope to be.

The train droned on. We left the beautiful blue mist hills of Missouri. After an hour or two, I leaned out the jolting boxcar door and felt the wind's invisible hands on my face. Great waving fields of wheat stretched everywhere, sweeping on in a great golden carpet off to the horizon in the west.

"You're in Kansas now, fellow worker," I heard the older man named Mac say behind me, and at the words "fellow worker," I felt a thrill of acceptance flood through me.

Kansas! And this was just the beginning. I resolved that I would see the whole world before I was through, every nook and cranny of it. I remembered my first rule of life I had formulated a few months before while lying in my bunk back in Springfield: *Anything is possible.* And I felt a sudden overpowering love for life and the world and all its plants and trees and mountains and men and critters.

After soaking up the beauty of the undulating golden waves of wheat for a while, I popped back into the car and sat listening to my new friends and brothers tell one another tales of their travels, of women, of great strikes and free speech fights, of Bill Haywood and Elizabeth Gurley Flynn, of Joe Hill, of the great Negro waterfront organizer Ben Fletcher, of half-Indian Frank Little who had been lynched in Butte, Montana, and of "the Saint."

"Who is this 'Saint' everyone keeps talking about?" a new recruit asked.

Mac sat straighter, a glint of light in his eyes. "Why, that's Vincent St. John, the greatest Wobbly of them all."

"Did you ever meet him?"

"*Meet* him — why, I helped him organize Goldfield, Nevada back in 1906 and '07." He paused, rocking gently with the motion of the train. "Yessir, there's never been anyone like the Saint. Bill Haywood is no slouch, but the Saint has that personality. You know he's interested in your welfare the minute you meet him. He first made a name for himself as secretary of the miners' union in Telluride, Colorado.

"Have you ever been to Telluride? You expect a gold mine to be a hole in the ground, something you look down into. I'd never seen a mine way up in the sky like that before, like the Smuggler–Union in Telluride. There was a mile or two of switchbacks leading

Vincent Saint John

straight up to it from that beautiful little mountain town, so it looked like the whole shebang was just about to fall down on top of you. That big black hole up there in the sky, hovering over you. There was something evil about it, and something dramatic and majestic too. You wondered if that hole led to heaven or hell.

"Well, one day there was an explosion and fire in the mine. After a while, everyone gave up hope of rescuing the dozens of men trapped in there. But St. John wouldn't give up. He led a rescue party in there through the smoke and fumes, and got almost everyone out alive. He suffers from a bronchial ailment from it to this day, from all the smoke he inhaled.

"But that didn't stop the Saint. He went on to become the greatest organizer the country has even known. He was absolutely incorruptible. He was a handy man with a six–gun, too. He was in ten gunfights, and arrested ten times, but in every case he was found not guilty.

"Back in '06 and '07 he organized Goldfield almost single-handed. It was the biggest mining camp in the history of the West. Twenty or thirty thousand people lived there. They even had an opera house. The world championship fight between Gans and Battling Nelson was held there in 1908. And the Saint organized it all. It was the closest thing to a classless society we've ever had in America. Newsboys and dishwashers and miners made the same pay. We treated one another with respect, the way it's supposed to be. And we didn't go begging to the slave–masters for better pay or conditions. The union tacked up on the wall of the owners' offices what the pay scale would be and that was the *law*.

"But I guess we were too much of a threat to the men who want to walk all over other folks. The hero of San Juan Hill, Teddy Roosevelt, sent his hired killers in there and that was the end of it. And the Saint lost his first gunfight there—he was wounded in the hand, and that hand is crippled to this day.

"He's all for the workers, the workers over the politicians. Until 1908 the IWW constitution called for struggle on the political as well as the economic front. We all suspected that Daniel De Leon, the marxist who headed the Socialist Labor Party, wanted to take over the IWW and run it with an iron hand. But St. John's a syndicalist—he believes the workers are smart enough to run the government themselves, and deserve to.

"A bunch of migrant Wobblies who called themselves the Overalls Brigade rode freights to the 1908 national convention.

They voted De Leon out and elected St. John as our general secretary–treasurer. And his was the guiding hand that made the IWW what it is until Big Bill took over in 1915. Then the Saint went out to start a cooperative mine in New Mexico."

The men continued talking of Wobbly heroes, past and present. I lay on the scratchy floorboards of the rocking boxcar, taking it all in eagerly. But finally the long night of sleeplessness got to me and I nodded off.

2

A REAL WOBBLY

When I awoke, the stuttering boxcar was rocking along in darkness. The interminable clack–clack of the wheels on the tracks, the relentlessly beating heart of the train, seemed like a continual background to my life now, like a mysterious inner metronome beating softly within my breast. "Where am I?" I wondered for a frightened lost moment.

I sat up and rubbed my eyes and saw the dormant bodies beside me. With a thrill of discovery, I remembered: I'm a *Wobbly*! Or almost one, anyway. Then I heard a staccato counterpoint to the drumming music of the train: So Wobblies snored just like normal men. Then, so as not to wake the others, I crept carefully to the door and peered out.

The waving tops of the grain shimmered softly in the moon-light, like a vast silvery protective membrane spread over the sleeping earth. A few far-off lights punctuated the darkness, seeming impossibly far away and disconnected as if from distant ships on the ocean. And I wondered if farm families were having their pre-dawn breakfast, preparing to go out and milk the cows or harness the horses or crank up their harvesters.

The train rumbled on. I lay down on my stomach with my head on my arms, looking out at the vast panorama stretching off into darkness. How strange life was: the nightmarish events of last night, my new Wobbly friends, and now sailing off into this vast sea of wheat. I hoped again fervently my assailant hadn't died. I closed my eyes and strove with the most intense concentration I could muster to relive those terrible seconds. I felt certain that I'd only wanted to scare my attackers off and had not intended to use the knife, and that it had been no movement of mine that had resulted in the tragedy. But who would ever believe me in a court of law? It would be the word of three—or four—against one. I knew that the farther I got away from Missouri, the safer I would feel, and I began to urge the train on faster.

I opened my eyes and looked again at the dark fleeting landscape. On the other hand I began to feel a sharp pang of loneliness, deeply missing my parents and my home. Already I wondered if I would ever see them again. I wondered how my dad was taking my leaving. I knew he had wanted me to apprentice in the railroad shops in a year or two, so he could help show me the ropes and help me to lead a steady life. But I knew I was too restless for a life so monotonous and uneventful—as far back as I remembered, I had wanted to see the great world. And anyway, lots of kids went out on their own at twelve or thirteen to make their own way and help relieve the burden on their parents. And if I could just find my older brother Emmett, it would be almost like being back home again.

What did I want out of life, I wondered, feeling the comforting rhythm of the train beneath me now on a stretch of smoother track, staring into the blackness. What was life, anyway—what was most important in life? Looking warmly into the eyes of your fellow human beings, I thought, the people you loved and who loved you, like the warm laughing looks I'd exchanged with these men now sleeping nearby, sharing a mutual joy in living, feeling one with the whole earth—that was the best life had to offer. I hungered for more of that sort of companionship and joy of life.

It got colder, and I began to feel the pangs of hunger. I remembered the sandwiches my mother had fixed for me, and I took them out of my pack, wrapped a blanket around me and sat up against the bouncy wall of the boxcar eating them, filled with gratitude for having such loving parents. I would make up for the shame and pain I was causing them, I resolved—I would make them proud of me.

The train droned on and on. I started to worry again. I realized suddenly that I shouldn't have given my real name to my new companions. What if the police had already circulated my name

*Elizabeth Gurley Flynn addresses striking silk workers
in Paterson, New Jersey, June 1913.*

and a description of me? Could I really trust all of my new friends? Maybe I should jump off into the darkness the next time the train slowed down and make my way on to Harper on my own, using a new name. Or maybe when I finally joined the IWW officially, I could get a different name put on my card—Emmett had told me many Wobblies used different names, or nicknames like Boxcar Blackie or T-Bone Slim or Side-door Shorty. Well, I decided, it was useless to worry about it now.

Dawn came. Long shafts of light came shooting up from the rear of the train, like strange fleet-footed animals leaping along beside it. A golden light suffused everything, sparkling the heads of wheat. I felt very alive.

My companions began to stir. I smelled the tang of coffee in the air. Limbs and torsos came to life about me, and soon I felt like I was in the midst of a jovial traveling circus, with morning greetings and homespun wisecracks flying everywhere.

"How you sleep, fellow worker?" asked Mac. Again I felt the thrill of being addressed by that companionable term, which I later was to learn contained the soul of Wobblyism: You earn respect and a voice in things by contributing to the necessary work of society.

"Not too bad," I said. "Sort of a bumpy mattress, though."

"Joe was holdin' his own," said another Wob with a toothy grin. "He was holdin' his own all night long." I felt myself blush.

We bumped and rattled on, passing through little lost towns. Occasionally I would see a girl or young woman standing near the tracks or walking along in the early sunlight and my pulse would quicken. After the morning java I found myself sitting near the open door with a friendly grizzled man of about forty who, like most of the Wobblies, always seemed to have a half-smile on his face, as if knowing something normal people didn't.

"You ever been in Emma Goldman before?" he asked.

"What?" I said. Then, uncertainly: "No-o-o-o…"

"Me and Ed here have. And a coupla the other 'bos. We named this here boxcar Emma Goldman, up in the berry harvest in Michigan last year. Never thought I'd get into old Emma again. Shows how small this ball o' wax is. Take a look when you hop down—name's still on there. We scratch names on a lotta cars—Tom Paine, Gurley Flynn, Boxcar Bertha… Hope Emma don't mind havin' her name on a B & O car…"

We rocked and roared on through the wheat. After a few minutes Mac came and sat beside me in the open door, our legs dangling down. He didn't say anything for a while, and I just felt the pleasant warmth of the older man beside me. Finally he turned toward me and said with a kind of wink:

"As Big Bill's son you probably know all this already," he began. "But just in case, I thought I'd fill you in on what this proposition is all about, Joe." And he began to explain in a simple unpretentious way what the IWW was after: decent pay and conditions; the industries run democratically by all the workers; an end to war, poverty, prostitution and oppression; a decent livelihood and a home and voice for everyone. I thanked him and told him it sounded pretty good to me.

Around seven in the morning we came in to Harper. I looked around anxiously, thinking perhaps I could spot Emmett along the tracks. The Wobblies decided to jump off near the outskirts when the train was still doing about ten per, just in case there were some hostile bulls around. Mac reminded me to run in the same direction the train was going, to keep from falling down. To my surprise, one of the Wobs took a small stub of a broom and swept out the car just before we jumped. "We believe in leaving things *better* where we've been — not worse," he explained.

I saw men jumping off all up and down the length of the train. There must have been sixty or seventy who dropped off. I strapped my bindle on securely and dropped. When I hit the grit I began running as fast as I could and managed to avoid falling. Some of the men from the other cars began walking in to Harper, others came towards us.

When we had all congregated, there must have been about forty Wobblies. We had a brief powwow and then the group began walking out toward the countryside, away from town. "We're gonna chow down first out in the jungle, the deluxe IWW hotel," Mac explained to me, "and coordinate our plan of action. An' some of the boys want to boil up — they took on a few free riders during the night."

I didn't want to show my ignorance so I said nothing. We walked about a mile and came to the Wobbly jungle in a small wash. Along the way, when we passed a couple of farms, Mac showed me some examples of the hobo code language cut into fenceposts. On one gate were cut four vertical lines with a tail attached, indicating a watchdog. On another were four horizontal lines indicating you might get a meal if you chopped enough wood. A "C" indicated a cheap town with low wages. A pair of handcuffs indicated hostile bulls. And so on.

We came to the jungle, hidden from the level plain down in the wash. It was an amazing sight: All was very neat and clean, with bedrolls laid out in an orderly fashion and the clothes of the thirty or forty men congregated there well-mended for the most part. Several men busily attended to cooking, dishwashing and other chores. "St. John Arms," a crude sign at the edge of the enclave announced, and I knew it referred to Vincent St. John, the famous Wobbly Mac had told us about the day before.

Mac and some of the others flashed their red cards. Several men rushed up to greet us eagerly. There were hearty slaps on the back, handshakes and even a couple of kisses on the cheek from a couple of stiffs who looked like Frenchmen. I spotted a Chinese, two Negroes, two Indians and a couple of other swarthy men. Four or five of our greeters shook my hand warmly. It was just like a big happy family reunion. Soon we were all gathered around the communal stew pot, lapping up the remains of a tasty mulligan.

The camp ran efficiently. There was a systematic division of labor, with everyone volunteering for a job. Some men went to boil up clothes to kill lice. Some gathered wood. Some went off to town to try and bum some meat from the butcher, others to the bakeries, others for other necessities. I ended up as a "pearl diver," helping wash up the tin cans and pots and pans we ate out of. They were always left spick-and-span for the next Wobbly guests, I learned. As things proceeded, I asked every Wobbly I could if he knew anything about my brother Emmett, but no one had any news of him.

After we'd chowed down, we newcomers got together with the fellow workers already there to discuss the job situation and organizing strategy. There had been considerable success in signing up new members, we learned. The IWW tactic of ca'canny, or slowing down where wages or conditions were substandard, had shown good results on many farms. This conscientious with-drawal of efficiency had brought better pay and reduction of the workday to ten hours. In some cases the crews had been fired. Where possible, a new Wobbly crew was immediately sent in to carry on the struggle where the last group left off.

We learned that a Wob crew had just been fired for a slowdown they'd staged at a farm a ways to the north. After a little discus-sion a vote was taken, and it was decided we would ride the freights north and try to get hired on there. There was a slow freight that stopped at a little burg near the farm.

There were about fifty of us now. It was a jolly group. We walked into Harper, singing Wobbly songs and swapping yarns. I was beginning to learn the jargon of the migrant workers: *Bull* was cop; *'bo* was hobo; *flop* was a room; *chuck* and *slum* were food; *balloon* was a bedroll; *slave market* was an employment agency. The new words felt and sounded good on my tongue.

As we neared town a friendly "shack" (brakeman) told us there would be a slow drag headed north in a couple of hours. I knew this might be my last chance to find Emmett. I told Mac about it and he agreed I should go to town and give it a try. A young Wobbly named Gary, who was about sixteen, decided to go along with me.

We went in to the dusty town. I was terrified of the police, but I was determined to find my brother. I asked almost every person I came to, especially those who looked like farmers, but no one had heard of Emmett. Finally, in desperation, almost expecting to see a "Wanted" poster with my name on it, I walked into the post office. The clerk had not heard of Emmett.

Then, just as we were leaving, another clerk said: "I remember that name. He came in here last about two or three weeks ago. I think he said he was heading north. But wait a minute—I remember now—he was a friend of my next-door neighbor. *He* probably knows where he went. If you'll jest wait ten minutes till noon hour, I'll go ask. I live right out back."

"Gee, thanks," I said. "I'd really appreciate that. We'll wait right out front." Then, to my surprise, the postal clerk disappeared through a rear door.

Panic shot through me. Had I told them Emmett was my brother? I couldn't remember. Maybe the clerk had heard a kid named Murphy was wanted by the police. I was trembling as we walked out to the street. I debated whether to tell my new friend Gary the whole story.

After a minute, I said: "Aw, come on. I probably couldn't find him anyway. And besides, I want to stick with you guys. I don't want that train to leave without us."

Though I tried not to show it, I was shot through with disappointment. When would I see Emmett again? And all the way back to the railyard I expected at any second to hear some town clown or harness bull ordering us to halt.

It was getting hot. The slow drag came in a few minutes late. About fifty of us lay in wait in some bushes a little out of town, and nailed it just as it was picking up speed. I was getting pretty good at hopping freights now. As soon as we clambered aboard I began to feel better. I was getting farther and farther away from the police in Springfield, and closer to Gary and Mac and my other new Wobbly friends.

We came to our stop about two in the afternoon. It was a little burg about three blocks long. Fate must have been in cahoots with us. There was one horse-drawn wagon on the dusty main drag. Almost as soon as we hoofed it over from the tracks, its owner rode up beside us. He was a big stern-looking guy with chinwhiskers, about fifty years old. He said his name was Schneider — and I remembered that was the name of the farmer who'd just fired his whole Wobbly crew.

We stood and jawboned with him. Mac had been elected to talk for us. He was still offering what our fellow workers had balked at — an eleven-hour day at thirty cents an hour.

"You guys ain't Wobblies, air yuh?" the farmer snorted.

"What's a Wobbly?" somebody asked.

"Well, I'll give yuh a chance," John Farmer said. And he gave us directions to his spread.

We hoofed it out there through the intense afternoon heat, thinking that if he was half a man he would have sent in a wagon for us, or at least taken a few of us along on his surrey.

We got to the farm about four in the afternoon, foot-weary and dripping with sweat. There was a big farmhouse, a much bigger barn, a silo, a long dilapidated bunkhouse and a few smaller buildings. We saw what must have been Schneider's wife and a couple of his sons up by the farmhouse. There seemed to be no work at all going on out in the wheat.

One of Schneider's sons, a big strapping kid of about eighteen, came out and showed us to the bunkhouse. It was an old converted chicken coop with a dirt floor and two long rows of old canvas cots with dirty blankets strewn across them. The adjoining john stank to high heaven. We filed in and spread out our bindles. Some of the men lay down to rest, their faces covered with sweat. A few others stood around outside in small groups, talking or smoking.

About an hour later, another of Schneider's sons came and marched us into another long low building near the farmhouse to put on the feed bag. The farmer's wife and a big rawboned daughter came in carrying plates of chicken, fried until it was almost black. But I was hungry, so I didn't mind too much.

I sat down next to Gary and dug in. After a couple of bites of the burnt chicken, I took a drink of water to wash it down. I immediately spat it out on the floor, feeling embarrassed. "What in the — ?"

The man on the other side of me laughed. "Never drunk alkali water before, eh Joe?" he said. "That's all they got all through this country. But at least you won't have to worry about this burnt bird fouling up your plumbing — you'll be shitting it all out with the runs in an hour or two."

He was right. I was to learn it was the worst thing about working in the wheat belt — the damn alkali water that gave you the runs. It took me a long time to get used to it.

The next day I became acquainted with the facts of life. We were up at dawn. Schneider came and asked some of us to harness up the horses. As a result we had a very rushed breakfast.

Then it was out to the fields. The air was beautiful and clear, but at six-thirty in the morning it was already getting hot. I was assigned to work on what was called a binder. It was a long wooden platform pulled by four horses. Attached to the front was a long sickle bar that moved back and forth, cutting the wheat and throwing it up on a moving belt. Another mechanism bound the wheat into bundles. It was the job of me and Gary and some of the others to walk alongside the binder, grab the bundles of wheat and stack them up in shocks. Then wagons would come along, and the shocks of wheat would be loaded on and taken back to the thresher near the farmhouse.

This was nothing like the strawberry harvest in Arkansas. The farmer's son who ran the binder drove the horses so fast we almost had to run to keep up. Before the first hour was past I was sweating buckets. The sun got hotter and hotter. So this was what life was all about, I thought, struggling to keep up. No wonder the IWW came into existence. If this was the way most people lived out their lives, then God should have stopped with the worm and the salamander. After two or three hours my muscles began to ache. I began to have blurry visions of our cool porch back in Springfield, of my mother's good cooking. Why had I let myself in for this nightmare? But I couldn't go back now, I knew — unless I learned the police were no longer after me. By the time the lunch bell finally sounded, I felt I was about to collapse. It was all I could do to stagger back to the mess hall.

The afternoon was worse. It must have reached over one hundred degrees. By three o'clock, I felt sure I was going to collapse. To make things worse, Schneider showed up and began walking along near us, watching us work.

Suddenly he came closer to me, shouting over the noise of the machine. "You're built like a gorilla," he yelled in my ear. "If you cain't work any faster than that, I'll have to let you go." He stalked off, sneering.

I felt humiliated, shamed, enraged. "What do you think I am—a mule?" But I didn't say it, I just thought it, and gritted my teeth and tried to work faster.

One of the Wobblies took my arm. "Don't let him get your goat, Joe-boy," he said. "We'll settle his hash before this operation's done with."

That evening, after dinner, I didn't even have the energy to say a few words to Gary. I just lay down on my cot and fell asleep.

The work went on. Next day every muscle in my body was sore, but I was getting better at the work. The third day it was a little cooler and things went better still. But still it was hard backbreaking work, eleven hours a day in the hot sun. And at night now lying in my bunk, I began to feel more and more homesick, to have an aching desire to see my dad and mom and brothers and sisters and friends.

But in another part of my mind I relished this new independence, the feeling I was a real man and self-sufficient. Now that I had a taste of freedom, I had an irresistible urge to see more of the great world. And especially to enjoy more of the comradeship of the Wobblies and to help them in their struggle for a better world.

Our first payday arrived. Schneider acted like it was pulling teeth for him to dole out our wages. It wasn't so much for the money but for another reason I had chomped at the bit for this day. After we got our pay I cornered Mac out near the bunkhouse. "Well, can I join?" I asked.

"You'd *better*, if you know what's good for you," he grinned. "But don't be in such an all-fired hurry, Haywood," he winked. "The boys have got a little initiation cooked up for you."

A little later, when it started to get dark, Mac asked me to step into the bunkhouse. They were all there, all forty or fifty Wobblies, waiting to welcome me into the IWW. Outside the doors, sentinels were posted. I paid my hard-earned money proudly, and bent with a feeling of deep solemnity to sign the pledge to be true to the principles of the IWW. Then Mac made out my red card, and I felt like I was a member of king Arthur's court being admitted to knighthood. I had to choke back a tear.

As I took the small well-made dues book in my hand, I made an inner vow that I would be a Wobbly forever and never cease to fight for freedom and justice. I carefully slipped the book into my pocket and buttoned it down, feeling that at last I was one of the select members of the greatest organization in history.

Everyone clapped, then began to stomp and holler. "Speech, speech!" someone cried.

I wasn't sure if they were serious. But before I had a chance to get flustered, I felt something soft and icy clamp down over my head. It was a bucket of ice cream. I lifted it off my head, licking the sweet-tasting stuff into my mouth. "Thanks — fellow workers," was all I could get out. Then more ice cream from other containers was served to all. It was my happiest day since I left home. That night I went to sleep smiling.

3

FIRST LOVE

Farmer Schneider had ignored all our requests for better pay and conditions. The next night after work we held a meeting in the bunkhouse. It was to be my first official IWW meeting. The call was made to choose a chairman. To my amazement and alarm, someone suggested me. This was carrying democracy too far. But before I could back out someone else had seconded it, and I was chosen by acclamation.

"But I don't know a damn thing about *any* kind of meeting," I protested.

"Ain't a thing to it, Joe," one of the harvest stiffs said. "You just call out what it says in this here book." He handed me an IWW constitution with the order of business for meetings in it.

I was flabbergasted. Stuttering and sputtering, I read off the list of procedures and got the shebang going. Under "new business," Mac was the first to speak.

"Well, boys, we've shown this slave-driving hoosier we know how to work," he said. "Now let's see if he knows how to appreciate it." A roar of approval went up.

Then we all voted and approved a list of demands: a ten-hour day, forty cents an hour, and less greasy grub. A committee was selected to present our demands to Schneider next day, just as work was about to begin. We were pretty sure he could afford to pay more, because one of the boys had overheard him talking to his wife about buying one of the new combines sometime soon.

We all sat tensely through breakfast next morning. When it came time to go out to the fields, our committee walked up to the farmhouse. Three minutes later, we heard about the longest and loudest string of curses my tender ears had ever been subjected to.

Our committee came walking back. "He says we can work at the same rate and hours or hit the road," one of the members said.

I expected a blanket of gloom to settle over the group. But some of the members seemed to get gleams of mischief and merriment in their eyes. "All right, boys, you know what to do," said Mac.

We began our work. But almost immediately the man next to me said: "You're working too hard, Joe. Slow down and watch your pay go up. Ca'canny, we call it. A good old Scotch word. Almost as good as Scotch whiskey. The members of the great American Fakeration of Labor lose their pay and waste their time picketing. This makes much more sense."

So we fumbled and puttered along, going at about half our normal pace. After a while, I saw one of Schneider's sons head back to the farmhouse. We didn't see any of them for two or three hours, so we knew they must be having one hell of a powwow.

We got about half the normal work done that day. We didn't see Schneider until he barged into the mess hall in the middle of our dinner. He knocked a big plate of chicken off the table and stood up on a bench.

"You think you're smart, don't you," he bellowed. "Well, you ain't—you're dumb. You're a bunch of goddamn Wobblies, that's what you air."

"What *is* a Wobbly?" someone squeaked.

"An' if you don't make up your minds to put in a good day's work tomorrow," Schneider went on, "I'm gonna run you all off. I've got a few kinfolk around here who know how to work like men who can help me bring in the wheat." He sneered at us and stalked off.

After dinner we called an emergency meeting in the bunkhouse. It looked like Schneider was one stubborn hoosier, and this was one time our slowdown tactic wasn't going to work.

"So whata we do, boys?" Mac asked. "Leave? Picket? Try to call in another crew of Wobs?"

No one had an immediate response. To my prideful surprise, Mac turned to me. "Joe?"

I felt nervous with everybody looking at me. I felt I had to say something, anything.

"Well... Maybe we could lose some of his farm equipment," I offered meekly.

"Lose it?"

"Or hide it," I said.

" 'Hide it,' " someone snorted. "Look around you, Joey boy— there ain't a tree or bush or ditch or even a crawdad hole as far as the eye can see."

I felt my face getting red. I looked out at the big farmyard desperately. I jerked my thumb toward the big haystack twenty or thirty yards away. The men stared.

A gleam of delight came into Mac's eyes. "Joe, you're a genius," he said. Some of the other men began to laugh and shout their approval. A couple of them came up and slapped me on the back. I felt a flush of exultation sweep through me.

Fortunately our bunkhouse and the huge barn were between the haystack and the farmhouse. About midnight we began burying the two binders in hay. It was hard work, but we were all giggling and joking so much under our breath that it was more like fun. We had the job done by about four. To the casual observer, the haystack looked the same as ever.

The next morning as we were finishing breakfast, Schneider came into the mess hall with his two sons and four or five other men. Some of them looked sort of shamefaced.

"Well boys," he said. "You highblown master craftsmen make up your minds?"

Mac spoke up and told him our demands were the same as ever.

Schneider turned to his kinfolk. "Okay, boys," he said. "Show them what God-fearing men who believe in honest work can do." He turned back to us. "I'll expect you I **W**on't **W**orks out of here within an hour." He turned and stomped off.

Within five minutes he was back, his face red with rage. "All right," he shouted. "What did you do with 'em? I'll have you all in prison for theft!"

Mac spoke up calmly. "We haven't stolen anything, Mister Schneider. I'll swear on a stack of Gutenberg bibles we haven't... But if anything's missing, maybe we can help you get it back..."

Schneider stomped off again. Ten or fifteen minutes later he came back, a little calmer now. He sat at one of the mess tables, the look of a beaten man about him. When he spoke again, it was almost with a whine. He seemed to be speaking to the tabletop. "Weather report says it might rain," he muttered. "I've got to get that wheat in. Whatayou boys want, anyway?"

"Our terms are the same as ever, Mister Schneider," said Mac.

Schneider threw his hands up. "Okay boys, you've got me buffaloed. Ten hours and forty cents an hour."

"And less greasy food," a voice piped.

"And less greasy food."

We worked there another week or so until the grain was in, then went to work for another farmer in the next county to the north. Perhaps because he had heard of some of our novel and rambunctious tactics, he was more reasonable. He hired us on at forty cents and ten hours a day right from the start, and the food and lodging were better.

Better yet, the farmer had a tall, slender, friendly wife of about twenty-two with long chestnut-colored hair. Perhaps because her much older husband treated her like a slave, like so many farmers did their wives, she seemed sympathetic with us workers. A couple of times I felt her hair brush against me as she bent to serve our food, and I couldn't help wondering whether it was an accident. Her name was Sarah.

The first Sunday at the new farm I stayed in the bunkhouse writing a letter home, while all the other Wobs went in to the nearby town. About noon I noticed the farmer's buggy was missing too. Hoping to get a stamp, I meandered up to the farmhouse and knocked at the back door.

"Oh, Joseph." Sarah came to the door, seeming a little out of breath. Unlike her husband, she had learned the names of all the workers.

I told her my mission. She seemed a bit flustered, and invited me in and found a stamp for me. Then she offered me some coffee and pie. Such a set-down seemed too good to be true, and I accepted eagerly. Soon I was shoveling huge forkfuls of pie into my mouth, while she sat watching me with what seemed a wondering look.

"Life is so lonely here," she suddenly burst out, and I thought she was going to burst into tears.

"Yes—I reckon so," I said, surprised at her outburst.

"If only I were a man," she said. "I'd be off with you men, seeing the world."

I brushed a crumb from my lip. "Yes—but it's awfully hard work, I said."

"Yes, but I'd do anything to leave here."

I didn't know what to say. She seemed restless and fidgety, and presently went to do something in the nearby pantry. I watched her beautiful white ankles beneath her swishing skirt.

I finished my pie and coffee. Presently she said from the pantry: "Joseph, there's something I can't reach in here—could you come and help me for a moment?" Her voice seemed to have something wild and plaintive in it.

I went and stood at the pantry door. Sweet and pungent odors wafted out to me. She pointed at something on the top shelf. "That jar of jam—could you fetch it down?"

She was tall, maybe five eight or nine, and it seemed to me she could reach it if she tried. But I went and stood close beside her and reached up and got the jar and held it out to her. But instead of taking it, her whole body seemed suddenly to collapse against mine. The jar fell to the floor and broke. I felt her soft hair against my face and suddenly we were in each other's arms. I had never known anything like it. She seemed to be devouring me and I wondered why her mouth against mine was so wet. She was making little moaning sounds as she kissed me. We were grabbing each other all over, grabbing and kissing and moaning. I felt something strange in my lower body press against her. I felt like my whole body was burning up. Then I felt her long slender hands sliding in and undoing my pants.

"I've never…"

"I'll show you," she whispered against my cheek.

Then she raised her skirt, standing on tiptoes. I seemed instinctively to know I had to bend down a little, and then she was guiding me into her. I felt like everything was going to explode, like the earth was going to end. Why had all the childhood stories made fun of this, when it was a thousand times greater than anything else in life? "I love you, I love you," I heard her moan over and over, and I whispered the same words back to her. It seemed to go on forever, and yet for far too short a time. And then I felt the strange explosion and felt like I was losing all of myself into her. She screamed two or three times and then clung to me, moaning softly.

I was too excited to speak. All I could do was cling to her. We just stood clinging to one another for what must have been eight or ten minutes. Then I realized she was crying. I took out my handkerchief and dried her tears.

I finally got the courage to speak. "I've never done anything like this before," I said. "It's the most wonderful thing that ever happened to me." And, hesitantly, "Can we do it again?"

Sarah ran her slender hand along my cheek. "I want to, Joseph, oh, I want to," she said. "But perhaps you'd better go now—I don't know when he's coming back."

Leaving her seemed the hardest thing I had ever done. I grabbed her hand and kissed it, and then got up and walked out through the kitchen.

I went and lay on my bunk. I felt like I was burning up. So this was what all the endlessly agonizing hard work was for, these few moments of paradise. I'd never dreamed that the act of making love could be such strong medicine. I had actually had part of my body in another person's body. It seemed glorious, unreal, sacred, magical. I felt like I was forever part of Sarah now, as if she were a sister or a mother or a daughter—even closer—as if she were part of my own body and I of hers—that nothing could ever destroy the bond between us. I felt more wonderful and powerful than I had ever felt in my life, yet at the same time, more hopelessly dependent than I'd ever been on another person for my happiness. I knew that I was in love with her, and I forced myself to believe that she must be in love with me as well.

The next days I was not in this world. Sarah was all I could think of all day long in the fields. During the long hard hours in the hot sun I moved like a robot, a man in a dream. Part of the time I felt like I was on fire, and part of the time I seemed to be floating among the clouds, serenaded by the voices of angels. Gary and the others would give me strange looks, and then for a while I would force myself to concentrate on my work. Every time I caught sight of her during meals I felt too sick at my stomach to eat. And I felt a catch in my chest, and thought my heart was about to stop.

Once when no one was looking she threw me a kiss, and once she waved at me as we rode out to the field. The first night after our lovemaking I couldn't sleep at all, and my sleeping and waking periods began a new cycle: one night lying awake all night thinking of her, then next day falling asleep immediately after dinner and sleeping twelve hours straight through; then the cycle was repeated.

Over and over in my mind I would relive the moments of bliss we'd had together. And once, getting less emotional, I began to wonder why people made love standing up. I had always assumed, for some reason, they did it lying down. Was it perhaps that that was the only way the woman's hole would open up? Or was it that it had just never occurred to anyone to do it lying down, which it seemed to me would be more natural and comfortable? Then my imagination ran wild, and the thought occurred to me that I might become famous and acclaimed all over the world by being the first person in history to come up with the vastly superior idea of doing it lying down. I would be a hero—it would be a greater innovation than the electric light. But then when these thoughts left my mind, I was left with my loneliness and frustration and miseries again.

I wondered how long I could go on this way. The following Sunday all the boys went into town again and I stayed behind. But the buggy sat near the stable all through the agonizing day. I sweated and tore my hair, and felt like I was going to die.

The next day at the breakfast table Sarah tucked a note into my shirt pocket. I felt like an angel's hand had touched me. When no one was looking I pulled it out eagerly, lovingly, and sneaked a look. "I love you," it said.

Four more days went by. I couldn't eat, I was losing weight. I knew it couldn't be long before I was fired. And perhaps even my fellow Wobblies could not, in good conscience, stick up for me— for the Wobblies prided themselves on doing good work for good pay.

I got up before dawn next day and waited for her to come out to set the places in the mess hall, too desperate and heedless to worry about her husband catching us.

"Joseph!" she said, startled, when I appeared from behind a small shed. Then she came and flung herself into my arms. We covered one another with kisses. We were both crying.

"I don't know if I can stand it any longer," I said.

"Nor I," she said. "Nor I."

"I love you," I said. "If I have to leave, that will be the reason."

"I know, Joseph, I know." Then we heard a noise and I ducked behind the shed.

The next few days, watching her furtively as she served food, were pure hell. And the third Sunday was hopeless too.

That night I told Gary I was thinking of hitting the road, that I was anxious to get out and see the great cities of the West. I asked if he'd like to join me, and he agreed.

Next morning before he woke, I waited again behind the shed. Finally Sarah came out, carrying a pail of milk. I was all torn up inside. I grabbed her hand. "I think I'd better be hitting the road," I said, barely able to get the few words out.

She seemed to gasp a little. "Yes, Joseph—perhaps it's the only way..."

My voice was hoarse. "If I ever come back, and you're not married, could I maybe..." Words deserted me.

"Sure," she said. She smiled a funny smile and put her hand on mine. "Anything is possible," she said softly.

My own first rule of life, and she was giving it back to me!

"Goodbye, Joe," she said. "I'll always remember you." And she darted on into the empty mess hall.

I went to my bunk and cried for half an hour.

After breakfast, before the men went out to the fields, Gary and I went around and shook their hands. We told them we were going to hit the high lonesome.

"Every time I see a haystack I'll think of you, kid," said one.

"And me too, every time I hear the name Bill Haywood," said another.

They all slapped Gary and me on the back. Someone stuffed the latest copy of the Wobbly paper in my pack.

As we picked up our bindles to leave, Mac came up to me, reaching in his pocket. "I want you to have this, Joe," he said. "I have a feeling you're gonna do great things for the One Big Union someday." He held out a small black, red and gold IWW lapel button. "The Saint gave that to me," he said. "In Goldfield."

I felt deeply touched. The beautiful gleaming pin seemed like a magic talisman to me. And it had belonged to Vincent St. John! "I'll treasure it forever, Mac," I said. "And I'll always remember it was you who first lined me up...fellow worker."

Gary and I turned and headed for town and the railroad. I wanted to get away fast, before I had the urge to look back.

By noon we had glommed the guts of a rattler. I didn't care where it went, I just wanted to wipe Sarah from my mind. We worked all up through the wheat belt, into Nebraska, the Dakotas, and across Canada and down into the Palouse in eastern Washington. Sometimes we worked with other Wobblies and sometimes we worked alone. And sometimes we took part in strikes or slowdowns that succeeded, and sometimes we lost. But little by little we were bettering the pay and conditions, building up the IWW and spreading the dream of the cooperative commonwealth.

A couple of days after we'd hit the road, and the danger of any gossip was past, I finally told Gary of my love for Sarah. And I told him of my idea for introducing horizontal lovemaking to the world.

"Oh, Joe," he said. "Oh, Joe..." Then I thought he never was going to stop laughing. "Farmers' wives do it that way 'cause they're less apt to get knocked up. Most people *already* do it lyin' down."

My love for Sarah took a long time to simmer down. Sometimes I lay in my bunk or in a lonely boxcar and thought of her and cried. But gradually my mind awoke again to my surroundings. Passing through the Rocky Mountains I felt like I was about to burst with the beauty of the world around me. It occurred to me that the whole fantastic world of nature was like a woman, another Sarah, and that I could love her too, and she would always be faithful to me.

By mid-October we were in short log country near Wenatchee, east of the Cascades. The harvest was over, and we rustled jobs working as roustabouts for the lumber lords in a big logging camp in the deep woods. I bought my first pair of caulked boots and black logger's jeans, and felt I was joining a great new brotherhood of workers.

This was a new type of land, and it grew on me—the woods and rushing rivers, the cool crisp mornings, the dampness in the air, the breathtaking views of snow-clad mountains, the hearty vibrant people—and the great living tradition the IWW had carved out of this land with struggle and blood.

In some ways the work was not as bad as slaving in the hot sun ten or eleven hours a day for John Farmer, shocking wheat. In the loggers' strike of 1917 the IWW had won the eight-hour day, and it was still in force in most camps. But our beanmaster shoveled out slop I wouldn't have fed to my dog back in Springfield, and the tumbledown bunkhouse was so crowded I felt like I was living in an ant hill.

Anyway, I was hungry for new sights and adventures, to see the great cities of the West Coast, and to be in an area where the IWW was really active. So the night of November 10th I said goodbye to Gary and caught a rattler heading west over the Cascades, and next day I was in the big IWW hall in Seattle.

4

CENTRALIA

It was one of those cold, gray, overcast autumn days. There were about a hundred of us in the hall in Seattle, mostly timber beasts like myself in our stag overalls and caulked boots, but a few harvest stiffs too. In the wintertime there were always more slaves in the Wobbly hall, because it was a place to go to keep warm and out of the wind and rain.

It happened on Armistice Day, November 11*th*, 1919, just four days after my fourteenth birthday. But I felt it was more like ten years since I'd left home than only five months ago, considering all the travel and varied experiences I'd had in those few months. When I left home I was a boy. But now, only five months later, I felt like I was a real man — as capable of getting along in the world as anyone twice my age. And now I had a religion too.

It was about mid-afternoon when the news came in to the hall. The secretary suddenly came and stood up on the little stage at one end of the big room and asked for everyone's attention. His face was white as a sheet. Struggling for words, he told us what had happened: Earlier in the day, during an Armistice Day parade, American Legionnaires had attacked our hall in Centralia, 120 miles to the south, and three of them had been killed. Dozens of Wobs had been jailed, and some of our boys were now being hunted by posses in the woods. It was urgent that we go to their defense.

For a moment after he stopped speaking you could have heard a pin drop. You should have seen the looks on the faces of the fellow workers there. At first stunned astonishment—then anger, outrage, compassion, fear—almost any emotion you could name. But mostly a fierce determination to rush to the aid of our fellow workers in need. Some of our boys burst out in tears. Wild shouts went up, suggestions about what we should do.

To calm the clamor for a few minutes, the secretary led us in singing a couple of Wobbly songs: "Hold the Fort," "All Hell Can't Stop Us," and "Workingmen Unite." After that it didn't take five minutes before our plans were laid to take the first rattler south to Centralia. We all had that "wild Wobbly dream" in our hearts, and we weren't about to stand idle and give it up when our fellow workers were in need.

We gathered up our bindles and rushed like an army troop advancing on the run down to the railyards. We saw a couple of bulls, but when they saw the size of our outfit and the looks on our faces they just slunk away into the shadows.

After a few minutes we found one of the shacks we knew who carried a red card. He told us there was a freight heading south in about fifteen minutes. It wasn't a long train, but fortunately it had three or four empty boxcars on it and a couple of empty flatcars. I ended up with a group of twenty or so who jumped into a boxcar back near the caboose. The first thing we did was all hide our Wobbly cards in our shoes, in case the bulls grabbed us.

It seemed like forever until that train got up steam and took off. We were all mad as hell and, at the same time, afraid for both ourselves and our fellow workers in Centralia. But most of all we were in a hurry to get there and get through whatever hell or salvation awaited us.

The wheels started going clickety-clack. For a while, nobody said much. We all just sat against the walls of the boxcar looking at each other occasionally, like men trapped in a mine or a sinking ship. A few of us knew each other, but there were also a lot of Wobblies from different areas who were strangers to one another.

Gradually the men began to talk. One bloke, trying to sound an optimistic note, told of being in the strike for an eight-hour day in 1917, when the lumberjacks finally carried the strike onto the job and simply pulled the whistle and walked off the job when the eight hours were up. It worked—they won the eight-hour day.

Then some of the men began telling stories about the terrible persecution the IWW had undergone because Wobblies had opposed the war, and because many people mistakenly lumped them in with the Communists.

One man told of how the delegate in his town, after many Wobs had been tarred and feathered, got word that he was next. He slit a pillow open and put it in his front window which faced on the street, with a note to the effect he was ready for them and would gladly supply his own feathers to be sure they were of good quality. He was left alone.

Then the horror stories began. One guy told how he had been on the steamer *Verona* in 1916 when hundreds of Wobblies had sailed up to Everett to help the AFL shingle-weavers on strike. Five of his Wobbly pals—a Frenchman, a German, an Irishman, a Jew and a Swede—had been killed by vigilantes as they came in to dock. It had shown the international nature of the IWW.

Another guy told of being in Sedro Woolley the year before, when he and the other Wobs had been whipped with rope ends and then had hot tar poured on their bleeding flesh. He unbuttoned his shirt to show us his scars: "So you can see why I'm going to Centralia—I have a little score to settle."

Then another fellow worker, who was from Centralia, told of being there the year before when the Wobbly hall was raided. The secretary was taken out into the woods, made to run the gauntlet and almost beaten to death. The mob had completely wrecked the hall, even ripped the planks off its walls. Then they'd lifted the Wobs by their ears onto some trucks one by one, knocked them unconscious, and hauled them out and dumped them at the county line.

Others told of Wobs they knew who had been hanged out in the woods. Another Wob who had also been in Centralia told of how a few months before, the local newsie, who was blind, was kidnapped and dumped over the county line for selling the IWW paper. What a coincidence, I thought, because back at the hall in Seattle I had just been reading a brilliant essay by Helen Keller about why she had joined the IWW—maybe that's what had made that blind news vendor pro-Wobbly.

After a while, as the train rolled south, we began singing again to try to bolster our spirits: "Solidarity Forever," written back in 1915 by one of our members, Ralph Chaplin; and some of Joe Hill's songs like "Mister Block" and "Pie in the Sky" and "Get the

Bosses Off Your Back." We were a bunch of singing fools in those days. It was the glue that held the IWW together.

As the train slowed coming in to Tacoma, we all braced ourselves and prepared a plan of action in case the bulls tried to grab us or dump us off the train. But fortunately we didn't see any bulls.

Just before we pulled out, a few Wobblies from Tacoma jumped into our boxcar. One was a guy in his late thirties who had a look on his face like he'd just been taken on a guided tour of hell. Some of the Wobs in my car knew him and gathered around him in the center of the jolting boxcar. He'd just come up from Centralia to round up more fellow workers to go down there, and he filled us in on what had happened. He had a far-off look in his eyes, like he was still in a state of shock.

He had been in the Arnold Hotel earlier that day, right across the street from the Wobbly hall, and he had seen the whole thing. The Legionnaires had come marching along and stopped right in front of the hall. Some of them were carrying Wobbly neckties, others carried clubs or pipes. This time the Wobs were ready for them. They were good and fed up with having their halls wrecked all over the state. Their lawyer, Elmer Smith, had advised them the day before that they had the legal right to defend the hall. "A damn good shyster, Elmer Smith," our informant said with reverence in his voice. "You know what the plutes say: 'A lawyer with a heart is as dangerous as a working man with brains.'

"So there they were in front of our hall. All of a sudden a whistle sounded and somebody yelled, 'Let's go! At 'em, boys!' And then all hell broke loose. A bunch of the marchers rushed for the hall. Some of 'em busted the door down and glass was flying everywhere. Then one of our boys—Wesley Everest, still in his army uniform—yelled out: 'I fought for democracy in France and I'm going to fight for it here!'

"And then as the Legionnaires busted in and the shooting began, one of the attackers keeled over right in the entrance. Then two more of them fell. Then the shooting stopped and the rest of the marchers swarmed into the hall. And a couple of minutes later I saw Wesley Everest hightailing it down the street with a mob behind him, down toward the river.

"I sneaked out the back way from the hotel and ran out into the woods to wait for a freight. By the time one came along, the whole town was like an armed camp."

Wesley Everest

The newcomer paused, catching his breath, the look of fear still in his eyes. Then he advised us, if possible, to jump off the train outside town and hide in the woods until we could size the situation up.

We discussed what to do as the train jolted on south. But we couldn't come up with any plan better than what he'd suggested. Finally, after the conversation subsided, I just sat listening to the clack–clack of the wheels on the rails, hoping it would all turn out all right.

We got into Centralia a little before dark. But the train didn't slow down enough for us to jump off until we were almost into town. Maybe a few of our boys managed to escape out into the woods, but most of us didn't have a chance. The whole town was patrolled by hundreds of Legionnaires and the plug–uglies of the lumber barons. As soon as I was yanked out of the boxcar I heard someone yell, "Let's lynch 'em here, boys!" And I could see that at least one of the hooligans was carrying a Wobbly necktie over his arm. Then three or four of the scumbags grabbed me at once. I managed to slip loose and deck one of them, but then something hit me on the back of the head and I passed out.

Next thing I knew, we were being herded downtown to the jailhouse. And all along the route those hoodlums kept yelling profanities at us, throwing stuff at us and trying to break through the cordon of vigilantes to jab something at us or punch us out.

We finally got to the jail. I could see at once that the local bulls weren't in control: The Legionnaires and other cat's paws of the lumber trust had taken over. Legionnaires were strutting around everywhere, barking orders at the cops and the poor stiffs in the slammer. The jailed Wobblies were a sorry–looking lot—their clothes all ripped, bruises where they'd been hit or jabbed or clubbed, but they stood there peering out as defiant and unbeaten as if they had the world by the balls.

I was thrown into a cell with several other men. At first we newcomers just stood there numb–like, looking around us, hearing the yells and curses and threats of the mob outside.

Maybe because I was the youngest, this red–haired fellow about thirty came up to me and put his arm on mine. "Don't be afraid, son," he said. "We'll be outside and they'll be in here before this shebang is over."

Then he introduced himself. I was surprised to learn that he was our lawyer, Elmer Smith, who had advised the local Wobs they had the right to defend their hall.

Like a fool, I asked him what he was in for. He gave a grim smile. "We call it self-defense. They call it murder," he said. Then he added: "Just for advising the boys of their constitutional rights, apparently."

It was a cold November day, and the jails provided no blankets in those days. Elmer Smith was one of the few who had any blankets, and he insisted on giving me one. And shortly after that, he gave his last blanket to another young Wobbly who didn't have one.

A little before dark we heard a deafening clamor—even louder than the clamor that had been going on outside the jail all along. It must have sounded like this in the early days of Rome when they brought in the Christians to be eaten by the lions, I thought. Through the high barred window we could barely see the crowd parting as a big party of men dragged somebody down the street toward us by a leather strap around his neck. Hundreds of people kicked and beat the prostrate form as it was dragged along.

As the crazed mob got closer, the Wobblies about me in the jail suddenly fell silent. We could see that the form being dragged along the street was in uniform. "Wesley Everest," somebody gasped. We watched speechless as the body was dragged closer. Some of the men had tears running down their cheeks.

Then, when the mob was only a few dozen yards away, we could see that the bleeding figure being dragged along still showed signs of life. He was twisting and turning, being dragged by the neck, constantly kicked and slugged, his protruding eyes peering out helplessly like those of a dying dog run over in the street.

When they got to the front of the jail they yanked him to his feet and slammed him against the wall. Several voices clamored to hang him on the spot, and somebody slipped a noose around his neck. Then we heard from that form which most people would have thought too near death to think—let alone talk—a high, ringing, vibrant voice yell out: "You haven't got guts enough to lynch a man in broad daylight!"

Then someone smashed the muzzle of his rifle into Everest's face, and all we could see was a mass of broken teeth and blood where his face had been.

A moment later, to everyone's astonishment, a solitary woman stepped through the mob and accused them of being a gang of cowards and criminals to treat anyone like that. And she calmly stepped up to the bloody hulk and removed the noose from Wesley Everest's neck.

Next thing we knew, the front door of the jail opened. They dragged Everest's body in and slammed it down onto the concrete floor of the corridor between the cells—for all of us to see as an example, I guess. Everest just lay there bleeding, apparently almost unconscious now, and we were helpless to do anything but watch.

Night came on. The furor in the street grew even louder. Through the bars we could heard snatches of the Legionnaires' conversation, about sending posses out to search for Wobblies in the woods, of breaking into all the homes in town to look for IWW literature, of lynching all of us.

Elmer Smith filled me in a little on what had happened. A few days before, when they heard rumors of the impending raid, he had asked for protection from the local police and even traveled to Olympia to ask the governor for protection. Nothing had worked. Then he pointed out to me, in adjoining cells, the men who had been captured in the hall: Bert Faulkner, Ray Becker the former minister, Britt Smith the stocky secretary, Mike Sheehan, and James McInerney. They all had the cool but defiant look of strong, intelligent men who knew they had done the right and the moral thing. Smith told me they had been taken one by one all afternoon into an adjoining room, brutally questioned, threatened and assaulted.

As he was saying this I heard a scream. Smith told me that must be the youngest of the captured men, Loren Roberts, whom they'd been questioning for hours. Roberts was finally brought out and thrown into a nearby cell, trembling from head to foot. He sat up on the cell floor, sobbing. We could see the men about him try to comfort the youth, but he just sat there talking to himself. And it gradually dawned on everybody that his mind had snapped.

A few minutes later some of the mob suddenly rushed in, grabbed James McInerney, and dragged him out to the street. I don't know why they singled him out. When they got him out in the street, the mob howled like hogs at feeding time. They put a noose around his neck and threw it over some kind of crossbar. Then one of the chief tormentors asked McInerney to confess that the Wobblies had shot before the Legionnaires rushed the hall.

McInerney replied, "Go to hell." And so they yanked on the rope and lifted him off the ground by the neck—and after a minute, lowered him again. They asked him again to confess. Again he said, "Go to hell." So they jerked him up again. The same process went on and on for maybe twenty minutes. Finally the mob gave up or got bored and threw him back in his cell.

About nine or ten at night suddenly all the lights in the town went off. You can imagine how terrified we were. This is it, we thought. The howling of the mob outside grew louder. Then we could see the headlights of three big expensive automobiles coming slowly through the crowd.

The front door of the jail opened and a crowd of men surged in, foaming at the mouth, yelling and cursing at all of us. It was soon evident what they wanted. The one in the lead kicked at the body of Wesley Everest, and the prone figure seemed to come to life faintly. Then, as they began to drag him toward the door, one last glimmer of life force seemed to rise in him, and he gasped out to us in a hoarse voice: "Tell the boys I died for my class." Then we saw them dump him in the back seat of one of the cars, and they sped off into the night.

Several times later in the night the lights went off again and the mob came in and dragged someone out. We never saw any of those Wobblies again. They must have dragged eight or ten of us out that night. Rumor had it later they had been burned alive in the big incinerators at the mills.

I don't think anybody slept that night. We were too afraid the mob might break in at any minute and lynch us all. And every so often they dragged in some new Wob they'd captured to join us.

Along towards dawn a Wobbly was thrown in jail who knew what had happened to Wesley Everest. When Everest first escaped from the Wobbly hall, he said, they had chased him down to the banks of the Skookumchuck River. Everest had waded out into the river, but found the current too strong and turned back to face the mob. "If there's a bull in the crowd, I'll submit to arrest," he said. "Otherwise, stand back." But a Legionnaire named Dale Hubbard, a nephew of the owner of the lumber trust, rushed for Everest. Everest shot him dead. Then the mob was on him, beating him almost senseless. Many wanted to hang him on the spot, but instead they tied the leather strap around his neck and dragged him to jail.

When they dragged him back out of jail after the night lights went out, Everest was put in the back seat of one of the big cars, between two men. One of them, a doctor, castrated him on the way to the river. Then they hung him from a trestle. They seemed to have trouble getting the rope tied right, and they threw him off the bridge three separate times. Then they played the headlights of the cars on his dangling body and spent a long time filling his body with slugs.

The new inmate, finishing his story, sat down on the concrete cell floor and sank his head in his hands, tears running down his cheeks. The howling of the mob outside went on and on, and I felt like my head was about to split open. Finally, about dawn, I wrapped myself in the blanket Elmer Smith had given me and managed to get a little sleep sitting against one wall of the cell — there were no bunks in the jail at all.

When I woke up, things had calmed down a little. The jailers begrudgingly gave us a little food — if you could call it that. It was the worst chuck I ever tried to swill down. Slumgullion would be much too fancy a term to describe it.

There were still a few dozen Legionnaires and other people milling around outside the jail. Occasionally we could hear what they were saying. At one point somebody rushed up to what appeared to be some big shot and said: "Everest's body has disappeared. I was just down at the river, and somebody's cut it down." A look of alarm came over the big shot's face. "We've got to get that body," he said. "Or the Wobs will find it and raise hell over its condition." They immediately began organizing search parties, and they all rushed off toward the river.

A few hours later they brought Wesley Everest's body — or what was left of it — back to the jail and dumped it in the corridor again, for all of us to see. It was an almost unrecognizable, bloody mess. And they left it there for two days, within a few feet of us, before they finally took it out and buried it in an unmarked grave.

5

LAWYER FOR THE DAMNED

Not long after, we got the news that our most famous shyster, George Vanderveer, the brilliant "lawyer for the damned," was on his way to Centralia to undertake the defense of our fellow workers. It was Vanderveer who had gotten our men off at Everett, Washington when they were charged with murder after their attackers shot one of their own men by mistake, and who had defended our 101 top leaders in the big trial in Chicago the year after. Also coming to cover the trial was Ralph Chaplin, one of our best writers and publicists, author of "Solidarity Forever." After this news the prisoners rested a little easier.

After a few days they released us Wobblies who hadn't been in Centralia at the time of the shootings. But those other poor stiffs had to stay in. They had jailed two or three more now that they claimed had been firing from outside the hall. We parted from our fellow workers in jail, telling them we'd do everything we could to get them released. We spent the next couple of days visiting the families of the prisoners, contributing food and money to them and helping out any way we could.

While we were still in Centralia, we heard some of the ghouls of the Legion laughing about a speech the coroner had made at the Elks Club a day or two before. In explaining the death of

Wesley Everest, the coroner told the audience that Everest had broken out of jail, gone to the Chehalis River bridge and jumped off with a rope around his neck. Finding it too short, he climbed up the rope to the bridge and put a longer rope around his neck. Then he jumped off again, broke his neck, and shot himself full of holes. They said the people at the Elks Club had roared over the story. We Wobblies found it about as funny as a crutch.

It didn't seem we could do much more around Centralia, and we were taking our lives in our hands every second we stayed in that sorry burg. So while we were waiting for the trial to begin the following year, some of us began to spread out over the state to tell the truth about what had really happened in Centralia. Both the IWW and the AFL papers in Seattle, and a lot of other labor papers in the state, had been shut down immediately after the raid, and the plute press was spreading a barrage of lies.

An Associated Press reporter was run out of Centralia in fear for his life when he learned the truth of the matter as revealed at the coroner's inquest: A local doctor who had been in the parade testified that the marchers had broken into the hall before the first shots were fired.

Posses were looking for Wobblies everywhere, houses of suspected Wobs were being broken into, and over a thousand Wobs were arrested under the new "criminal syndicalism" law for just having a red card. We felt our only hope was to get the truth out. So I went around the state with a few other Wobs spreading the word, and at the same time trying to keep undercover. I worked here and there in the woods under a fake name, trying to make a stake for the winter.

The trial was held in the county courthouse in Montesano, in the next county to the west, one of the most reactionary areas in the state. I was in Montesano the first day of the trial, in late January 1920. Mounted policemen swarmed through the town. And the Legion had raised enough money to pay fifty uniformed Legionnaires four dollars a day to sit in the courtroom every day of the two-and-a-half month trial.

I started up toward the courthouse with some other Wobblies to give our moral support to the defendants. We were decked out in our usual attire—caulked shoes, overalls, stag shirts and mackinaws—because we couldn't afford fancier duds. But before we could even get up into the courthouse, some bulls came after us and asked us where we thought we were going. When we told them they said, "Oh no, you're not—you're coming with us to the bucket."

"On what charge?" we asked.

"On suspicion."

"Suspicion of what?"

"Just suspicion."

We were carted off to jail. It had never occurred to us that, right there by the courthouse, where a trial that had nationwide publicity was going on, with dozens of reporters around, anything could happen to us.

In the police station the bulls found a red card on one of my fellow prisoners, and one of them said, "So you're an IWW, huh? We'll fix that." And he tore up his red card. Another bull said, "Well, you're not an IWW anymore." My fellow worker replied, "But you can't tear it out of my heart." And so we spent a month in jail, just because we were dressed like loggers.

While we were in jail, we would hear from other, more recent inmates what was going on at the trial. One of our lawyers had been run out of town, and our head shyster Vanderveer had had his life threatened several times. He and Ralph Chaplin had to commute to court every day from Aberdeen, sixteen miles away, because no hotel in Montesano would rent a room to them.

At the beginning of the trial, when the first two defense witnesses told of seeing the hall door broken down before the first shots were fired, they were immediately arrested on charges of perjury. It was obviously a scare tactic to intimidate later witnesses. But even that fascist court didn't have the audacity to bring them to trial on the perjury charges.

I finally got out of the hoosegow. The trial was still in progress. And now a new touch had been added. The lumber barons had circulated a rumor that over a thousand Wobblies were lying in wait in the surrounding hills, about to pounce on the courthouse and kill everyone in sight. On this pretext they got a squad of U.S. army troops billeted on the courthouse lawn, tents and all, to further intimidate the witnesses and jurors. When I saw this I really got my Irish up, and I decided to try again.

This time, strange to say, they let me in the courtroom. Maybe because some of the facts had come out by now, and things were beginning to look a little better for my fellow workers. Vanderveer had uncovered conclusive evidence that, three weeks before Armistice Day, some of the town's leading officials had met at the

Elks Club and conspired to raid the Wobbly hall. And a whole slew of witnesses had sworn the break-in came before the shots were fired. Several more testified they had seen the postmaster and a minister carrying ropes in the parade.

At one point Vanderveer did something very clever. The prosecuting attorneys had coached three witnesses to say they had seen Eugene Barnett, one of the Wobblies, in the upstairs window of a hotel across the street from the hall just before the raid. The first two identified him as the third man in line in the row of defendants in the dock. Then Vanderveer asked for a recess. When the trial resumed a few minutes later, Barnett was no longer the third in line. The prosecution's next witness broke down in confusion and failed to identify Barnett.

It was inspiring to see the brave front put up by those Wobblies on trial for their lives. They never flinched or stammered once in their testimony or changed it one iota, no matter how long or hard the six prosecution attorneys hammered at them. Ray Becker, a former preacher, idealism shining from his eyes; Eugene Barnett, who had a gentle backwoodsy strength about him; Britt Smith, the Centralia secretary, solid as a rock; and Elmer Smith, the milk of human kindness in his eyes, on trial for murder only because he had advised the others of their constitutional rights.

The best-known reporter at the trial was the IWW's own Ralph Chaplin. He was a handsome cuss, with his big shock of wavy black hair and those penetrating eyes that seemed to love everything they looked at but seemed to see right into you, too. I met Chaplin at a little get-together one night after the ordeal of court. I surprised everybody by reciting by heart his poem about the Paint Creek, West Virginia miners' strike, "When the Leaves Come Out." Afterward he came up to me and gave me an autographed copy of one of his books of poems and shot the bull with me for a while.

The courtroom was full of drama. Through the entire two-and-a-half months, the wife of the slain Legion commander and the wife of Eugene Barnett sat near each other but never once exchanged a glance. All the while, their two young children played together in the aisle.

Around the middle of March the trial finally drew to an end. There was drenching rain that day, and the court was so packed the reporters had to climb over chairs and tables to get to the press room. Vanderveer summed up our case: "I am asking you to

The Centralia defendants outside the Montesano jail. Front row, from left: Mike Sheehan, John Lamb, Eugene Barnett, Bert Bland, and Elmer Smith. Back row: Loren Roberts, James McInerney, Britt Smith, O. C. Bland, Bert Faulkner, and Ray Becker.

decide the fate of organized labor in the Northwest, whether its fundamental rights are to survive or be trampled underfoot."

The jury's first verdict was manslaughter for some of the defendants, but the judge refused to accept it and ordered them back to the jury room. In their second verdict they exonerated Elmer Smith and one other, declared the boy whose mind had snapped under torture insane, and found the others guilty of second degree murder, with a recommendation of extreme leniency.

Then came a hush as the judge read the sentence: twenty-five to forty years in prison.

None of us could believe it. Such a harsh sentence, with the recommendation of leniency completely ignored. I saw tears running down Vanderveer's cheeks. Many people in court were openly crying, myself among them. But the men in the dock looked as defiant and righteous as ever, their heads unbowed.

Two years later, six of the jurors signed affidavits declaring the trial unfair. But the Wobblies remained in prison. Later I traveled all over the West, sometimes with Elmer Smith, who spent the rest of his life working for their release. And every year I would take several boxes of apples out to the prison at Walla Walla to those innocent men who had been buried alive.

6

DISHES ON THE ROOF

The Centralia episode left a bad taste in my mouth for a long time. It did for all of us. When you see the cards stacked completely against you like that, with nowhere to turn, it makes you feel pretty hopeless—and at the same time, fighting mad. As we used to say: "Justice can only be found in the dictionary."

And when people are killed, even if some of them are your enemies, it makes you do a lot of serious thinking. Thinking about what's wrong with the whole goddamn system, and about whether there's some better approach to trying to fix things up, or whether it's possible to fix things up at all. A lot of us Wobs felt that if the courts were going to ignore the laws and the U.S. Constitution like that and screw us all ways coming, then anything goes: If they play dirty, then we will too. That is, up to the point of killing. Unlike the capitalist class, we believed in violence against people only in self-defense.

But let me backtrack a little. The winter of 1919–1920, while we were waiting for the Centralia trial to begin and I had been working at various jobs in the area, a number of important events occurred. One was the Palmer raids, when U.S. attorney general Palmer and his assistant, J. Edgar Hoover, led raids on dozens of IWW halls all over the country and seized tons of our files and literature. And this time they didn't even have the phony excuse that we were impeding the war effort. Seizing our membership lists, they deported hundreds of our members. But every action has its reaction: Not long after this, the American Civil Liberties Union was formed—by Roger Baldwin with IWW orator and organizer Joe Ettor and a few others, to try to uphold the Bill of Rights and protect personal freedom.

Also that winter the United States invaded Siberia, joining England and France to help the Russian forces fighting against the Bolsheviks. We didn't know much about the Bolshies, but at least we knew they had overthrown the terrible dictatorship of the czar. So Wobblies on the waterfront refused to load ships with arms for the U.S. forces in Siberia.

While I was working in Seattle, president Woodrow Wilson visited the city. Many Wobblies had divided feelings about Wilson. Some admired Wilson for supporting the League of Nations and trying to foster international cooperation. But we Wobblies all hated his guts for coming down on the IWW so hard, merely because we were asking for a tiny percentage of the vastly increased profits big business was making from the war. Whether he opposed us out of ignorance, malice or an opportunistic desire to placate the owners of industry, I don't know. Or perhaps he didn't even give it a thought.

The owners of industry and their flunkies have access to the White House and the halls of Congress, and can offer their bribes and political support in a "civilized" way. But the oppressed have to raise hell, usually at great risk to themselves—to interfere with production and profits or commit some "outrage"—before they get any attention. And that, in a nutshell, is why we need a syndicalist law-making body, a workers' Congress, so the workers can get their voices heard without having to resort to desperate measures.

When Wilson came to Seattle, the Wobblies were ready for him. After the success of our strike for the eight-hour day in 1917, we had signed up over 25,000 members in the Northwest among the lumber workers alone.

The presidential procession started through Seattle. And there was the chief bull o' the woods himself, standing up in his limousine in his silk hat, waving to everyone. Thousands of hero-worshippers were going crazy, yelling and applauding. Then the procession came to a stretch of four or five blocks where there was nothing but Wobblies lining the streets. There we were, thousands of us, in our blue shirts and jeans and our caulked boots, standing with folded arms, not emitting so much as a whisper. After all the tumult and shouting, suddenly there was total silence. After half a block or so you could see His Highness visibly melt. After two blocks he sat down in his car. And didn't stand up again until the yapping slave ruckus began again two or three blocks farther on.

The first job I got that winter was as a dishwasher in a greasy spoon down near the docks. At first I was so broke the only place I could afford to stay was in the notorious Hotel de Gink on the skid road near Profanity Hill, the red light district. Every type of flea, bedbug and louse ever seen—both animal and human—could be found between its musty walls. Some 'bo had tacked up a little placard in the stinking hallway outside my room that read:

Put no ham sandwiches on my casket, but give me a mulligan stew through the path of life, Amen!

After my first payday I was able to move to a boardinghouse I had heard about. It was run by the mother of the soon-to-be-famous "Boxcar" Bertha Thompson. I hightailed it down there as soon as I got my pay and rented a room. Mrs. Thompson was a very nice woman, and she would rent rooms to only Wobblies or socialists.

Sitting around the dinner table there one night, when she and her daughter Bertha weren't around, I heard one of the boarders tell their story. A few years before, our landlady and her then husband, Walker C. Smith, had been speaking in favor of free thinking in the Midwest. Just before Bertha was born they were thrown in jail for giving these speeches in some little town in Kansas or Nebraska. And Bertha had been born in jail. Later the parents split up.

Now Walker C. Smith edited our IWW paper, the *Industrial Worker*, here in Seattle. He was well known, especially as author of a little book called "Sabotage" which he'd written a few years before as a guest of Jack London at his ranch in Glen Ellen, California. By "sabotage" the Wobblies usually meant the *slowdown*, a withdrawal of efficiency on the job commensurate with their ill treatment by the employer. I got to know Bertha and her mother, and later I took a couple of hobo-ing trips with Boxcar Bertha.

The skid road in Seattle, down along Washington Street, was an interesting place. It was called that because originally that's where the loggers had skidded logs down to the docks to be loaded on ships. Now you could find almost everything there: Sky-pilots preaching pie in the sky and trying to lure you to their churches. Con artists selling snake oil. Health fanatics trying to sell you exercise programs or special diets. Pimps and whores. But the most interesting and entertaining of the denizens of the skid road were the Wobbly soapboxers.

One day, shortly after I got my dishwashing job, I was walking along through the crowd at the edge of the skid road, and this guy suddenly shouted out: "I've been robbed! I've been robbed!"

He began grabbing at his pockets as a crowd gathered around him. Then he jumped up on a box and said: "I've been robbed by the capitalist system!"

Then he launched into a brilliant spiel about how workers were robbed of most of the product of their labor. Somebody said his name was Jack Phelan.

A couple of the other Wobbly orators were "Red" Doran and C. B. Ellis. The latter was an accountant, and he would set up a blackboard and carefully draw detailed graphs and charts illustrating just how much the master class was exploiting the workers.

But the best speaker was Big Jim Thompson—"silver-voiced Jim." He was an enormous blue-eyed guy with a huge mustache who had played a leading role in some of the biggest strikes in the country. He had a loud, clear, beautiful voice that could be heard a mile away. He liked to quote from Lincoln's 1864 address to Congress: "Labor is prior to and independent of capital. Capital could not have existed if labor had not first existed... Labor is superior to capital and deserves much higher consideration... To secure to each laborer the whole product of his labor is a worthy object of any government." And he told how Lincoln went on to warn laboring people never to surrender their power—which, if they did, would lead them into slavery.

At the end of his speeches, Thompson would invite his listeners to come and line up with the One Big Union at the Wobbly hall. You would see all these loggers going down the street after him, looking like an army of fireflies as the metal strips on their caulked boots struck the sidewalk and threw off sparks.

I spent a lot of time in the Wobbly hall reading—when it was opened up again after the Centralia terror. Some of my favorites were Jack London's *The Iron Heel* and "Dream of Debs," and Markham's "The Man with the Hoe." And Robert Service's poem, "Song of the Wage Slave." And Robert Burns' "A Man's a Man for a' That," with the line about how the time is coming when "...we'll brothers be the world o'er for a' that."

And I read the anarchist prince Kropotkin's book, *Mutual Aid*, in which he tries to show how, in the animal kingdom, there is as strong a tendency toward mutual help as there is for self preservation and survival of the fittest—citing the case where Darwin found pelicans bringing fish to a blind pelican. Kropotkin thereby hoped to lay the foundation for a more democratic sort of organization for society than the capitalists or the marxists advocate. And there was Upton Sinclair's anthology of proletarian literature, *Cry for Justice*. I was amazed to read in it how, at one time in ancient Rome, there had been a syndicalist society where the workers had called the shots. If they could do it way back then, why can't we do it now, I thought. After doing all this reading I began to write my first poems, most of them on proletarian subjects.

While washing dishes, I did a lot of thinking. The Centralia case and the wave of anti-Wobbly terrorism the press had whipped up after it made a lot of us realize that if we were going to stay in the IWW, the battle ahead might get tougher and tougher, and we had better be able to defend ourselves. I decided to start working out in gyms every chance I could and learn to handle myself really well—so that, if I did have to fight, I'd be ready for the plug-uglies of the master class. I started going to this gym down on Second Avenue every chance I got.

I had mixed feelings about fighting. My dad always said: If you must use your fists, do it in a good cause. I had always been gentle like my dad. I had never wanted to fight. When I was a little kid of eight or nine, several times I was beaten up by kids smaller than myself. Then one time my mother said: "Why don't you hit them back next time?" It had never occurred to me.

The next time I was attacked, I remembered what my mother had said and lashed out blindly. I connected and really laid out the bully who was attacking me. I was amazed, pleasantly surprised at what I'd been able to do. At the same time I felt pity for the guy I had decked. Then the bullies laid off me for a while.

Later I was forced into more scraps. And the worst of it, the really unbearable part, was getting beaten. You could get your face messed up. Strange to say, I didn't get much satisfaction out of laying somebody out either. I always felt sorry for him.

If I had to fight, the greatest satisfaction came when I was trading blows with someone I was evenly matched with. The good exhilarating feeling of the other guy's blows on your flesh if they weren't too awfully hard. Looking into your opponent's eyes and seeing the look of respect, almost brotherly love and comradeship, when you got in a good punch. The sense that you were really pals and both damned good at what you were doing and filled with a delicious youthful strength and energy.

One day when I was working out at the gym, this guy who helped out at the Wobbly hall saw me sparring and said, "Hey, why don't you come and box at the hall? We have a smoker with four three–round bouts once a month."

I thought it over. Hell, I was only fourteen. I was almost six feet four, and I weighed a good 195 now with the free grub from my job. But I was still a little unsure of myself, so I turned him down. In the meantime I started practicing in the gym more and more. The next time I was asked to box at the Wobbly hall I finally agreed.

There's a big difference between roughhouse brawling and real boxing. In roughhouse brawls I probably could have licked ninety–nine stiffs out of a hundred. But, like many others, I learned the hard way that real boxing was different. It takes a hell of a lot of technique, training and stamina.

The night of my first bout there must have been five hundred members crowded into the Wobbly hall. It wasn't just boxing. First there was singing, led by Katie Phar, the "Wobbly songbird." She was a little gal, only about four feet tall, but how she could sing! It was Katie—and not Elizabeth Gurley Flynn, as the history books say—who inspired Joe Hill's song, "The Rebel Girl." After the singing came a couple of lectures on the class struggle by Big Jim Thompson and a woman named Kate Sadler, who was also a terrific speaker. And then a skit about the Everett massacre, by Walker C. Smith. And through it all I was shaking like a leaf.

The fight finally began. My opponent was a twenty–year–old Swede logger called Battling Swensson. He was only about five feet eleven, but he was solid muscle. I was so much bigger than he was, I figured he would be a pushover. The bell rang and I put my dukes up. Before I knew what hit me the lights went out. I was down flat on my back. I just lay there shaking my head until the count of nine. I was more careful from then on, but by the end of the third round I was out on my feet. It was all I could do to last the three rounds.

I was determined to find out what I'd done wrong. Now I spent every available minute at the gym working out. A month later I figured I was ready for another try at it.

This time my opponent was an East Indian, one of those big Sikhs who had terrified the Germans in the war. He called himself the Punjab Jabber. Most of the Indians who went in for fighting preferred wrestling, but the Jabber was an exception. He stood about six feet one. He had a big easygoing smile and looked like the friendliest guy on earth. But when that bell rang he was all business. This time I wasn't knocked down, and I gave a better account of myself than I had with the Swede—but when the final bell sounded I knew I wasn't the winner. What Kipling wrote about Gunga Din was the real goods, all right—some of these East Indian stiffs were plenty tough and plenty smart.

I decided I'd try one more time. This time my opponent was a guy about twenty-two who called himself Slugger Kelly. He looked like he was made of solid steel. Just before the fight, this Wobbly delegate I knew sidled up to me. "I hope you settle his hash, Joe," he said in a low voice. "We're pretty sure he's a stool-pigeon. He's been seen twice in the company of undercover bulls. And he said before he blowed into Seattle he worked at the Neversweat camp over by Humptulips. We checked with some of our boys in that misnamed insect laboratory, and they'd never heard of 'im."

That was all the motivation I needed. This time I was determined to win. In the few minutes remaining before the fight I mapped out a new strategy.

The fight started. I deliberately held back, concentrating on defense, letting Kelly wear himself out as I slowly retreated round and round the ring. As the first round was coming to an end I got a worried look on my face and started backing up faster. He took the bait and advanced on me more aggressively, dropping his guard. Then, as he rushed at me for the kill, I suddenly stepped back, stopped, and let him have it in an uppercut with everything I had. "That one's for Frank Little," I said under my breath. He just stood there stunned. "This one's for Wesley Everest," I said, and pile-drived a left into him. He started to fall. "And here's for Joe Hill." I clobbered him with another right-hand uppercut as he fell toward the mat. He was out for about fifteen minutes. Nobody saw him any more around Seattle after that.

After the fights, two of the editors of the *Industrial Worker* came up to me and asked for an interview. One was Walker C. Smith, the father of Boxcar Bertha. The other was one of the earliest Wobblies of all, a man of about sixty named Mortimer Downing. In the course of the conversation it came out that he was one of the 165 top Wobs convicted of opposing the war effort in the big trial of 1918, now out on appeal. The trial had been divided into three parts: the Chicago trial, the Wichita trial and the Sacramento trial. After Bill Haywood and the other hundred top leaders had been shafted by the government at the Chicago trial, Downing and the others in Sacramento had figured it was hopeless. So they had staged the famous "silent defense" in which none of them had said a single word during the entire trial, to show their contempt for the stacked deck they knew was against them.

Naturally I was flattered by Smith's and Downing's interest in me. They asked me if I had a nickname as a boxer, and I said no. So they dubbed me "Kid Murphy," and the name stuck. They gave me a nice write-up, and later I began submitting some of my poems to the paper. I continued boxing now and then, polishing my technique little by little, gradually winning more and more of my bouts. But unfortunately—or perhaps fortunately—like most Wobs I had to hit the road and look for work, so I never was able to give my undivided attention to boxing. Anyway, I was more interested in the class struggle and organizing for the IWW.

About the same time all this was going on, the waitresses at the restaurant I worked at went on strike. The waitresses were nice gals. A couple of them had been left in the lurch with young children by their scissorbill boyfriends, and they were just scraping by. The café owner announced a cut in pay. My pay was going to be cut, too. It didn't bother me too much, because spring was coming and I was about to shake the lousy job and go back to work in the crops. But I felt sorry for those poor waitresses.

"Look," I told them. "You don't have to put up with this. There are a couple of hundred out-of-work Wobblies hanging around the IWW hall who could help you if you went on strike." I convinced them to have a meeting with one of the delegates from the hall, and they all lined up—joined the IWW. I think it was mainly because I told them about a strike tactic I'd heard about, that Seattle Wobblies had used in a café strike a few years before.

It worked like this: The waitresses gave the owner their demand that he rescind the pay cut, and he locked everyone out, including me. Just before that, seeing the handwriting on the wall, I had made my own special contribution: While the boss was in the front of the café arguing with the waitresses, I got a ladder and put all the dishes on the roof. I've never believed in stealing, but this was more in the order of temporary misplacement.

About eleven in the morning the waitresses began picketing. The owner was mad as hell. I didn't stick around to see the look on his face when he went back to the kitchen. But I did circle around a couple of blocks and took up my station in another little greasy spoon across the street to watch the action. The owner, tighter than the bark on a tree, had managed to rustle up some other dishes somewhere, and to get some of his family members to wait on customers.

About eleven-thirty, Wobblies began arriving from the hall. The waitresses made a big pretense of shouting and cussing at them as they went through their picket line. The Wobs took every available seat at the long counter and in all the booths. And all, to the last man, ordered a cup of coffee. One cup of coffee. And dawdled over it for an hour. The few plutes or scissorbills who crossed through the picket line gave one look inside and gave up and left. When the lunch-hour rush was over, the Wobblies paid up and left. Except for a couple who had ordered T-bone steaks and, when it came time to pay, said, "Charge it to the mayor" and ran out the door—an old Wobbly tactic.

Well, the skinflint owner endured it for three days, then finally gave in. After that he stayed away from the place most of the time and let the ladies run the place pretty much as they liked.

7

'WE'RE <u>ALL</u> LEADERS'

It was getting along toward spring now. There wasn't much work around Seattle. I was getting restless and wanted to try to make some money doing farm work. I wrote a long letter home to my folks, and another one to my brother Emmett, and then went around and said goodbye to my friends. Then I got my bindle together, went down to the freight yards, and glommed the guts of a rattler heading east toward Wenatchee and the orchard belt. This time I was lucky and didn't run into any railroad bulls.

When I got to Wenatchee I had some java and a doughnut in a greasy spoon, and then found my way to the Wobbly hall. A couple of the stiffs there surprised me by coming up and addressing me as "Kid Murphy." They had seen me clobber the fink, "Slugger Kelly," in the hall in Seattle and they gave me a good reception. The only trouble was that now, whenever they expected trouble, they came to me because they knew me as a good fighter —a reputation I couldn't shake.

Sometimes it seemed like trouble followed me around. I hadn't been there ten minutes when a couple of Wobs burst into the hall and told us a strike had just started at a big apple orchard outside town where hundreds of saplings were being planted. The farmer had told the workers he'd pay a certain wage, then cut the pay once they started working. They had all quit and begun picketing.

There were about forty Wobs in the hall. The secretary called an impromptu meeting and we discussed our strategy. There were only a couple of slave markets in town open that time of year, and it was almost certain the farmer would be coming in to them looking for strikebreakers. We decided *we* would be the "strike-breakers."

It was decided that the new Wobs in town, myself included, would go down to the slave markets first, to make it less likely the farmer would spot any known Wobblies. As luck would have it, just about that time a freight came into town from the east and about fifty new Wobs came traipsing up to the hall.

We started off toward the slave market in ones and twos and threes, the out-of-towners first. Our plan was to get hired, go out to the farm, stage a slowdown and finally join our fellow workers on strike.

Sure enough, just about the time we got to the first slave market, Farmer John came chugging into town in his Maxwell— no small-time operator this one. He sort of squinted at us, then asked if there were any Wobblies in the group. None of us had even heard of the term. He offered to pay us a couple of cents more an hour than the strikers, and took on about forty of us. Then he gave us directions to his plantation a couple of miles outside town.

It was getting along toward mid-afternoon. When we got to the place we found our fellow workers picketing and dancing around and singing Wobbly songs, generally enjoying themselves. No one had dared cross their lively picket line, not even the farmer's sons. At first they stopped singing and started giving us downright mean looks as we approached. Then, when they recognized some of us, they began putting on the best performance of fake hostility I've ever seen, calling us everything in the book.

The farmer put-putted up in his limo. When we drew back a little in pretended fright he upped the pay a couple cents more an hour, gave us a few instructions, then beat a hasty retreat to his farm house—or maybe to look for the sheriff. Both groups of men kept up our opera bouffe. Our fellow workers gave us a few playful nudges as we crossed their picket line, just in case Farmer John was still watching in his rear view mirror.

We came to the long rows of saplings we were hired to plant. A bleary-eyed kid about my own age who said he hadn't slept since he'd climbed on a freight in Idaho the day before, looked down at one of the small saplings and asked with apparent sincerity: "Which end of these things do we stick in the ground, anyway?"

I looked down at the saplings. Actually, with the leaves not out on the tiny branches yet, the two ends didn't look awfully different.

Then I had a flash of inspiration. "Ain't you ever planted saplings before?" I said. "I thought any fool knew you plant *this* end." And I grabbed one of the saplings, stuck it in the ground with its roots in the air, and commenced to fill up the hole around its branches with my shovel.

Without a thought, the other kid did the same. Then the next man down the row saw what we were doing, and he followed suit. Soon everybody was planting the trees upside down. It was a beautiful sight. The pickets retired to a little rise off to one side and just sat there watching us with big grins on their faces, as if they thought it was the greatest show on earth.

In around twenty minutes we had planted about a hundred trees with their roots in the air. It looked like the ceiling of hell. When the farmer came back about half an hour later and saw what we'd done, I thought he was going to die of apoplexy. He actually fell down across the seat of his car for a minute, tearing his hair.

After he'd calmed down a little, some of our more experienced members went up to him. "I'm beat," I could hear him say. "I'm beat." And then, after moaning and huffing and puffing for a while, he asked: "Who's your leader?" In the time-honored Wobbly tradition, we said: "We're *all* leaders." After he had finally digested that, the bargaining began, very low key. He agreed to pay the second group of us a dollar each for our performance and the trip out, and to hire the original crew back at what he had originally promised them, including their time picketing. The rest of us walked back to town singing "Solidarity Forever" and a few other Wobbly songs.

I got a job with another chinwhisker outfit around there for a while. When that job was over, a bunch of us beat our way back to Seattle on the freights. It was the end of April, and the IWW was having a big May Day picnic at Renton Junction near Seattle. Bill Haywood and Ralph Chaplin, both of them out of Leavenworth on appeal of their twenty-year sentences, were going to be the speakers. Naturally we all wanted to see Big Bill.

I had never seen so many people in one place before. Half of Seattle must have turned out. There were big IWW banners all over the place, and everybody was laughing, singing and jabbering away and in generally high spirits. There were a lot of cute girls there, too. And to the IWW girls our working-class duds were a badge of honor.

First Katie Phar led us in a few songs, and they must have heard our booming voices in Spokane. Then Big Bill got up to speak, and the crowd went wild. There he was, our top official, the one-eyed giant who had walked through the bayonets at Denver, who had fought the plutes to a standstill at Coeur D'Alene, at Silver City and Telluride and Leadville and Lawrence and Paterson, who had built the IWW up from less than 20,000 to over 100,000 members.

They said Haywood had suffered a lot in prison and had diabetes and wasn't quite his old self. But still his booming voice was the most impressive I've ever heard, and his straightforward reasoning the most concise, direct and effective statement about the class struggle I've ever listened to. He had us all spellbound. He delivered that famous "I have a dream" passage he had used in speeches before, about his vision of a cooperative common-wealth where everybody shared the work and wealth of society as equals, where nobody would ever be in need. When he finally stopped punching the air with his big fists and his powerful voice, we all felt we had shared a momentous moment in history.

Then the charismatic form of Ralph Chaplin arose. He reviewed the horrors and iniquities of the Centralia case, and spoke of the great spirit the IWW prisoners had had in Leavenworth. In his inimitable and poetic style he phrased his own visions of the new society. I think the thousands of us in the crowd felt that, with such remarkable people in our ranks, we were invincible.

Afterward I went up and shook hands with Ralph Chaplin. He remembered me, and took me over to introduce me to the big man himself. As Bill Haywood shook my hand with his firm warm miner's grip, I had the mystical feeling that some of his power and intelligence and determination were entering me, to help me in my own struggles for the organization. For hours afterward I was in seventh heaven. A sort of luminous dancing film seemed to float between me and everything I looked at. We Wobblies believed that all people are equal, and weren't accustomed to hero worship. But I was only human.

I hung around Seattle for a couple of days and then I headed back for John Farmer's fields. Revolutionary euphoria didn't fill the stomach. I started beating my way east on the freights with some other 'bos, following the crops again all through the Midwest, up into Canada, and back again to the Northwest in the fall of 1920. I was in a few small strikes, some of which we won and some of which we lost, and a few fights with hijackers and bulls on the freights and in the jungles. It seemed the more we were able to bring the wages up, the more hijackers—many of them cops—began to rob the workers of their hard-earned pay. It was becoming a bigger and bigger problem.

In the late fall when the harvest was over I began working in the woods again, up northeast of Seattle. And occasionally, when I had a little money saved up, I'd get into Seattle for a boxing match. I was getting better now. Almost everywhere I went people knew me as Kid Murphy, and I was winning about three-fourths of my bouts.

I spent a lot of time doing serious reading and trying to make up my mind about the Bolsheviks. I knew a few of the most prominent Wobblies had already joined them. But I had a hard time making up my mind. Maybe because I was from Missouri, the "show me" state, I was something of an agnostic in everything. I always tried to see all sides to an issue and had to be damn sure before I made up my mind definitely about something. I knew that large segments of the working class were oppressed and that the IWW was doing something to remedy the situation. But as to the exact form an ideal new society should take, I was far from certain—and I don't think anybody else knew for sure, either. I figured it was going to take a lot of experimentation to achieve the ideal society.

The Bolsheviks had formed what was called the Red International of Trade Unions, and they wanted the IWW to be part of it. They invited us to send delegates to a big conference in Russia to discuss it. We sent a very savvy Wobbly named George Williams and another delegate.

But when they got to Russia, it turned out what the Bolshies wanted us to do was to dissolve the IWW and infiltrate the AFL. You can imagine our reactions to that. John Reed, who was in Russia then, took our side and opposed their plan, but the big-shot Bolshies wouldn't listen to him.

It's hard to figure. Maybe the Bolshies thought we were too popular, that our system would triumph over theirs. Maybe they were afraid they couldn't control us. All they had known was a very authoritarian tradition. They didn't understand democracy. People are often afraid of what they're not familiar with.

Our delegates came back and recommended emphatically that we not affiliate with the Communists. "The workers are not free in Russia," they said. And the rank and file voted not to affiliate.

After that, the Communist Party in the U.S. had orders to destroy us. They began trying to break up our meetings. Mobs of them would drown out Ralph Chaplin when he was trying to speak by singing his own song, "Solidarity Forever."

All this would spin round and round in my head when I was lying exhausted in my bunk at night. And I would often ask myself: Where am I going? What do I want out of life? I pretty much knew what I wanted, I guess: a decent job, a wife, a home —the things almost any bloke wants. But it looked like I didn't have the chance of a snowball in hell of ever getting any of those things, the way things were set up now.

I thought about the great Wobbly martyrs and some of our people who gave their whole lives to the movement to improve society, but I didn't really want to go to that extreme, either. I gradually came to the conclusion that neither approach was right for most people—complete selfishness or complete self abnegation. It seemed to me the most rational approach was to steer a course somewhere in between: to try to work toward both my own happiness, and also for the happiness of all the other people in the world.

Of all the speeches and essays I heard or read in those days, I think the words that impressed me most were those of Eugene Debs: "I don't want to rise *from* the working class; I want to rise *with* the working class."

And that became the plan of my life.

8

THERE'S A BEAUTY
ABOUT BOXCARS

A few weeks later I decided to make my first annual visit to the Wobbly class war prisoners in Walla Walla prison in southeastern Washington. I stopped for a while in Yakima to visit a friend. Then in the early afternoon I went down to the railyards to look for a freight headed east for Pasco and Walla Walla. My heart always beat a little faster when I got around trains. There's a magic about trains. And the paraphernalia of the railroad always seemed so much more solid, real, proletarian, democratic and exciting to me than most aspects of the world.

A big long freight was pulling in slowly just as I arrived. Off to one side, by some sheds, I saw a group of harvest stiffs waiting. As the train pulled almost to a stop, I saw a few 'bos hop off and mosey over to the stiffs waiting by the sheds. One of them, a guy about twenty, stood out from the others. He had a certain bright gentleness to his eyes. I walked up to him. He told me his name was Bill Douglas.

"Any empty boxcars?" I asked.

"Nary a one," he said in a friendly sort of voice. "Guess you'll have to deck it or ride the rods."

Bill was the sort of guy I could have told anything to. We had an immediate rapport. "I guess I'm too chicken to ride the rods,"

I said. "Seeing those ties flying by just a few inches under my nose gives me the creeps. But I guess I'll have to."

"The secret is to lay some boards across the rods," he said. "Then you're more comfortable and safer, too. Ther're some old boards around behind the shed there."

I had never thought of that. And apparently not many of the other 'bos had, either. I thanked him and went to look for the boards. I got three one-inch planks, and when no one seemed to be looking, I went out and slid them in over the rods beneath the end of the nearest boxcar. Bill Douglas knew what he was talking about: They made a neat little platform out of sight of the casual passerby. I threw my bindle into my cozy little nest and climbed in after it.

After what seemed an interminable wait, the freight started up with a jerk, derailing my train of thought. But it didn't go far. The shunting of train cars back and forth began as cars were taken off and added to the train. Each time a new car hit, it sounded like a round of heavy artillery coming in, and I felt like John L. Sullivan had just slugged me in the ear. Now I was really glad I had the boards to protect me.

Then, when I thought I couldn't stand it any longer, we began sliding along smoothly, with almost imperceptible acceleration. It still remains a mystery to me how boxcars can be slammed together with such murderous ferocity, and yet hundred-car-long trains can suddenly slip from a standstill up to fifty so smoothly you hardly know you've started. We glissaded along between other trains and packing sheds and warehouses for a while, and then exploded into the open countryside and were on our way.

There's a beauty about boxcars. Secure in my hidden perch, I could see them strung out ahead of me as the long train made big swooping turns along the river, red and green and orange and every color there is almost, each a world of its own, cars from all over the continent, waltzing along merrily in the bright spring sunlight, shooting off to who knows what far-off destination, like true romantic footloose adventurers. The train took on a long swelling, dipping roll like a large ship far at sea, and its distant whistle whined and screeched like the plaintive call of sea gulls.

I lay looking out at the ripening crops, rocking gently back and forth, and had the feeling that it was all one big throbbing beautiful mass, that I was part of the train and the passing countryside and all of it, and that even if I fell I would, after all, only be falling into a soft, watery, welcoming mass of earth and sky. And I often thought I'd like to stick with just one boxcar for a whole month, just to see all the places it goes. They were a home to us, the boxcars, and we felt about them just the way some people do about their houses or their boats, as if they were alive, individuals, each with a personality and human destiny. And trains were like many-colored caravans moving across the face of the earth.

As we swept past little lost farms and villages, I longed to look into the windows of the houses, to see the people there, to know what they were like, their views and feelings, their aspirations, to get to know and be friends with them all, to merge with all of humanity. Those fresh grassy vacant lots between the little frame houses seemed so real, so basic, so good, so unpretentious, so alive in a way the self-consciously famous places of the world did not seem alive, with the reality of mud puddles and kids with kites.

Yet, as all the sights and sounds appeared and then were swept away and lost forever, I felt the peculiar isolation of riding freight trains too — wanting to reach out and touch all that teeming life, but being unable to. But then I'd think: Sometimes it's good to communicate with humans and sometimes it's good to be cut off like this and communicate only with your own soul — but with the whole world waiting for you out there whenever the train stopped.

We passed out of the orchard country into winter wheat, which waved in the wind out there like a gigantic green-gold ocean, sudden breezes brushing currents across it like racing schools of fish riffling its surface, a vast, ever-changing spectacle.

I thought of bits of railroad memorabilia, of the notorious railroad bull, "Umatilla Red," who had terrorized migrants not far east of here. One day he tried to throw one 'bo too many off a moving freight and ended up hitting the grit himself; an Italian immigrant gandy dancer had come upon his corpse and phoned in to the section gang office to report: "There's a red-a bull lying on the tracks — what-a should I do?" The foreman, thinking he was talking about a bovine, said: "Toss him in the bar pit and throw some dirt over him." So...

As we swooped on east and darkness descended, I began to sing Wobbly songs, Joe Hill's "Casey Jones, the Union Scab" and "Hallelujah, I'm a Bum":

Migrant workers "taking five" on discarded railroad ties alongside a rail line.

'Oh, why don't you work
like other men do?'
'How the hell can I work
when there's no work to do?...

'I can't buy a job
for I ain't got the dough,
so I ride in a boxcar
for I'm a hobo...

'Hallelujah, I'm a bum!
Hallelujah, bum again!
Hallelujah, give us a handout
to revive us again!'

It got dark and cold. When we stopped at the edge of one little
town down near the Columbia I decided to make a quick dash
into the weeds to take a leak, not having the faintest idea how
long the train would be stopped there. As I started to climb back
under the car a couple minutes later, a brakeman or bull suddenly
swung down from the ladder at the end of the car and yelled: "Hit
the grit, bum!"

I dashed back out into the woods before he could catch me. In
the darkness, I didn't think he saw the boards I had laid under the
car. I ran through the bushes about two cars down. When he was
turned the other way I ran in between two cars and up over the
bumpers to the other side of the train. Then I walked quietly up
to my car and slipped back into my hiding place. As soon as I was
ensconced the train began to move. Soon we were rocking along
at fifty again, rolling from side to side like a ship at sea, plummeting and bucking as from the lash of waves, off into the night.

Now that darkness and cold had come, I began to get scared. I
thought again of Umatilla Red. What if the bull *had* seen me get
back on the train? I had heard stories of mean bulls or shacks who
would dangle a steel coupling pin on the end of a cord under the
cars and cut the poor 'bos riding the rods to pieces. Later we'd see
an obituary in the local paper about a tramp who apparently had
gotten drunk and passed out on the tracks.

The train rattled on east, picking up speed. The rushing wind
blew cold against my face. Suddenly I heard a kind of clattering
clunking noise getting closer to me. My god! I thought. It was like
a self-fulfilling prophesy—here I'd been thinking about that most

murderous of all the brutal tricks of the railroad bulls, and now could it actually be happening to me?

In another minute all doubt had been dispelled. So the bull had seen me get back on. The loud beating and ricocheting of steel on wood and metal that kept getting closer and closer could be nothing but a metal coupling pin at the end of a cord, bouncing around murderously under the car. In another moment it was hitting the tracks and the boards directly beneath me. And I felt more grateful to Bill Douglas than I'd ever felt toward anyone in my life for suggesting the boards—without their protection I would already be a corpse.

The pin seemed to beat right through the boards, and I felt like I was being pummeled in the ribs by a hundred expert boxers with brass knuckles. I wondered how long it would be before the boards would be battered into splinters and the pin would be hitting my bare flesh. I was so scared I even found myself praying to Jerusalem Slim that I'd survive the ordeal.

I suddenly got an idea: I remembered the gloves I always carried in my mackinaw in case I had to do some heavy shovel work. I fumbled around as the pin beat the boards beneath me, and finally slipped one glove on my right hand. My only hope, I reasoned, was to grab the cord and pull it out of the hands that were holding it on the other end.

The train roared on. A big piece from one of the boards was battered loose and fell out from under me. I could hear it being pounded to bits along the track bed as it bounced between the ties and the bottom of the speeding train.

I turned a little to one side and watched the bouncing coupling pin throwing out sparks as it jumped back and forth, helter-skelter, a few inches from my feet. The cord that held it whipped back and forth like some frenzied, constantly moving snake. I grabbed at it once, twice, without success. It lashed against my gloved hand like a high tension wire shooting electricity through me.

Then I concentrated for all I was worth. Remembering the speed I had used to kill flies with my bare hand back on our porch in Missouri, I reached out swiftly and grabbed the cord and jerked with everything I had. The cord suddenly lost its tautness. I dropped it and heard the pin go clunking back behind me along the length of the train. Did I just imagine that, a second later, I half-saw some dark mass pass under me on the road bed? But surely the bull or shack wouldn't be dumb enough to have kept holding on to the other end?

I gave a gasp of relief and lay back on what was left of the rattling boards beneath me. With a trembling hand I wiped the dripping sweat from my brow. My heart seemed to be beating a thousand times a minute.

After a few minutes, when I felt a little calmer, I started worrying about what to do next. If the bull was still there, he must be madder than ever by now. And if he was crazy enough to murder people deliberately in that way, I could imagine what he would do to me when the train came to a stop. I was just praying that when the train stopped next, there would be other people around so that maybe at worst he'd have me arrested for trespassing. A month in jail looked good about now. But what if there wasn't anybody around?

I looked out through the darkness at the rods stretching toward the other end of the car. There was no way I could get up on the sides or top of the car with it underway like this. But if I could just shimmy my way to the other end of its underside, at least I would have a few seconds' leeway at the next stop while the bull looked under this end for me—and maybe I could make my escape before he caught me. It might be my only chance.

I put on my other glove and gingerly began to crawl and slide my way along the jolting rods, trying not to see the flying ties and cinders inches below me. I would wriggle my way a few feet, stop to rest, then slowly go on a few feet more, holding on to the shaking rods for all I was worth. In twenty minutes I had made it to the other end of the car. I'd had to abandon my bindle, but that seemed a small sacrifice under the circumstances.

I lay crouched under the other end of the car, ready to spring down the instant the train came to a stop. It seemed it never would. But finally, at some indeterminate hour in the middle of the night, it pulled into Pasco. The instant I saw the wheels weren't going fast enough to run me over, I leaped down and ran for the bushes. I didn't take the time to look around to see if anyone was following me. I ran off through the darkness for three or four blocks before I stopped behind a shed to catch my breath. Nobody was in sight. Then I slowly circled around the town through the surrounding countryside before entering it a mile or two from where I'd left the train.

I sat shivering beside an abandoned shack until it began to get light. Then I found a greasy spoon and had breakfast, praying that a bull or shack wouldn't come in and recognize me. Later, after cleaning up in the rest room, I took a bus on east to Walla Walla. And all along the way I gave thanks to William O. Douglas for giving me that tip about laying boards across the rods—otherwise I would have been cut to ribbons. I guess the memory of his days as a harvest stiff stuck with him. Because fifty years later when he was on the U.S. Supreme Court he wrote the majority opinion on a landmark case aiding in the union organization of farmworkers.

When I got to Walla Walla I bought some tobacco and magazines and fruit and headed for the prison. It was a grim-looking place. I thought of Eugene Debs and Bertrand Russell and their years in prison for obeying the teachings of Jerusalem Slim and refusing to kill—what a weird world it was where working people were thrown in jail for refusing to kill and for wanting everyone to lead a happy life.

As I was entering the prison I met our Wobbly shyster, Elmer Smith, coming out after a visit with the prisoners. He remembered me and greeted me warmly. We had a long powwow outside the prison gates. I told him of my ordeal of the night before, and he told me he was trying to take some legal action to curb illegal activities of the railroad bulls. He had heard of my reputation as a boxer and urged me to join one of our flying squadrons, but he cautioned me to be careful. For the rest of his life Smith continued traveling constantly, speaking and working for the release of the Centralia prisoners. I finally bade him goodbye and went on into the prison.

The seven prisoners seemed a little gaunt but cheerful. Most of them remembered seeing me in the Centralia jail or in the courtroom in Montesano. They were extremely grateful for my gifts. I told them of my pledge to visit them at least once a year as long as they were in, and of a new vow I had just made to become an IWW delegate at the first opportunity. When visiting time was up, I gave them all a warm handshake and the clenched-fist salute Bill Haywood had used in the Lawrence textile strike to symbolize solidarity. I felt sorry for the poor stiffs as I walked out of the prison, but I felt good about having visited them and filled with a strange emotion—it was like a religious experience, like a pilgrimage.

9

FLYING SQUADRON

That night I caught a train north to Spokane. I didn't ride the rods. All I could think of along the way was of getting that psychopath who had tried to kill me off by himself someday and taking my revenge. I'd only caught a glimpse of his face when he'd first ordered me off the train, but I knew I'd remember it as long as I lived.

Next day I was back in Spokane. One of the first people I saw on the skid road was my hobo pal Dale Curd. He was with another Wobbly harvest stiff named Bad Axe Blackie. Blackie was a big friendly guy of French Canadian descent. People assumed his nickname came from the fact he used an axe as a weapon—but he was called that because he was from the town of Bad Axe, Michigan. Don't ask me how the town got that name.

We went to a greasy spoon for some coffee an'. I told them of my ordeal on the freight. "That's why we need you on the flying squadron," Dale Curd chimed in. He showed me under the table an Iver-Johnson .38 he had, to defend himself against any hijacks who were armed. I knew that our flying squadrons had put the fear of St. John into the hijacks and other crooks who preyed on the harvest workers in the wheat belt. But after my recent experience, I didn't have to be told that things were getting bad again. I told them I'd try it for a while. I was so mad at that bull who'd tried to kill me, I'd risk anything. Their plan was to head east through the harvest belt, working now and then along the way, and going wherever there were reports of hijacks or crooked gamblers operating.

I bought some new blankets and then went to the Wobbly hall and arranged to "take out the rigging." I was given twenty blank IWW membership cards and some blank report sheets and "silent agitators"—the little IWW propaganda stickers we plastered up all over the country. Then I bought a needle and some thread, and spent the next half hour sewing a secret pocket into the inside of my mackinaw to hide my delegate's supplies in. That night I slept in the Wobbly hall.

Next day we walked down to the railyards. We were just about to catch a freight east when we heard there were some bad forest fires over toward Wenatchee, and the government was paying firefighters thirty-five cents an hour. There had been some rumors of hijackers over that way too. All three of us needed the money and it sounded like they needed men badly, so we decided to go fight fires for a while.

We caught a slow drag going west. There were four or five other stiffs in our boxcar, going out to fight fires too. An hour or two out of Spokane we looked up to the northwest. The whole sky was like one gigantic gray cloud, shutting out the sun, obscuring everything. "Jesus," said one of the 'bos. "It looks like Armageddon's come to swallow us up."

In another hour we were at our stop. There wasn't much formality. They were taking on anybody who wanted to fight fires. We were given a quick meal and sent out to the front lines. We were put to work building firebreaks, working like madmen. Every now and then, if the wind shifted a little, we'd get a dose of choking smoke in our lungs. We worked till we dropped from exhaustion—about one in the morning.

We kept it up for two weeks, working nineteen or twenty hours a day, until we finally had the fires under control. It was the hardest work I'd ever done, but I was able to save almost a hundred dollars.

When Dale and Bad Axe and I and a few others were standing by a water tank waiting for a freight to take us back to Spokane, we saw a ragged bunch of men walking toward us up to the tracks. They had angry looks on their faces. When they got up to us they told us they'd been paid off as firefighters the day before, and last night had been held up by hijackers a few miles to the east. One of their members had been killed when he gave the three thugs some back talk. They gave us a description of the hijacks. We commiserated with them for a while and then they went on toward the firefighters' camp to report the incident.

We went off to one side and had a consultation, reviewing our plan of action if we ran into the hijacks.

About an hour later, a long freight pulled in. We got in a boxcar with about twenty other stiffs. As I was pulling myself up I saw three men rush out from some bushes and get on the train about thirty cars back, just as we began to move.

The train picked up speed. We fell to talking with the other 'bos. Most of them had been fighting the fires. We alerted them to the danger from the hijacks, and we developed a concerted plan of action.

About forty-five minutes later, I happened to look out of the boxcar door and saw a body rolling down the bank—apparently someone had just fallen or been pushed off the train farther up toward the engine. I jumped to the door and peered forward into the rushing wind. Then I saw another body shoot out of a car three cars ahead of us. I alerted the others to be on their guard. Bad Axe and Dale took out their guns. Everyone was tense, waiting for the worst.

I stood just inside the door listening. About ten minutes later I heard a voice right above my head say over the noise of the train and the wind: "You two hold your guns on them and I'll take the dough this time."

Then a rope ladder swung down over the side and the first hijack, pistol in hand, swung into our car. We knew it was them or us. I don't know who shot first. I saw Bad Axe's gun blaze and the first hijack hit the grit. An instant later the second hijack swung in and Dale began grappling with him. Then the third came in, right up against me, and as he tried to steady his gun I grabbed his wrist and swung him against the side of the boxcar. He kicked back at me like a mule, but I put my foot out and tripped him, then got on top of him and put a half-Nelson on him. When I had him down good, I reached out rapidly and snatched his .38 and put it in my pocket. Now I had a gun too.

When I looked up there was no sign of the second hijack—a minute later Dale told me he'd fallen out of the car. Several others were helping me hold my man down now. I got up and brushed off my clothes. Then we stripped the hijack—he had about sixty dollars on him—and we divided it up among everyone in the car.

"Enough excitement for you, Joe?" said Bad Axe when things were back to normal.

"Makes boxing seem like child's play," I tried to grin, still panting a little.

"You did real good, Joe," said Dale, patting me on the back. "With a few more like you on the flying squad, we'll clear out the crooks in no time."

My heart was beating fast. I felt a strong rush of confused feelings: shock, exhilaration, fear, power, self-righteous exultation. And I think that, for a moment, a kind of bloodthirsty lust for violence came over me. Yet, as things calmed down, I knew that what we'd done was right and had to be done by somebody. The cops and goons and hijacks were the slugging committee of the master class—so in self-defense we had to have a slugging committee of our own. And the more I thought about it, the prouder it made me feel to be enrolled in the shock troops of the labor movement.

The train roared on. It turned out there were three or four other Wobblies in the car. They showed us their red cards. When the others learned we were Wobblies, they began to voice their appreciation for what we had done for the workers. In the next few minutes we explained the principles of the organization and issued membership cards to all of the fifteen or so stiffs who hadn't lined up yet.

When the train slowed down on a curve, we dumped off the third hijack. He claimed he was sorry for what he'd done and said he had been pressured into it by the other two. We gave him the benefit of the doubt and dumped him off when the train was going slow enough that he wouldn't be killed.

The next time the train slowed down, the three of us jumped off ourselves. We didn't want to take a chance on going on into Spokane, in case the train crew got wind of what had happened and called the bulls on us. We were in a gently rolling area of piney woods. We decided we would spend a few days hiking leisurely through the woods back from the railroad tracks toward Spokane, then catch a freight southeast to the wheat harvest where the hijacks were thickest.

We began hiking up a gully alongside a stream toward the north. In the late afternoon we came to a small cabin. An old duffer was sitting on the front porch. And it turned out we were in luck: He was a Wobbly named Sven Lagerqvist. He had lined up as a miner in Goldfield, Nevada in 1907 and saw Vincent St. John get shot in the hand by a plug-ugly there. He told us how The Saint had organized the place so well that almost everybody in town was getting equal pay—the closest thing to a classless society and the brotherhood of man that had existed since the Indians ruled America—until Teddy Roosevelt ordered in federal troops to end it all.

Sven invited us in and cooked up a mess of venison stew. We bedded down for the night on the floor next to his potbellied stove. Next day as we were getting ready to leave, Sven told us he was taking off to visit his daughter in California when the first snow hit in the fall, and said we were welcome to use the cabin in his absence. I told him I might take him up on it.

Two days later we were in Spokane. The first thing I saw as we walked along Trent Street was a newspaper headline that blared: HOBOS MURDER POLICEMAN. And there was his picture to clinch it: one of our great public protectors, a city cop, who had been holding up migrant workers. Under the circumstances we decided not to go to the Wobbly hall. We found a fellow worker along the street and gave him a message to pass on to the secretary while we waited at the edge of town. In a couple of hours a messenger came out to meet us, bringing fresh literature and a new supply of membership cards. By dark we were on a fast freight heading for the early wheat harvest in Kansas.

Early next morning we were rattling along at about fifty in a car full of harvest stiffs in southern Idaho. I was pounding my ear in one corner of the boxcar and dreaming about sitting down to a big dinner at home in Springfield with my family. I suddenly realized Bad Axe was shaking my shoulder.

"What's up?" I asked, wiping the sleep from my eyes.

"Up an' at 'em," said Blackie. "Somebody just spotted some hijacks coming along the decks."

I looked up and saw the face of a young 'bo hanging over the top of the car. As I watched he swung down in to join us. "I was riding the decks," he told us, out of breath. "And I saw 'em comin'. They're about ten cars back."

We woke up the sleeping 'bos. Everybody got ready. This time we had a new strategy—not to even let them in the car. We couldn't get their money that way, but there was less chance of getting shot. Bad Axe stood in the center of the car with his rod out, and Dale and I stood by each side of the door with our pocket knives open.

We didn't have to wait long. In three or four minutes a rope ladder was thrown down from the deck above and a pair of legs began to climb down it. We had our knives ready.

"As T-Bone Slim wrote," Bad Axe said with a grim smile, "'Wherever you find injustice, the proper form of politeness is attack.'" We cut the ropes up near the roof of the car, and the hijack kept climbing right on down the ladder to meet his mother earth.

The second hijack had dangled his feet over the side. Dale grabbed him by the ankles and swung him down into the car, and he slid across to the wall on the other side. We saw a gun go flying out the door of the boxcar before we could grab it.

"Anybody else up there?" I asked him when he sat up dazed-like.

"Nope—this is it," he said, looking scared as hell.

"It'd better be—if you're lying, you'll never get off this train alive," Dale told him, going through his pockets.

We stationed two men by the door, just in case. This pecker-wood had about a hundred dollars on him. We divided it up among the men in the car. "To pay your Wobbly dues with," I said. We signed up every one of them. Then we stripped the hijack's clothes off and left him standing balls-ass naked at a solitary water tower the train stopped at, way out in the middle of nowhere.

We rumbled on east. You never knew what to expect riding the freights. Sometimes the cars were clean and the trains were fast and the rails were good and the ride was smooth and it was sheer pleasure. Other times the cars were filthy and the trains were slow and it was sheer hell. This was one of those slow drags. The wheels wept along so slowly it was maddening. You had to learn patience to ride the freights. But then, when we would top a rise and start down the other side, we skedaddled along like crazy, till we thought the train would shake apart. And there was the continual worry about the hostile shack or hijack or bull. There's a beauty about boxcars—but there's a horror about them too.

We held her down all night, and the next afternoon we were rolling into Pocatello, in eastern Idaho. A few of our fellow travelers were going there to plant spuds. We hadn't planned to stop there, but it had been one of those dirty dusty boxcars, and one look at ourselves with our grimy faces told us we needed a rest stop to clean up at. A hobo's life may sound romantic—and at times it is—but being covered with dust and grime, going hungry, and being shaken to pieces by a rattler bounding over old track can disillusion you swiftly. So we decided to join our buddies and plant spuds for a few days.

When our train got in it was too late to go out to any of the farms, so we decided to spend the night in one of the local jungles. Also, we saw carved on a post beside the tracks a replica of a pair of handcuffs—the Wobbly symbol for hostile bulls—so the sooner we got out of town the better. There were about a dozen of us. We bought some grub in a small grocery store and started out along the tracks. About half a mile out of town we came to a jungle. You could always tell a Wobbly jungle because it was so much cleaner and better organized than other jungles.

There were eight or ten men at the camp, all Wobblies. They greeted us warmly and offered us some java right off. We added our own contributions to the stew pot. As usual, there was a big can of water boiling off to one side. I'd begun to feel a little itchy after sleeping all night on the floor of the boxcar, so I decided to boil up. I never believed in supporting free riders or parasites, human or otherwise.

About the time I'd finished delousing myself, three strangers walked up to the campsite. I could tell by one look at them they were so crooked they had to screw their socks on in the morning. Also I noticed they had no calluses on their hands.

They joked around with us for a while. Then, when they thought they had us buttered up good, the old deck of cards came out. "Just to while away the time boys, nothing serious," the chief kazoo said. I noticed that one of the three stayed back from the others who were gathering around to join in the game, so I motioned to Bad Axe to keep an eye on him.

The game proceeded. The cards were so crudely marked you could have spotted it a mile away. So Dale and I played it close to the chest with our hands covering the backs of our cards, and it seemed to infuriate the two tinhorns. Also I noticed that, whenever one of them had a good hand, he'd look off into the distance for a second, and then the other one would raise. It wasn't long before we had all their money.

After raking in a big pot, I hoosiered up and in an innocent voice said, "By the way, why is it the backs of some of these cards look different than the others?"

The gambler started to reach into his pocket, but Dale's hand shot out in a flash and grabbed his wrist. I reached over and relieved him of his gun. Two other fellow workers took a knife away from the second gambler. Back away from the group, Bad Axe decked the third crook and took his gun away too. We took the rest of their money and divided it up among ourselves. Then we held all three gamblers down and made them eat the deck of marked cards, one by one. One of them threw up before he was through.

Later I was to hear the life stories of a number of these gamblers and hijacks and crooked cops—with a lot of lies sprinkled in, no doubt—sometimes before we unmasked them, sometimes afterward. It seemed like almost every one of them had a tragic story to tell: childhoods of desperate poverty, parents who beat them, being forced into long hours of hard labor at an early age.

Extreme hardship seems to have two main effects on people. If a bloke has any real brains, it makes him more sympathetic with others. If he's low on social intelligence, it often makes a criminal or exploiter of him—a hard guy. Just like treating a dog bad makes him mean. I realized that, despicable as these crooks were, they hadn't had my advantages of having fairly well educated, loving parents. I figured that if we could just manage somehow to improve the world, create a better society and provide a decent childhood for everyone, then there wouldn't be so many mean, mad-dog people in the world.

We sent the tinhorns on their way, posted a sentinel and hit the sack. Next morning at dawn we went looking for work. It wasn't long before we all got hired at a big spread, planting potatoes. It was long hours and hard work. But at least there was a fairly decent bunkhouse, and the pay was forty-five cents an hour—at least five cents higher than John Farmer paid in Kansas and Nebraska. The only thing really wrong was the rotten chuck —only two eggs for breakfast and a couple scrawny strips of greasy bacon.

Our all-Wobbly gang soon persuaded the other workers to take some job action. The second morning after breakfast we all started walking in to town. "Hey, what's goin' on?" the farmer yelled.

"We're just goin' in to town to get somepin more to eat," we told him. "Don't worry—we'll be back in an hour or so." It worked fast. From then on we had piles of eggs and all the bacon and ham we could eat.

After a few days, a Wob came into camp and told us of widespread hijacking starting up again all through Kansas. We had our work cut out for us. We told our master and our fellow workers goodbye and hit the hobo trail. The newcomer Wob had brought us all the latest IWW papers, and all the way going south and east on the freights we sat reading them.

The organization was growing fast again. Not only in the harvest belt here and in Canada, but Wobbly seamen were opening up new branches in England, Germany, Australia, South America and South Africa. One of our delegates had even led a successful fishermen's strike in Tahiti and taught the local stiffs to sing, "Hallelujah, I'm a Bum" in Polynesian. It was a wonderful feeling to be part of a great growing organization.

We held her down all the way into Kansas. And we spent the next few weeks going from one end of that state to the other kicking ass, working off and on, defending the harvest stiffs. It was a dirty business. But we put the fear of St. John into the hijackers and the town clowns who tried to shake down the workers.

There were some good moments now and then too. There's nothing quite like watching the sunset on the prairie from a speeding freight car. The beauty of the shimmering sea of wheat going on endlessly, the tall grain elevators silhouetted against the sun like altars to the harvest gods. But sometimes it has a monotonous sameness and loneliness about it too—a beautiful aching loneliness.

Sometimes I would look out of the freight car, out over the rolling prairie, and think: It's beautiful, it should be for everyone. How did we arrive at this weird situation where some people own it all and others rattle around in freight cars busting their ass to feed the human race? At least those animals out there, the coyotes and the gophers and other varmints, have a more or less equal chance to avail themselves of the earth—they don't rope it off and make other animals work for them. And through it all I would think from time to time of the railroad bull who had tried to kill me on the freight near Pasco, Washington, and would renew my vow to go back next winter to get my revenge.

As the harvest season came to an end we headed farther north, all up through the Dakotas, Manitoba, Saskatchewan, Alberta, and finally back down into the Palouse in eastern Washington.

It had been a long hard summer, dangerous and fascinating. I was no longer a boy. When I rode that last freight into Spokane in October at the end of the harvest I was ready for a long rest...and a lot of serious thinking. As I said goodbye to Bad Axe and Dale at one of our favorite joints on Trent, I thought of the old Swedish Wobbly who had offered to let me stay in his cabin for the winter.

10

THE HIGH LONESOME

I spent the rest of the day preparing for the trip. I bought some warm clothes, some more blankets, a big backpack, and some rice and beans and flour. Then I bought all the books there was space left for: *Les Misérables* by Victor Hugo, several books on economics and politics, and dozens of the "little blue books" published by Emanuel Haldeman-Julius in Girard, Kansas, with the editorial help of such brilliant minds as Eugene Debs. Last of all I bought some pencils and a notebook. I had decided to keep the poems I wrote from time to time in it, as well as poems and aphorisms of others that impressed me.

I spent the night at the Wobbly hall in Spokane, and the next morning I hit the high lonesome. I could see snow flurries off to the north as my freight whooshed westward. By late afternoon I was hiking up the gully to the old Swede's cabin.

Sven gave me a warm greeting. My timing couldn't have been better. He was just about to take a huge venison stew off the stove. And next day he was leaving for his daughter's. After we shot the bull for a while and I told him of my summer adventures, exaggerating only slightly, he insisted on giving me a mess of canned food he had stored up, and the use of his rifle and fishing pole and other supplies. That old Swede was a whole team and a dog extra and a dog under the wagon.

Early next morning we bade each other farewell. I watched Sven walk down the trail with his battered suitcase, until he was out of sight around a bend. After all the hurly-burly of the summer...delicious aloneness. I had learned that part of the secret of happiness in life is variety, a change of pace now and then. And everyone should have time alone to think about things from time to time.

And think I did. Watching the first snow flutter to earth, I thought up one side of my life and down the other. Then I took on the problems of the world. I spent the first few days just wandering around to get my bearings, and in deep thought.

Where am I going? I asked myself. Did I really want to spend the rest of my life battling vermin and rattling around in a dirty boxcar? I thought of boxing: Perhaps there I could make a career, rescue myself from poverty. But, for the time being, I'd had more than enough fighting on the flying squadron, and I just couldn't seem to get any real pleasure out of trying to bash someone's brains in. I thought of the 164 Wobbly leaders in dismal prisons at Leavenworth, Wichita and Sacramento—some facing twenty years behind bars—and felt a simmering determination to keep up the struggle for a better world.

I spent many hours mulling over the problems of the Wobblies and of the organization of society. The chief problem seemed to be how much to reward those who were most efficient at producing what society needed, versus how much compassion to have for those who, for a variety of reasons, produced less, or nothing at all. But in our dog-eat-dog economy we hadn't even come close to considering such refined ideas of right and wrong.

If the IWW seized state power, would it become just another heartless, bureaucrat-ridden government? If it could just remain democratic and more-or-less decentralized. If it could create a society of worker-run cooperatives loosely coordinated by its central body... Even now I saw the struggle between centralization and decentralization beginning to rend the organization: The lumber workers led by James Rowan were more decentralist, while the far-flung farmworkers were paradoxically more centralist. And there was the struggle between those who thought the main emphasis should be on promoting immediate revolution, and those who believed it should be on building stable job control. And between the migrants and the homeguards. Where did the best balance between these opposing tendencies lie?

And the human factor was so important. The only long-range guarantee of a decent society, I thought, was the creation of a general feeling among the vast majority of people that everyone should have a fair deal. But how to achieve that? The main danger seemed to be for anyone to have too much power.

November 7th came on a cold snowy day. I was sixteen—a real adult! I had a growing feeling that I was destined to be something in the world.

I plunged into my reading, hitting the books from dawn till after midnight, sitting up wrapped in blankets by the potbellied stove. And here and there I would glean some of the more trenchant statements of the great thinkers of the world and set them down in my notebook:

Goethe: "If you treat people a little better than they deserve, you might improve them a little."

St. Francis: "Strive to change for the better what can be changed, and learn to accept what cannot be changed."

Spinoza: "If you can understand how everyone is molded by circumstance, you can love anyone." (A little hard, at times).

Bill Haywood: "For every man who has a dollar he didn't earn, someone else worked for a dollar he didn't get."

As the winter wore on, I thought more and more of the sort of life I wanted to lead. The summer's events had been exciting and had made me proud, but I couldn't see myself going through my whole life living like that. I wanted a home, a wife, affection, security, decent food, maybe kids. And yet I felt a powerful dedication to the labor movement. But maybe something in between —a decent steady job where I could still do some low-key organizing. Often compromise was the soul of sanity, just as in labor relations. I thought more and more of my family, of Missouri.

Christmas came, the snow was piled high, and I had a bad case of the dismals. I had ceased being a Catholic, but all the associations of Christmas were still strong in my mind—family, gifts, friends, sharing. And if there really *had* been a Jerusalem Slim, it seemed obvious he had many of the same values as the Wobblies.

As Christmas faded toward the new year, I thought more and more of home. There was something about Missouri. Something special. Something about the word, even. Sometimes I would sit by the potbellied stove and say it over and over, "Missouri,

Missouri, Missouri, Missouri." Feeling the roll of it on my tongue.
It seemed to have a lazy sensuous ethereal beauty to it.

   Three days after Christmas I decided to return home.
   Missouri.

11

MISSOURI

I almost froze to death riding the freights back to Springfield. Through Idaho, Montana, Wyoming and Nebraska, my teeth chattering all the way. But finally on a gusty day in January, I dropped off a rattly boxcar in the Springfield yards and headed across familiar turf toward home. I ran the last two blocks of the way.

Home. Safety. How different from my usual way of life these past two-and-a-half years. My mother had written me back in 1919 that there was no record of a death or knifing in Springfield that fateful day I had left, so I had no fear of imminent arrest. But I still had a faint uneasy wariness of running into one of the toughs who had attacked me that nightmare night so long ago.

But when I ran up the steps of my parents' house, all was pure ecstasy. A moment later my mom and I were hugging one another, and two minutes after that I was seated at the kitchen table before the biggest piece of pie I'd ever seen.

That night when Pop came home from work we had a great family reunion, with several of my brothers and sisters there. Naturally I was called upon to recount my adventures. And I gave a carefully edited rundown of my time away from home, omitting all references to the violence I'd experienced.

Pop and Ma looked older and more careworn. But they both seemed delighted and relieved to have me back home, and after all the dangers and discomforts I'd been through I was relieved to be there.

I spent the next few days just sitting around home, talking with my folks and visiting a few friends. At first I kept a wary eye open for any hostile youths—the guy who'd been knifed was the only one I felt sure I could recognize—but I didn't run into any trouble and after a while I began to relax.

I knew I'd have to get a job before long. My dad told me there was an opening as a blacksmith's apprentice in the big railroad shop near where he worked. It paid less than forty cents an hour, but I looked forward to learning a skill that seemed almost certain, in time, to lead to higher pay. The railroad Pop worked for was called the "Frisco Line," because its founders had planned to extend it all the way to California, but its tracks had never extended more than a few hundred miles.

So a new mode of life began for me. Good food, security, the companionship and support of my family, and the steady grind of working and learning. In spite of the long hours and the monotony, I developed a certain interest in the work. It gave me a feeling of pride working on the big powerful locomotives, keeping them going, roaring across the width and length of the continent. And I knew that, when and if I became an expert craftsman, I could not only enjoy a better personal life, but be in a better position to advance the social struggle.

I renewed a couple of old friendships and had a few dates with a couple of girls I took a fancy to. But inevitably, after all my outlandish adventures, the slow and steady life began to weigh me down at times with boredom. If only we could find more of a balance in life, I would think—a balance between the steady necessary work of life, and adventure, excitement, the experiences that made the blood race in the veins and told you you were really alive. How I missed at times the great roaring lumber camps of the Northwest, the warm camaraderie of big Wobbly meetings, the fiery speeches, the action on the picket lines, the dedicated warmhearted rebel girls who really knew what life was all about.

I was torn. Sometimes in the long afternoons, I felt like throwing down my tools and hopping aboard the first lurching freight train headed west. At other times I would remember the cold and the hunger and the danger and the uncertainty and thank my stars that I had loving parents and a home and a steady job.

But the dynamics of the economic system were not to let me remain undecided for long. The leading industrialists, buttressed by a conservative Republican administration, were girding for a massive attack on labor—an assault designed not only to increase their profits and decrease wages, but to destroy the entire union movement. It began to look more and more like an all-out war. And it looked like the railroad shop workers' unions would be at the very center of it.

Our worst fears began to materialize. The big railroads, often in violation of union agreements, began farming out more and more of their work to non-union contractors who paid under union scale. Then the biggest roads announced a wage cut of twelve percent. An immediate storm of protest arose. The lower-paid shop workers like myself—500,000 of us—were hit the hardest. Efforts were made to forge a united front among the different rail unions. But when it came to the crunch, most officials of the better-paid trainmen's unions broke ranks and refused to join the strike.

So on July the first, 1922, half a million railway shop workers around the country hit the bricks on their own, destined to slug it out with the railroad barons.

12

THE GREAT RAILROAD STRIKE

The strike was on. Down at the railyards not a thing was moving. I got up before dawn. The house had an eerie stillness to it. Over breakfast there were more uneasy looks than words spoken—looks of mingled fear and hope. My mother had a worried expression on her face all through the meal. She knew about strikes and unemployment and hunger from long and bitter experience. Pop had a little more determination and hope in his eyes.

A knock came at the door. Everyone jumped. But it was only two young pals of mine from the shop who were going down to picket with me. My mother had tears in her eyes when she said goodbye to me on the porch. She took my hands in hers. "Be careful, Joe," she said.

Even the sun seemed to come up through the trees and houses to the east with a strange foreboding that morning as the three of us walked through the quiet streets. Gradually more figures appeared in the dim early morning light. Were they strikers or scabs or cops or goons? we wondered, keeping up our guard as we walked along slowly with our picket signs.

Gradually others joined us, one or two here, one or two a block farther on. We were like a secret militia assembling silently at dawn to strike some sudden and crushing blow at an invisible tyrant. Soon we were fifteen, then twenty, then forty, then eighty, then a hundred of us converging from all directions on the silent railyard.

Finally the sprawling railyards loomed before us. There was no sign of any activity at all. It was so quiet you could hear the temperature rise. There was something unreal and scary about it. There, in those big old buildings before us, we had always heard a cacophony of pounding hammers and shouted orders and engines letting off steam—and now, nothing. It was like one vast cemetery, the silent locomotives standing about like gigantic sarcophaguses waiting to be entombed, the steam drained from their veins, their giant drivers stilled. It seemed like the end of the world.

Then it began. Slowly, in ones and twos and threes, other forms began to appear in the first rays of morning sunlight. Some with their heads bowed, some avoiding our glances, others laughing defiance or scorn at us. The engineers and firemen and switchmen and brakemen who were not honoring our strike. Some walked toward us slowly, hesitantly, as if prepared to break and run. Others plowed forward rapidly as if determined to ram through any obstacle. I saw no police.

Our picket line was ready for them, spread out for a hundred yards or more along the edge of the tracks. Suddenly, like a circus cranking up, all was tumult and shouting. We became a long creature with a hundred heads and a thousand arms, barking defiance. I wondered if, among the shapes advancing on us, I would spot one of those forms that had attacked me so long ago. I felt a sort of horror of anticipation, mixed with vengeful longing. What if they spotted me here, beside my hundred comrades— what would they do? What would I do?

For one long moment the advancing forms seemed to pause before us and we stared into one another's eyes like opposing soldiers must do at the last second of a bayonet charge. What an irony, I thought in that intense moment: Just after I'd toned down my rebellious ways, I was forced into my biggest struggle ever.

The men who, by their actions in the next few minutes or days could make our lives much worse, were suddenly on us. Thought they could cut our miserly pay by twelve percent, did they? We'd show them. Shouts and curses exploded on all sides. The long picket line surged and ebbed like an irregular line of surf. Here a low-key discussion began, here a fistfight broke out, there a shoving match began. No one person could be aware of the multitude of individual struggles erupting all along the length of that long, constantly shifting line.

An engineer I knew began to step by me, followed by two firemen. It suddenly felt like a fight within my own family—the most heartbreaking kind of all. And I remembered, from my many times on picket lines before, my own theory of picketing: a graduated escalation from friendliness to hostility.

He was a big man, almost matching my six feet four. I looked dead into his eyes. "Why don't you help us out, Bill?" I said.

"I'd like to, Joe, but it depends on the Brotherhood's officials"— he had his answer ready.

"Anybody can do anything he wants to," I shot back.

Bill said nothing more and walked on by. I felt like tripping him, but held myself in check. The first fireman went by rapidly with averted eyes. The second fireman, whom I'd exchanged greetings with a couple of times in the shop, mumbled, "Good luck, boys," and followed the other two.

A fight was going on to my left. I started to slug a husky brakeman who had just shoved the picket next to me. But then we saw the bulls coming, and all was decorum. We resumed peaceful picketing, and the few remaining scabs made their way into the yard. It was infuriating to have to stand and watch them helplessly.

The repair shops remained silent. But out on the tracks a few of the engines began to get up steam, the men in the distant cabs with pinched dyspeptic looks on their faces.

How strange, I thought, looking into those silent sheds where I'd given so many hours of my life, with which I seemed so intimately connected. Once, workmen had owned their tools and could be their own men and have some pride and dignity in their craftsmanship. Now the tools had all been taken over by a master class of usurpers, lock, stock and barrel. "Progress." They and their cronies had taken over the land, the buildings, the homes, almost everything.

And walking the picket line, watching the first engines start to shunt freight cars back and forth, I thought: What a damn shame more Wobblies aren't involved. Then, instead of standing out here like a bunch of boobs, we'd still be in the shops, *our* shops, still collecting our pay, staging a slowdown—or ca'canny as the Scots called it — doing far more harm to our oppressors from inside than we could possibly do on a picket line. And if the IWW had been running the strike, a much greater effort would have been made in advance to get the cooperation of the other unions. With the One Big Union of the IWW — just as in Debs' successful strike against the Great Northern in 1893 — this nonsense could be settled in short order.

Later, when there were no more scabs crossing through our line, we went to the house of one of the boys to get the latest strike news on the radio. Up till now it had seemed like just one puny little strike in our hometown. It was hard to believe that it was going on anywhere else.

But now the news began coming in from all over the country. Hell was breaking loose all over the place — it put our middling efforts to shame. Hundreds of thousands of men out, boxcars and bridges burned, engines sabotaged, shoot-outs between union men and scabs, stranded trains, threats to call out state militias — it was mind-boggling. It was like a massive war on hundreds of different fronts.

I was so excited I could hardly sleep that night. Next morning when I got up a little after dawn, there was a surprise waiting for me: a banner headline from the *New York Times* shouting up at me from the kitchen table. (What had Pop been doing out so early? I wondered).

400,000 RAILROAD SHOPMEN QUIT TODAY BUT WAY MAINTENANCE MEN WILL DELAY; JEWELL DEFIANT, FLOUTS LABOR BOARD

"Trains Will Run, Strike or No Strike,"
Railway Executives Unite in Declaring

HOOPER REBUKES SHOP CHIEF

So it was real. And I, we, were part of it. A gigantic industrial army on the march. The dream of Debs and the IWW. I devoured the long article eagerly. When Pop came to breakfast, we had a long discussion about it. He had an excited look in his eyes but looked very sleepy. I wondered what he had been doing all night.

"I couldn't sleep," was all he would say. The consensus of opinion seemed to be that, if the maintenance-of-way men would join us, we'd have them by the balls. But they were still on the fence, apparently trying to cut a better deal on their own. The railroad owners were trying to play the different unions off against one another, and it made me madder than ever. "It's time we let the cat loose!" I exploded as I got up from the table.

Pop took me aside on the porch as I was leaving to go picket. "Look, son," he said. "Don't do anything too rash. Nothing they can put you in the can for more than a month for. If this was the revolution I'd say join me in the front lines. But it isn't—it's only a skirmish."

"Pretty big skirmish," I said. "By the way, Pop, how'd you bruise your knuckles?"

"Look, Joe," he told me. "I'm about to retire. You've got your whole life ahead of you. You won't be helping the cause by spending it in jail." He gave me a friendly pat on the back, and I grabbed my picket sign and headed off for the combat zone.

That day things got more interesting. There were more strikers on the picket line. There were also more cops and railroad bulls around with their usual dumb arrogant looks. I noticed the headlight was smashed out of one of the engines. "What's going on around here?" I asked my picket buddy, Art. "I thought we were the only two Wobblies around here."

"You know what they say," Art laughed. "'The IWW *advocates* sabotage, and the AFL *practices* it.'"

Then the engineers and firemen began appearing. They walked a little more warily today. I noticed that a couple of them had black eyes. One of our pickets had a black eye too. "Looks like our Sick Committee visited them last night," said Art.

"The Sick Committee?"

"Yeah—if the scabs aren't sick when the Sick Committee gets there, they're sick by the time they leave."

Presently Bill, the engineer I knew, and the same two firemen came walking toward us, their eyes set dead ahead. I decided to continue with my gradualism. "Thanks for your support," I said with heavy sarcasm. Bill ignored me, going in between me and Art. I decided to try a little humor: "You must have a *loco motive* for breaking our strike." Bill gave me a dirty look, and the three of them continued on.

"I get it—ho, ho, ho!" said Art, giving me a poke in the ribs.

I got another brainstorm. I had a few copies of the IWW's *Little Red Songbook* on me. I handed them out to some of the guys near me on the picket line and told them to turn to Joe Hill's famous song, "Casey Jones, the Union Scab." Art and I sang a few bars for them. When the next group of engineers and firemen came along, we burst forth in spirited song:

> The workers on the Frisco line to strike sent out a call,
> But Casey Jones, the engineer, he wouldn't strike at all;
> His boiler it was leaking and its drivers on the bum,
> And his engine and its bearings, they were all out of plumb.

> Casey Jones kept his junkpile running;
> Casey Jones was working double time;
> Casey Jones got a wooden medal
> For being good and faithful on the Frisco line...

Then we substituted the names of the engineers we were confronting in place of "Casey Jones":

> Billy White went to Hell a flyin';
> 'Billy White,' the Devil said, 'Oh, fine;
> Billy White, get busy shovelling sulphur;
> That's what you get for scabbing on the Frisco line!'

The train crews looked sheepish. But one tough-looking scab, the last man to cross through our line, gave us the finger and then made a grab for my songbook. I wasn't "Kid Murphy" for nothing. I gave him a little pat on the smeller with my left, and blood spurted out. He lunged for me, but I sidestepped and he went down. Some of the other scabs stood with raised fists facing me. But then we all saw a couple of bulls coming our way and the scabs backed off grumbling, and turned and went on into the yards. "I know who you are," the would-be songbook thief said. "You're the Murphy kid. I'll get you, you Mick son-of-a-bitch!"

Then we sang more songs, "There is Power in a Union" and "Mr. Block" and "Workingmen Unite" and "Solidarity Forever," and got the picket line all fired up. The next time we saw a train crew arriving, the scabs took one look at our spirited line and turned back the way they'd come, and we never did find out if they went to work that day.

People came and went all day long. At one point I looked at the picket next to me, who was shouting at the scabs in a more spirited and rowdy fashion than any of us, and I was in for a shock. It was the guy who had been pushed onto the point of my pocketknife that dark night three years before, whom I'd left gasping in the shadows.

So he hadn't died. I was looking right into his eyes, two feet away. But he didn't betray a flicker of recognition. I wondered if he had heard that engineer call me "Murphy." A hoodlum three years ago, now he seemed like one of the friendliest guys you could ever hope to meet—unless you were a scab. Maybe that bloody encounter had put some sense into him. What strange twists of fate life took sometimes. He gave me a big grin as if I were a blood brother. I grinned back my solidarity. But a minute later when he'd turned away I moved down to another spot on the line, wondering if he would ever recognize me—and if so, what he would do.

When my picket shift was over, I went by one of the lunchrooms where a lot of the shopmen hung out. There was a lively discussion about the strike going on. A heated argument began with a couple of old retired engineers who didn't think a twelve-percent wage cut was enough reason to go on strike. After the discussion seesawed back and forth for a while, I decided to inject a note of humor.

"I don't give a damn about the twelve percent," I said. "I'm on strike because the boss is an asshole."

"'The boss is an asshole,'" one of the engineers sneered. "Brilliant. You don't even know who your boss is. *What* boss?"

"All of them," I said. "They're all assholes. And I can prove it."

I had the attention of everyone in the place now. "All right, then, prove it Joe," someone yelled gleefully.

"Well," I began, "when the body was first created, there was this big argument about who was going to be the boss. The brain said: 'Since I'm the nerve center that does all the thinking, *I* should be the boss.' The feet said: 'Since we carry all the friggin' weight, *we* should be the boss.' The hands said: 'Since we have to do all the manual labor, *we* should be the boss.' The eyes said: 'Since we have to look out for all of you, *we* should be the boss.' And so it went with the heart, the lungs, and all the rest of the body, till there was nobody left but the anus. When the anus made his claim, all the others laughed: Whoever heard of an anus being boss of anything? This upset the anus so much that, in a fit of anger, he closed himself off completely and refused to function anymore.

"Soon the brain was feverish. The eyes burned. The feet were too weak to walk. The heart, the lungs and all the rest of the shebang had a rough time to keep going. So they all finally gave in to the anus, and he became the boss. And while *they* did all the work, the anus just basked and let out a lot of hot air.

"And the moral of this little yarn is that it takes no special talent to be a boss. So why have one if everybody knows how to work together in harmony...?"

Everyone broke up in laughter except the two sour old engineers. They just looked disgusted. I went on to give a five-minute lecture about the IWW and how the workers should be running things themselves. Before I was through, I actually had some of them agreeing with me. I didn't tell them my "Boss is an Asshole" yarn was something I'd read in one of the Wobbly papers.

A while later someone brought in some newspapers, and we all crowded around to read what was going on in other parts of the country.

RAIL STRIKE ON, 90% OF SHOPMEN OUT; A FEW TRACKMEN JOIN, LITTLE DISORDER; TRAINS ALL RUN, SOME DELAYS HERE

HOLIDAY THRONG HALTED

President Smith Helps to Speed Trains at Grand Central.

PENNSYLVANIA UNDELAYED

Handles a Record Crowd of 300,000 Pleasure Seekers on Schedule Time.

FOOD SUPPLY SAFEGUARDED

Department of Markets Will Use Motor Trucks—Port Authority Also Acts.

In the midst of the greatest rush of outgoing holiday travel New York City ever has experienced, the railroad shopcraft men, in defiance of the Railroad Labor Board's wage award, walked out yesterday. The strike had little effect on the schedules of most of the roads.

Hooper Pledges Government's Protection To All Railroad Men Who Are Willing to Work

Special to The New York Times.

CHICAGO, July 1.—Ben W. Hooper, Chairman of the Railroad Labor Board, issued a statement late today which placed the strikers outside the pale of Government assistance or sympathy. The workmen who take the place of the strikers, he said, are entirely justified and are entitled to support. His statement, which throws open to all workers the jobs abandoned by the strikers, follows:

"There is one new thought in connection with this strike that should be impressed upon everybody concerned.

"The man who takes the work that has been abandoned by a striker always has been called a 'scab' or a strikebreaker—terms to which much opprobrium attaches in some quarters.

"In the present case the men who assume the work abandoned by the striking railway employes cannot be justly reproached with the epithets mentioned.

"This is not the customary case in which the employer and employes have a controversy about rules or wages, and each tries to impose his views on the other. In this case the controversy is not, as in the former sense, between the carriers and their employers. The people, by Act of Congress approved by President Wilson, established a governmental tribunal charged with the duty of and vested with the power to fix rules and wages for railway employes.

"Disputes as to rules and wages were submitted and the evidence and arguments fully presented on both sides. Decisions of these disputes were handed down by the United States Railroad Labor Board. It is these decisions against which certain of the employes strike.

"Regardless of any question as to their right to strike, the new men who take their places are merely accepting what is equivalent to an open position, the wages and working conditions of which have been duly established by a governmental tribunal. They are not accepting wages and conditions which an employer is attempting arbitrarily to impose upon the striking employes.

"Under these circumstances it is a foregone conclusion that both public sentiment and governmental power will protect the men who remain in the service of the carriers and the new men who take the service."

SUCCESS, SAYS STRIKE HEAD

Jewell Looks for No Effect on Train Operation for Several Days.

MEN STAY AT WORK IN SPOTS

While Unexpected Help Is Given by Groups of the Maintenance-of-Way Men.

SOME SABOTAGE ON WABASH

And Strikers Clash With Guards in Maryland in Belief They Were Strike-Breakers.

Special to The New York Times.

CHICAGO, July 1.—Quietly and with no disorder, except in a few isolated and minor instances, the strike of the railway shopmen began throughout the country at 10 o'clock this morning, as scheduled.

A big cheer went up as we read the headline. And in the following days dozens of more articles told of the huge struggle that was erupting all over the country.

WALKOUT IS GENERAL ON NEW ENGLAND ROADS ———— *But Some Remain at Work and Road Officials Say There Will Be Cut in Trains.*	ILLINOIS TROOPS MOBILIZED ———— RIOT IN CHICAGO SUBURBS ———— Mob Throws Stones at Workmen's Houses—Jewell Hears Molders Are Quitting.

Our blood boiled when we read some of the stories, especially those that told of strikers being beaten, shot or arrested. Then we got the news that one of our local men had been shot by a scab-herder and was barely clinging to life.

Next day, Springfield had the atmosphere of an armed camp. People seldom went about except in large groups now. People eyed each other warily. Nobody smiled on the streets. There were more fights on the picket line, and a few arrests. Some of the wives and girlfriends of the strikers were now out on the picket line, yelling epithets at the scabs or throwing rocks at them.

It was war. And standing on the picket line I would think how, in the usual sort of war, the millionaires and rulers of nations got the lower classes to kill each other, and that was considered noble. But when we, the producers, had a *just* cause to fight for—a living wage and the right to have a union—*we* were made out to be unpatriotic scoundrels. But it made a lot more sense to wage the kind of war we were waging than to go off to some foreign country to die in the mud for the rich capitalists.

It was the Fourth of July, and some of the superpatriots who loved to die for the rich were planning the usual hullabaloo. But I heard bits and pieces of conversation on the picket line about how some of the boys were planning some Fourth of July fire-works more spectacular than any the superpatriots or Legionnaires had planned.

Late in the afternoon, one of the other pickets came up to me and said in a low voice: "How are you with a crowbar, Joe?" I told him I was ready to pry off the hinges of hell if it would help win the strike.

As soon as it got dark Art and I and four or five others got our crowbars and started walking along the tracks away from town. Then the fireworks started. After we'd been walking for about fifteen minutes we looked back toward the town and saw several boxcars on a siding go up in flames. When we'd walked for about an hour we saw a more spectacular sight: Off across the gently rolling plains, on another line, we saw what looked like a gigantic horizontal Roman candle whooshing across the countryside—it was a freight train, several of its cars afire, racing for the nearest water tank.

When we were several miles from town we came to a place where the railroad ran along beside a small river. "This is the place, boys," the main kazoo said. And we spent the next several hours huffing and puffing, prying up several lengths of rail and dumping them in the creek. Then we chopped down some trees and laid them across the tracks at each end of the big gap, so there wouldn't be a train wreck. We were exhausted but proud of our night's work. I didn't get home until almost dawn.

To my surprise, as I went into the yard, I ran into my dad just coming home from somewhere. "Are you on the Sick Committee, Pop?" I asked him in a whisper.

"Joe, it's not only you young bucks who are entitled to have all the fun," he sort of laughed.

I punched at him playfully. "It's great to have a hero for a Pop," I said. We went in to bed.

13

AN OBJECTION
TO DESPOTISM

There were more cops and railroad bulls than ever on the streets next day. But what really infuriated us was seeing the first contingent of "shopmen" scabs, surrounded by cops, being escorted into the shops to take our jobs. If it hadn't been for a few cool heads on the picket line, there could have been a massacre. We shouted every contemptuous epithet we could think of. A few rocks came hurtling from somewhere, and the scabs looked scared as hell.

Later I went to our hangout to read the papers. Everybody was edgy and filled with venom. We crowded around to read the latest reports. A big moan of disappointment and anger went up when we learned the maintenance–of–way men weren't going to support us. And just after we'd provided them with all that extra work last night! We read on through the latest dispatches:

RIOT GUNS ISSUED AT HORNELL

**Erie Guards Are Doubled—Clerks at
Syracuse Vote to Strike.**

ILLINOIS TROOPS OUT, MISSOURI TO ACT; RAIL GUARDS FIRE INTO MOB, KILL YOUTH; FEDERAL ACTION AUTHORIZED AT CHICAGO

Federal Officials Are Authorized to Use Force At Chicago to Protect Mails and Commerce

Two Roads Obtain Court Protection—Federal Marshals Enter Slater, Mo.

The fury of the strikers was growing. If the other railroad workers wouldn't support us, that meant we'd have to be that much more militant on our own.

The railroad company had set up a mess hall for the scabs who'd taken our jobs. They were looking for dishwashers and kitchen helpers. Art and I were running low on money, so we decided we'd try to kill two birds with one stone: work a few days to earn some money, and see what havoc we could wreak on the strikebreakers.

As far as I could see, no one who might recognize me was around the scab mess hall. But just to be on the safe side I gave a phony name when we applied for the jobs. Sure enough, the chowderhead of a cook took us on, and we went to work peeling spuds and washing dishes.

It almost made me puke to look out into the mess hall and see the sorry ignorant specimens of humanity who were stealing our jobs. One look at them and we knew a lot of them were going to foul up the equipment more than some of our best efforts at sabotage, but we were still out to get the conscienceless creeps. With the belly-breaker biscuits, the shoe-sole hotcakes and the rancid cow-paste they called butter, it was a wonder they could work at all—but we were determined to put the finishing touches on the job.

The first hot night, we opened some cans of pineapple and tomatoes and let them stand out overnight. By next day around ten or eleven, dozens of the scabs were holding their bellies and running for their bunks with the collywobbles. The head biscuit-shooter gave us suspicious looks and made an inspection of the kitchen—but fired one of the bull cooks instead of us.

To entertain myself at that miserable job, I would recite the poem "The Dishwasher" by a Wobbly poet named Jim Seymour, which had appeared often in IWW publications:

Alone in the kitchen, in a grease-laden steam
I pause for a moment, a moment to dream,
For even a dishwasher thinks of a day
Wherein will be leisure for rest and for play...
...You leeches who live on the fat of the land,
You overfed parasites, look at my hands;
You laugh at them now, they are blistered and coarse,
But such are the hands quite familiar with force;
And such are the hands that have furnished your drink,
The hands of the slaves who are learning to think,
And hands that have fed you can crush you as well
And cast your damned carcasses clear into hell!

After a couple of days, Art and I decided to strike again. This time we got several bottles of croton oil and put it in the food. It was by far the most potent laxative you could get. We sauced the food up good with it. Within fifteen minutes that railroad yard looked like an Olympic track meet: Scabs were running for the outhouse faster than a gold medal track star. After an hour or so, the chief scab–herder threw up his hands and laid them off for the day.

Art and I knew the boom was bound to fall soon. Next day I heard a gruff voice out in the mess hall ask the chief cook: "Is Abraham Lincoln here?"

I looked out through a slit in the doorway. A big harness bull was standing there with what looked like an arrest warrant in his hand. "Hey, Thomas Jefferson," I whispered to Art, who was peeling spuds nearby. "Let's amscray."

We tore off our aprons and skedaddled out the back door just as the cook and the bull were entering the kitchen. I was afraid to go home, so we went to the hangout where we always read the strike news.

This time, an article in the *New York Times* that caught my eye really set my Wobbly blood to racing:

STRIKERS SEIZE SHOPS OF C. & A. IN MISSOURI

They Drive Out Non-Union Men at Slater and Maintain Possession of the Works.

SLATER, Mo., July 5 (Associated Press).—Striking shopmen have seized the Chicago & Alton Railroad shops here, driven out non-union men brought in to work, and are holding the shops.

Eighteen men were ordered from the shops today, and yesterday twenty-five were ordered out. Union officials said the non-union men were placed on trains and sent from the town.

This was Wobbly tactics! Perhaps the beginning of sit-ins all over the country! Perhaps the beginning of the massive nation-wide or even worldwide strike of the One Big Union that would result in the workers taking over the whole shebang! Art and I couldn't contain our excitement, and we immediately began making plans to join our fellow workers in the liberated railroad shops in Slater.

As soon as dark came, we got friends who weren't under suspicion to go to our homes and get some extra clothes and traveling supplies for us. Ma came out to where I was waiting in the shadows half a block away. She begged me not to do anything rash, and I assured her I wouldn't.

Slater was about two hundred miles directly north. We decided to walk to the next town, where we weren't known, to catch a train. On the way out of town we passed the high school, and I got an idea. I had an older friend there who had a class in chemistry, and he'd been showing me some of his experiments. He had set up a little chemistry lab in a shed in his back yard. We were in luck and caught him alone in the shed. He gave me the chemicals I needed.

We caught a freight north to Kansas City. Twice there were long delays where railroad equipment had been sabotaged. We got into KC early next morning. There was heavy picketing in the railyards, and we joined the picket line for a while. Then we went into the passenger terminal, got cleaned up and bought tickets to the next town east.

About five minutes before we got to our stop, I took a coffee can out of my pack, slipped it between my feet and poured some hydrochloric acid into it. Then I took out my five or six lumps of iron sulphide and dropped them in. I slipped the coffee can under the seat. A minute later we got off the train. Next day we heard that, ten miles outside town, they'd had to stop the train out in the boondocks and let the whole carload of coughing passengers off, because of the "rotten egg" gas I'd generated.

We caught a freight headed toward Slater. As we neared Slater, we saw more and more heavily armed railroad bulls standing guard along the tracks.

We got into Slater a little before dark. There were armed guards spaced here and there all along the approaches to the town. As the train began to slow going through a little copse a mile or so outside town, we dropped our bedrolls off and jumped into some weeds. We hid our bindles in some bushes and ambled into town.

A heavy air of suspicion and fear hung about the little town. And yet, little groups of people here and there had a brightness of hope and excitement in their eyes too, as if for the first time in their lives they were part of something that was changing the world.

The railyards were surrounded by a cordon of police. But a spirited picket line, including many women, was there in spite of it. The people on the line had looks of a rather astonished happiness on their faces, as if they had the whole world by the balls. And beyond we could see the railroad shops, with a few smiling faces peering out through an open window here and there. The workers had retaken what was rightfully theirs.

"Maybe this is where it will start," said Art.

"I hope so," I said. "Wouldn't it be great to be in on the very beginning of the world's first really civilized society?"

We had wide-brimmed hats pulled well down over our faces to disguise our identity. The pickets were suspicious of us at first, but we produced our red cards and finally were accepted as the real goods. When we told them we wanted to join the men inside the shop, they were hesitant. But when we told them we'd brought some food and other supplies for the occupiers, they consulted with some people on the strike committee and decided to let us go in.

As soon as it got dark we went outside town and got our packs. Then we were taken to one of the strikers' homes. About midnight we headed for the railyards, accompanied by two of the locals.

There weren't as many guards around now. It was a very dark night. We made our way to a spot where there was cover almost up to the shops. One of the men with us gave a low whistle, and a railroad guard came up to us, gave me and Art a double take, then let us sneak through to the shops. When we start getting the cops on our side I guess that's progress, I thought.

After another signal we were let into the compound. It was a great feeling, joining our brothers in what might be the beginning of the revolution.

Fifty or sixty men were holding the place. There was a festive atmosphere. Some of the boys were playing cards, and others were talking in little groups. They all rushed up to see what we had brought and gave us a little cheer. Our guides explained who we were, and we took out our red cards. It turned out two of the men inside were Wobblies too. We should have known the IWW had something to do with such a revolutionary proceeding.

"Well, you boys are sure welcome," said one of the strikers, coming up and shaking both our hands strenuously. "We were beginning to wonder if the outside world knew what we were doing here."

"They know," I said. "And the ones who don't know now, will know soon. You're making history." The men gathered about us smiled their appreciation.

"Think you boys can run the railroad as well as the plutes?" said Art.

"Hell, I *know* we can—an' damn better," piped up another man.

Our two companions left, and the others began plying us for news of what was going on in other areas. We gave out newspapers and other literature, and the thirty or forty little red songbooks we had brought. Soon we were making the rafters shake, roaring out the lyrics to "Casey Jones" and "Mr. Block" and "Solidarity Forever." A few lights went on in nearby houses, and soon we could see a few people standing at the edge of the railyards cheering us on.

The next couple of days we had a number of educational sessions in which we explained to the others about the One Big Union of the IWW, and we signed up a number of the men. There were some great people in that group, heroes all.

We began making plans as to how to proceed if troops were sent in to remove us. It was agreed that we would not initiate any violence. We also agreed that our only real hope for success was in initiating similar takeovers all over the country. It was decided that Art and I and several others should fan out across the country, trying to persuade other workers to do what the brave men of Slater had done. Who knows, everyone thought: If we had some real success, it might be the beginning of a real revolution.

The third night we sneaked back out the way we had come, Art and I and several others. We got a few hours' sleep at one of the strikers' homes. A little before dawn we started off on our mission. Art and I were to be one of several two-member teams. Our host gave us a ride in his old flivver to the next town where the trains were still running. In a couple of hours we were in a rattling boxcar, on our way to the next town east that had railroad repair shops.

We went from town to town, stopping wherever there were pickets. A lot of the strikers seemed cheered by what the Slater workers had done, but damned few wanted to risk doing it themselves. When only four or five workers at a railyard wanted to take over the shops, we cautioned against it. Unless a sizeable number were involved, it might make the sit-in look unpopular and hurt the cause more than help it.

A couple of days later, riding a flatcar into Jefferson City, we saw a headline: FEDERAL MARSHALS AT SLATER.

> SLATER, Mo., July 8.—The full power of the United States Government was thrown into the strike of railway shopmen here tonight when I. K. Parshall, United States Marshal of the Western District of Missouri, sent eleven deputies into the shops and roundhouses of the Chicago & Alton Railroad here to serve as protection for non-union workmen.
>
> Parshall, in a conference with strikers and a declaration of intentions made to Mayor T. J. Gaulding, outlined the Government policy his armed force represents.
>
> "I am here to see that the shops run," the Government officer said.
>
> "My position has been taken on the line between the railroads and the strikers. I will be just. I am neither for the railroad nor for the strike. I am for the public."

The next day we read that the rebels in Slater had peacefully abandoned the shops. Well, that was the end of that. Our hopes seemed shattered. Still, we felt proud to have been part of the shop takeover. And even if this opportunity for victory was lost, the strikers' example might help spark some future revolutionary action by the workers.

Then my eye lit on a tiny item that made us both sit up and take notice:

> ST. LOUIS, Mo., July 7.—J. M. Kurn, President of the St. Louis-San Francisco Railway, today issued a statement saying that "strikers succeeded in driving off sixty-three men with threats of lynching," at the road's shops in Springfield, Mo., and that "another lot of twenty-eight men were taken away by the Chief of Police of Springfield shortly after they had been unloaded at our barracks."

It turned out that the twenty-eight were a group of Negroes from Memphis who were taken into the shops under armed guard. Apparently they hadn't been told they were being brought there as strikebreakers. The chief of police went in to interview the Negroes, who were being held as virtual prisoners, and asked them if they wanted to work. They said no. So he forced the railroad company to release them.

My god! While we were out trying to foment revolution elsewhere, all hell was breaking loose right in our own backyard. We had to get back to Springfield, arrest warrants or no.

Riding freights back south toward Springfield, we fell in with four or five strikers who had been burning railroad trestles. They asked us to join them. We agreed to do it, partly for precautionary reasons: We wanted to be sure they cut down some trees across the tracks or posted some sort of warning when they took out a trestle, to prevent people from being killed—there might be some innocent hobos or migrant workers on those trains. The IWW had always been against killing, except in self-defense.

A little before dark we crossed a big trestle over a river, and we all jumped off the train two or three miles farther on where it slowed for a turn. We hiked back through the woods lugging several cans of gasoline. When we came to the trestle, Art and I proceeded to drag some heavy limbs across the tracks on either side of the bridge, about two hundred yards away. Then we slid down the riverbank to join our cohorts. The tall underpinnings were already beginning to go up in smoke.

We all started scrabbling our way along the riverbank through heavy underbrush. Suddenly we were aware of several railroad bulls standing up on the bank about fifty yards away. We started back in the opposite direction. But after rounding a little bend, we saw even more bulls back that way. And there were more now on the opposite bank of the river.

Art and the others began to scramble through some trees and bushes up the bank. Then I saw a guy directly above me. I heard him say to someone I couldn't see: "Hey, I know who that guy is —that's the Murphy kid from Springfield!"

I felt my mouth go dry. I had to do something fast. I could see the bulls grab one of our pals up on the levee top. I rushed back around the little bend and was out of sight of my pursuers for a minute. Then I spotted a clump of reeds in the water. I waded in, grabbed one of the reeds, cut off a section, then looked around frantically for what else I needed. I was in luck: I found a small piece of jagged driftwood and was able to fasten one end of the reed to a niche in the wood. Then I set the device to floating and dived under the surface of the muddy water. After a few gasps, my underwater breathing apparatus began to work.

At first I just held myself down on the river bottom for all I was worth, not moving a muscle. I could hardly hear a thing and hadn't the faintest idea what was going on in the upper world on dry land. Once I heard what sounded like a big rock plunging into the water a few feet away and my heart almost stopped.

Then, after a few minutes more I began faintly, very faintly, pulling myself along by the tree roots at the river's bottom in a downstream direction. When it seemed like an hour had passed, and I had come to another clump of reeds, I finally edged my head up above the water line.

It was almost dark. The only thing I could hear was a few bullfrogs and crickets. I looked around carefully and then breathed a huge sigh of relief. The coast was clear.

It was a warm night. Fireflies pirouetted about me. I cleaned off my wet muddy clothes as well as I could, and worked my way slowly back to the spot a few hundred yards away where I had hidden my pack. It was still there. Hefting it, I saw silhouetted against the moonlight the charred, stilt-like legs of the trestle—it would be a while before it was back in operation.

I wondered what had happened to my fellow workers, whether they had all been arrested. I wondered what I should do. It would be too dangerous to head back to Springfield right after someone had spotted me. They might be looking for me all through this country. I could always join the wheat harvest in Kansas—I might find my brother Emmett there. I decided my best bet was to head off across open country to the west, avoiding farmhouses, then catch a freight at the first opportunity and not stop until I was in Kansas. I got my bearings from the moon and began walking slowly westward.

Then I remembered some distant cousins who lived on a small farm near here. I seemed to recall that one of them worked on the railroad and was a strong union man. I finally found their farm around daylight, and got a big friendly welcome. When I explained over the breakfast table what I had been up to, they treated me as if I were some kind of hero.

I arranged to help out with the chores for a while in exchange for my room and board. It was an easy, pleasant life. But the best time was when the father, Clayton, came home from town each night with the daily papers. I eagerly devoured every word about the growing strike.

TRACKMEN NOW THREATEN TO JOIN STRIKE;
ASKED TO DO STRIKERS' WORK, THEY SAY;
EFFORT TO WRECK TRAINS AND A BRIDGE

One New England Train Is Wrecked, Two Escape;   GRABLE ISSUES WARNING
Texas Attempt Fails; B. & O. Bridge Dynamited

Mob Raids Scranton Armory for Guns
Roused by Alleged Attack by Strikebreakers

And one hot July day there was a front-page article in the *New York Times* about Debs:

CHICAGO, July 17.—Eugene V. Debs, leader of the great American Railway Union strike in 1894, today issued a statement to the striking railroad men and other unions that the time has come for the rank and file to unite and "strike together, vote together and fight together."

"There has been some slight disorder and a few scabs have been hurt," Mr. Debs said. "This has been the extent of the violence, but it has been sufficient to bring to the strikers what they fought for in the late World War. The Federal Government announces through the Department of Justice that it will stand no trifling on the part of the strikers, and that if necessary armed force will be employed at once for their suppression.

"The Governors of seven States have simultaneously announced that they have the National Guard in their respective States mobilized and ready to move at command when the exigencies of the situation demand action.

"You will have no trouble in guessing what kind of action is thus meant on the part of our national and State Governments; which you shouted for, voted for, invested your last dollar for, and crossed the Atlantic to fight and be gassed and die for in the war to make the world in general and America in particular safe for democracy and liberty.

"And now that the war is over and Kaiserism is dead and democracy and liberty are on top, this same crowd to a man, to whom you rallied in such frenzy of enthusiasm, to compensate you for your noble patriotism, is now lined up against you in battle array and ready to shoot you down like dogs.

"It is true, Mr. Union Man, that your craft union leaders with scarcely an exception stood with the Wall Street profiteers in howling for war and rushing you, the common herd, into the trenches to be gassed, mutilated and murdered, while they remained in the rear to receive the plaudits of the plutocratic press for their patriotism. But that does not excuse you, for you chose those leaders and were responsible for them, and, after all, the leaders are about as fit or otherwise as the rank and file that elects them.

"If in the light of this situation you do not realize the crying need for unity, for solidarity on every front, regardless of creed or color, you are indeed in a pathetic plight, and your case is all but hopeless. Your weak craft unions have got to be converted into a powerful industrial union, and you have got to cut loose once and for all from the rotten political parties of your masters. * * *

BATTLE IN WEST VIRGINIA	NORTH CAROLINA TROOPS OUT. Disorders at Several Points Cause Governor to Act.

Strikers Defy Police Until Latter Charge—Toledo Women Assail New Workers.

Rebel girls! Joe Hill would have been proud! Now why couldn't *I* find a woman like that? I wondered.

And:

BROTHERHOODS TIE UP THE SANTA FE BY CALIFORNIA WALKOUT AGAINST GUARDS; WESTERN GOVERNORS WANT MINES SEIZED

HALT THROUGH MAIL TRAINS 24-HOUR ULTIMATUM GIVEN	"This Looks Serious to Me," Says the Postmaster General.	Passengers Left Stranded in the Arizona Desert.

And then a real doozie!

Daugherty Believes I. W. W. Is Busy in Strikes; Told the Railroads of Plots Against Bridges

WASHINGTON, Aug. 15 (Associated Press).—Attorney General Daugherty declared today that reports had come to the Department of Justice indicating that "the I. W. W.'s are quite active in connection with the railway strikes."

The Attorney General added that there was no detailed information in the hands of the department, but he said he was satisfied from the general information received that a relation existed between the strikes and activities of the I. W. W.

"There are indications," said Mr. Daugherty in a statement to newspaper men at the Department of Justice, "that the I. W. W's are ever willing to take over some of the responsibilities of railway transportation and even the Government itself in the West."

And the IWW's answer:

ADMITS I. W. W. ACTIVITIES.

Leader Says There Are Many Members Among Rail Strikers.

CHICAGO, Aug. 21.—Many members of the Industrial Workers of the World are numbered among the railroad strikers and a number of them "have demonstrated their objection to military despotism by quitting their jobs," according to a statement of Martin Carlson, general secretary of the Railroad Workers Industrial Union, a part of the I. W. W. organization, according to an announcement by the General Defense Committee today. Carlson's statement was called forth by recent statements of Attorney-General Daugherty that he believed there was a relation between the railroad strikes and the I. W. W., and that there were "indications that the I. W. W.'s are willing to take over some responsibility of railway transportation and even the government itself, in the West."

"It is true that there are I. W. W. members among the railroad strikers in various centres who have demonstrated their objection to military despotism by quitting their jobs," Mr. Carlson was quoted by the defense committee. "There are I. W. W. members also among the men at work in other railroad departments, and they too would be out on strike if the majority of the workers in those departments had not been under the domination of their grand lodge officers."

Carlson was quoted as saying also that the I. W. W.'s were "willing and eager" to take over "all responsibility for railroad transportation and for the conduct of all other productive industries." He denied, however, that the organization sought control of the reins of government.

Incredible! I thought. I couldn't have put it better myself. The IWW running the railroads! Why not? Hadn't we run a good part of the harvest operation back in the war years and, according to Thorstein Veblen, done a better job than the farmers? Many statistics had proven the U.S. government had done a better job of running the railroads in the world war than the private owners had in peacetime, and the IWW could do an even better job. It could be the real beginning of "building the new society within the shell of the old."

I worked at the farm for almost a month. At times I would join Clayton and his oldest son in some extracurricular night work on behalf of the strike. Then I got restless and decided to risk returning to Springfield.

I got into town after dark. I went to the house of a friend and dispatched him to my folks' place. My mother sent word that no bulls had been looking for me, so I went on home. But the next few days I stayed inside in the daytime, just in case.

The fortunes of the strikers ebbed and flowed. More and more injunctions were issued, and there was more and more violence. Over the next couple of weeks I continued to follow the newspaper articles:

VIOLENCE INCREASES IN THE RAIL STRIKE

Attempts to Wreck Trains, Explosions and Tampering With Tracks Occur at Several Points.

DAUGHERTY SAYS REDS FAN FLAMES IN STRIKES

WASHINGTON, Aug. 22.—Reports to the Department of Justice indicate that "agitation" of railroad strikes at Shawnee, Okla., is at as high a pitch as any point in the United States, with "I. W. W.'s fanning the flame," Attorney General Daugherty said today. Trains are being stopped and the mails are being interfered with to some extent, he added.

WOMEN ATTACK SHOPMAN.

Throw Pepper and Wield Clubs in Strike Riot at Olean.

Special to The New York Times.

OLEAN, N. Y., Aug. 22.—Throwing black pepper and waving brooms and clubs, 500 women, wives of striking Pennsylvania Railroad shop craftsmen, took part in a riot in the North End tonight when they surrounded an automobile carrying a shop workman, his three armed guards and a chauffeur. Warrants for eleven women, said to be leaders, have been sworn out, and they will be served tomorrow.

CALL FOR A GENERAL STRIKE

Sioux City Urges All Unions to Back It—Denver Refuses.

FORD SHORT OF COAL, TO CLOSE PLANTS; LEADERS BALK AT GIVING HARDING POWER TO TAKE OVER COAL MINES AND ROADS

HE BLAMES 'MONEY BARONS'

"State and national public officials are impotent in this national crisis," Mr. Ford said, "and the greed of the 'money barons,' who by subsidized agents control and manipulate the labor unions of the country will compel the average citizens to force a readjustment."

ALTON WALKOUT ENDS; MEN WIN CONCESSIONS

Official Offers 'Everything but the Railroad'—Men to Decide When Engines Are Safe.

SAYS BANKERS ARE RICH ANARCHISTS

Connolly Declares Wall Street Firms Have Done Country Incalculable Harm.

About this time I found another good aphorism for my notebook. Bertrand Russell: "A true revolutionary becomes more revolutionary the older he gets."

Events see-sawed back and forth. The federal injunction had little effect in curbing the strike. Finally one of the nation's biggest railroads, the Baltimore and Ohio, suggested that each company settle separately with the workers, and several railroads offered to cancel the wage cut and take the strikers back to work. Gradually around 225,000 strikers got more or less favorable settlements. Around 175,000 lost their jobs or their unions, or both. But the nationwide drive to cut wages and destroy the unions lost much of its momentum after that. And after the loss of so much of their equipment, the railroad bosses and other heads of industry were much more wary of antagonizing their workers. I felt proud of having been part of the struggle.

But at this point the strike in Springfield was still dragging on. I felt restless and useless just sitting around the house all day. Often I thought of the teeming exciting towns of the West, Spokane and Portland and Seattle, and of my desire to get revenge on the railroad bull who had tried to kill me. I wanted to *live*. "Life is real, life is earnest," Longfellow had written, and I yearned to live life fully and vividly.

One day I happened to read a line in a book that stirred my soul: "Something lost behind the ranges—something lost and waiting for you—go!"

Then one day, I heard an ominous knock. A minute later my mother told me the police were looking for me. That decided it.

Next day before dawn I hefted my pack and said goodbye to my mom and dad. I made my way down to the tracks at the edge of town. Before long a slow freight came along and I jumped up onto a flatcar, whoopity-scoot.

I felt the wind rush against me. The vast rolling countryside began to unfold before me. A great rush of freedom surged through my veins. As I felt the rhythmically bouncing planks beneath me, a few lines of Whitman sprang into my brain:

Passage—immediate passage! the blood burns in my veins!
Away, O soul!...
Have we not stood here like trees in the ground long enough?
Have we not grovell'd here long enough, eating and drinking
    like mere brutes?...
Reckless, O soul, exploring, I with thee, and thou with me...

The train picked up speed. I heard the whistle of its distant engine shriek.

This was life!

14

THE LABOR SPY

I held the rattler down as far as Coffeyville, Kansas, just above the Oklahoma line. I had always wanted to see Coffeyville because of its reputation as a romantic bastion of the Old West, where some of the most famous—or infamous, depending on your point of view—outlaw gangs had holed up.

On the trip west I had time to do a lot of thinking. My hatred for the capitalist system was at its peak. Here I'd spent several months conscientiously learning a craft, thinking that at last I could settle down and marry, be near my folks, and lead a decent life. And it had all been shattered by the greed of the railroad barons—with the collusion of the government—in cutting our pay. I vowed eternal vengeance against the slave-driving rich and their whole rotten system. And if I couldn't help change their dirty system, at least I was determined to get my revenge on their railroad bull lackey who had tried to murder me near Pasco, Washington.

Pulling out of Joplin, I was startled when a guy about thirty with an extra large bindle swung up into my car just as the train was picking up speed. He was a farmworker called Shortfuse Shorty from Whitefish, Montana. It turned out he was a Wobbly delegate, and the extra padding in his balloon was copies of IWW newspapers. After we rattled our teeth at each other for a while, I set to reading.

I was amazed to learn that, with increased sign-ups in the lumber and farming industries, the IWW now had the biggest membership in its history, close to 100,000. And with over 150 of our top leaders in prison and the new rule limiting officials to one year in office, it showed what the rank and file could do, given half a chance. Not only that, but our Marine Transport Workers union was continuing to open branches all over the world—in Australia, Germany, South Africa, Argentina, Chile, Peru. Maybe there was hope for the revolution yet—a *real* revolution, not just changing one set of tyrants for another as the Bolshies apparently had in mind.

We ditched at Coffeyville a little before dark. Though not exactly a wide-open cowboy town, it was a lively little place, with a thriving red light district. We found a flop in a little fleabag hotel and hit the sack.

Next morning we had some flapjacks and java and hit the main stem looking for work. This late in the summer the harvest was petering out this far south. But finally we got hired by a small farmer shocking wheat. He was one of those who had acceded to the IWW demand for a ten-hour day and fifty cents an hour, and the bunkhouse we shared with ten or twelve other stiffs was fairly clean. So there wasn't much chance of job action, especially with the harvest about over. We did our work in the blistering sun for a week until the job was done, then headed into town with our pay.

I was anxious to catch the first train on west, but Shortfuse had other ideas. I had assumed that, mild-mannered as he seemed, he had gotten his nickname from his quickness to take offense when treated badly. But I was to discover it had been given to him for another reason.

I had good intentions that sultry evening. But when Shortfuse steered me by one of the sporting houses where the scantily clad ladies sat on the porch swinging their gams around, my pulse quickened. When Shortfuse grabbed my arm to steer me into the place, I didn't put up much resistance.

With the harvest almost over and most of the stiffs gone, there weren't many customers. We were treated like royalty. Some bootleg booze was passed around. As Wobblies we were opposed to booze, especially during strikes. But hell, nobody should try to be too perfect—you'll never know what makes other people tick.

We let ourselves be conned into trying some, and the festivities picked up.

First thing I knew, it was two in the morning. It was still hot as the hinges of hell. We were all sitting out on the porch, joking and laughing now, me and Shortfuse and a couple of other stiffs with seven or eight of the girls—stark naked. Suddenly one of them got it in her head they should have a foot race—right down the main street of the town. So the lot of them lined up in the middle of the street. We bet on who would win, and then Shortfuse yelled, "Let 'er rip!" They took off in their birthday suits right down the main drag, past city hall, all the way to the other end of the business section and back.

My gal won—a tall striking redhead with green eyes. I spent my winnings on drinks for everyone. Then, with fond farewells and embraces all around, Shortfuse and I took off for our flops.

Next day I glommed a freight going northwest. Shortfuse said he had to stay in Coffeyville a day or two on "unfinished business." I lay back and dozed off. When I awoke it was late afternoon, and the long train was approaching familiar territory around Harper, Kansas. Much as I despised its tightwad farmers and their political stooges, I always felt a warm spot in my heart for the area, remembering it was near here I had first joined the IWW. The late summer wheat was a vast golden shimmery ocean, and after the excitement and danger of the railroad strike I almost felt like wading into it and venting some of my pent-up anger in furious and unrelenting work.

I wasn't disappointed. I got on with a crew shocking wheat, and we worked like maniacs through the long hot days. Here they paid only forty-five cents an hour, they still had the twelve-hour day, and I had the usual trouble with the damned alkali water. I think my plan to get even with the railroad bull in Washington was the only thing that kept me going through the long exhausting hours of boring and backbreaking work. Those cavemen who gave up a life of hunting and fishing for farming must have been stark raving mad, I would think at times. And every time I saw a lonely freight train going west across the prairie, I felt a fresh feverish longing for the day I would hop such a train and head west to get my revenge. In the meantime, some of the other Wobblies in the crew and I were debating job action to improve conditions.

One day I was shocking wheat next to a friendly young Wob. He said he had seen my brother Emmett just the day before in the Wobbly hall in Kansas City. I suddenly felt an overpowering urge to see Emmett, my favorite brother, to reminisce with him about our experiences together, and to see if maybe he could help me figure out where I was supposed to be going in this mess called life. That evening I collected my pay and, by midnight, I was riding in a side-door Pullman on a fast train to the east.

Next morning, when I woke up somewhere near Osawatomie, I thought the world war was still going on and I'd suddenly been transplanted to the Western front. A huge clattering machine, like ten tanks welded side to side, was charging toward me and the train, as if bent on sending us to Kingdom Come. I rubbed my eyes and began to recoil. Then I noticed a couple of 'bos who must have gotten on the train at some stop when I was asleep— they were laughing at me. The huge contraption, which must have been a good sixty feet across, came rumbling right up to the edge of the track, made a wide sweeping turn, and rattled away from us through the wheatfield like some kind of weird juggernaut.

"What in hell was that?" I asked the laughing men.

"Hain't you never seen a combine before?" chuckled one.

I should have known what it was. I had heard and read enough about the huge new contraptions and even seen photographs of them. But this was the first time I had seen the real thing. I sat in awe watching it disappear behind us, eating up the wheat like some insatiable metallic monster.

"That there shebang can do the work of fifteen men," one of my new companions said. "Pretty soon, all we'll have to do is ride around the country in style and eat up all the free bread."

I had an ominous queasy feeling in my stomach. If that thing really caught on and put all those men out of work, I reflected, pretty soon we'd have the biggest depression the world has ever seen. Great if it reduced work. But if the financial benefits weren't spread out among all the people, nobody would have the money to buy the wheat or bread, and we'd be in a real fix. One more reason to hasten the revolution.

We got in to Kansas City about noon. I went straight to the Wobbly hall to look for Emmett. But the secretary told me he'd left the day before to work in the harvest up around Fargo, North Dakota.

Depressed, I wandered down to the banks of the Missouri. The Kansas City riverfront was a lively place with the river traffic, the big railway station, the hospital and the teeming hotels nearby. This had been the beat of Ernest Hemingway five or six years before on his first job as a cub reporter for the *Kansas City Star* at age eighteen.

That night, as I was wandering along the riverfront, someone handed me a flyer about a meeting for the defense of twenty-two miners facing murder charges in Herrin, Illinois. The railroad workers and miners had given a lot of help to one another during their two big strikes which were just winding down, and my sympathies were immediately aroused. I offered to help the miner distribute the leaflets, and afterward went with him to the meeting that night.

I had read about what was called the "Herrin massacre" a few weeks earlier. And before the meeting started, I was able to look through a collection of clippings about the incident from the *New York Times* that the miners had assembled:

5,000 STRIKERS STORM ILLINOIS MINE, FORCING SURRENDER UNDER WHITE FLAG; 14 REPORTED KILLED, SCORE WOUNDED

Union Leader Says Men Will Fight It Out
If It Takes All Summer to Win Coal Strike

Special to The New York Times.

CINCINNATI, June 21.—The 680,000 striking coal miners are determined to " fight it out if it takes all Summer," William Green, Secretary-Treasurer of the United Mine Workers, declared in a statement here tonight.

Warning that a coal shortage was inevitable this Fall and Winter, Mr. Green said it was incomprehensible why the representatives of the Government and the public as well could not foresee this impending situation. He expressed the hope that before the strike had gone too far " reason, sense and good judgment will so influence the minds and actions of the coal operators as to bring about a conference and settlement that will be fair and just to all concerned."

" Along with the suffering of the miners," said Mr. Green, " must inevitably come great inconvenience to the public and perhaps suffering as well. If this coal strike is to continue, the supply will be wholly inadequate to meet public requirements when Fall and Winter comes."

Officials of the United Mine Workers organized in the anthracite coal fields, who arrived today to attend the convention of the American Federation of Labor, predicted that the 150,000 hard coal miners would declare a strike on July 1.

Thomas Kennedy of Hazleton, Chairman of the anthracite Wage Scale Committee, said that all negotiations had ended, and that the referendum vote now being taken by the membership was overwhelmingly for the declaration of a strike.

MINE GUARDS SUFFER MOST

Passing Train Crew See Heap of Bodies Lying in Pit on a Hillside.

ATTACKERS RAID FOR ARMS

Rifle Three Hardware Stores and Scour the Countryside—Fire on Truckload of Guards.

DISORDERS IN PENNSYLVANIA

There were varying versions of what had actually happened. When the strike had broken out, the owner of the Herrin mine had asked permission to strip the dirt off a layer of coal, pending a settlement; he promised not to touch the coal itself, and the union agreed. The owner brought in the members of a steam-shovel operators' union from Chicago. Later he went back on his word and had the men start excavating coal for sale at exorbitant prices, despite a plea from president Harding that owners not take advantage of the strike situation in this way.

The Herrin miners' local wired their president, John L. Lewis, asking what to do. Lewis wired back that the steam-shovel operators' local had been expelled from the union years before, and its members should be treated as strikebreakers. That much of the story was established fact.

Within hours, five thousand miners and their womenfolk assembled and began to march on the mine. They later claimed they were only trying to talk to the workers to ask them to leave, when mine guards opened up on them with machine-gun fire. An all-night gun battle ensued. The owner claimed the strikers captured the mine next day and executed nineteen of the imported workers and guards. The miners claimed those strikebreakers and guards were killed in the course of the battle, along with two or three of their own men. Later over two hundred miners were indicted for murder. The number was later reduced to twenty-two, and it looked bad for them.

The miners and their wives and sisters who spoke at the meeting that night had heart-wrenching stories to tell about their poverty and the oppression by the mine owners. But unfortunately, they did not have much of an audience. No matter who initiated violence, it scared most people off. They might drool at the thought of their sons and brothers and husbands dying in some foreign land in the name of "patriotism"—but fighting in America for a living wage hit too close to home.

After the meeting I stuck around to talk with some of the miners. One of them opined that their only chance was if they could feel out the opinions of the prospective jurors, so their attorneys would know which ones to challenge. They had access to the list of prospective jurors, most of whom were small farmers, but the big problem was to find out their real views. The locals tended to be very guarded around other residents of the county.

But if they could just get some innocuous-looking outsider to come in...

I saw what they were getting at. I guess partly because of my youth, I tended to fit the description "innocuous."

"Sure, I'll volunteer," I said.

Then a discussion arose as to what was the best sort of front for me to have. I didn't especially like the idea of sailing under false colors. But this was an emergency. And anyway, it probably wouldn't involve telling any outright lies, just keeping my ears open.

Finally somebody remembered he had a brother in St. Louis who had a sewing machine franchise. They decided to fix me up as a legitimate sewing machine salesman—I could keep the commissions from any machines I sold. The miner phoned his brother in St. Louis to check on it, and he agreed to hire me.

By next day, the whole deal was arranged. I was to be outfitted with a Model T, half a dozen sewing machines, and an advance on expenses for my first two weeks of operations.

The more I thought about it, the more the idea caught fire in my mind: doing a mighty chore for the labor movement, while having the freedom to putt-putt all over the country in my own car, and maybe make some good money in the deal. My dad had let me drive his flivver in Springfield a few times, just enough to whet my appetite for automotive travel, and I knew I could handle the contraption.

Next day I rode the cushions to St. Louis with some of the miners. I spent the following day being broken in to the sewing machine business. Actually it was a great contraption, a tremendous boon to the poor overworked housewife who had ten kids to make clothes for and cook and keep house for. Just before I left, loaded down with machines, I was given an address in the countryside near Herrin where I was to pick up the list of prospective jurors. Then I was on my way.

It was thrilling to cross the great river toward East St. Louis, Illinois. Of course I had read *The Adventures of Huckleberry Finn*, like most kids. But the great flowing expanse of water was even more majestic than I had imagined. Someday, I thought, I'd like to get a raft just like Huck and Jim, and ride it from its headwaters all the way to New Orleans and the Gulf.

I headed down toward Cairo and Little Egypt, really letting her rip. I waved at pretty girls along the streets of sleepy little southern Illinois towns, wishing I had time to linger with them.

The country was lovely going down toward Herrin, green and gently rolling, wooded here and there, kind of like I'd been told Ireland was. But as I got deeper into mining country, a gradual change came over it. The little houses became more hovel-like, the people looking out the doorways seemed to have an air of desperation and hopelessness about them, almost to be a different race of people. I had read and heard a lot about the lives of miners, but I wasn't prepared for the reality: teenage youths who already had the look of death in their eyes, men in their thirties or forties dying of black lung and other occupational ailments, children in rags, people totally devoid of hope. They were at the bottom of the social pit in more ways than one.

Why did they do it, work in the mines? I wondered. No one should be subjected to that kind of hell. But then Bill Haywood was brilliant and he'd done it, as had John L. Lewis and some of the smartest men in history. Because they were desperate. Because there was no other work. Because the owners paid them so little they couldn't save enough to move on. Because they didn't want to leave friends and relatives. Because not everybody could be a farmer, and many of *them* could barely scratch out a living. Because it was the only thing they knew how to do. Because it got in their blood...and their lungs.

Things were rough in the mines—they had always been. There was a much-quoted truism that if a mine disaster was reported, the first question the superintendent asked was: "Did we lose any mules?" Then his next question was: "Did we lose any men?"

As I got closer to Herrin, I felt the air of desperation and suspicion grow. I lingered in little village cafes so I wouldn't arrive at my secret destination before dark. People looked at me warily, obviously leery of any newcomer to the area. I did my best to act jovial and innocent, feigning surprise when a waitress and the man sitting next to me began to talk in baleful tones of the coming trial. "I might as well say goodbye to my brother and two cousins," my counter mate mumbled, getting up to shuffle out of the place.

A little before midnight, I pulled up at the miner's shack where my local contact lived. It was the home of a brother of one of the men on trial. In hushed but eager tones, he and his wife invited me into their small home. They seemed surprised at how young I was. I was a little embarrassed at how grateful they seemed for my help. "You're our only chance," they told me, almost with tears in their eyes. They plied me with food, filled me in on the local situation, and then gave me the coveted list of prospective jurors. Almost all the people on the list were farmers. They handed it to me as if it were some secret talisman to be guarded with my life. I promised them I would do my level best, then cranked up the Model T and headed back to Carbondale, about fifteen miles southwest, where I'd rented a hotel room.

Next day I got a map of the county and started on my rounds. I decided to start with the area closer to the mine and the scene of the battle, because I'd heard the farmers there were friendlier to the union. I soon discovered the reason: Before the battle, the mine guards had illegally stopped everyone who passed along the public roads close to the mine, subjecting them to humiliating questioning and harassment.

The first place I stopped at was a small dairy farm about two miles from the mine. There was a stand of hollyhocks in front of the small frame house, and it looked like a reasonably friendly place. I parked behind an old wagon, took a deep breath, and walked up to the door.

A frail middle-aged woman answered my knock, peering out a little warily. I gave her my sales pitch.

She sighed. "I'd sure enough like to have one of those contraptions," she said. "But with business fallin' off the way it has been on account o' the strike I don't think I'd dare ask Pa to buy me one."

"I heard about the strike," I said. "Everybody sure looks down in the dumps around here."

"Who wouldn't be—with twenty-two of our poor boys facin' the hangman's noose." Something clicked in my mind—mark one up for our side—but I didn't let anything register in my face. "Why don't you let me talk to your husband?" I said.

"Wouldn't hurt any, I guess. He's out back mending a stretch of fence."

I found the man. He squinted at me even more warily than his wife had done. He got a little friendlier when I told him my business, but winced when I told him the price of a sewing machine.

"Come back next year," he said. "Maybe things will be better after this god-awful mess is settled."

"Your wife told me about the labor troubles," I said.

"I've never had much use for the damned miners," the farmer said. "Mainly a bunch of lowlife foreigners. But after seein' how them mine guards run over ever'body around here, I can better understand why they got up on their hind legs. I think somepin should be done to those boys, but I don't think they should have to croak."

I thanked him for his time and went back to my flivver, waving goodbye to the farmer's wife. I drove down the road a ways, then stopped and got out my list. I'd decided to make a different mark for five different types of response: sympathetic, mildly sympathetic, doubtful, unsympathetic, and no response. I made the mark for "mildly sympathetic" for my first stop. This was progress!

At the next little farm I got a different response. After berating me for wasting his time, a dyspeptic-looking sodbuster said: "We've got enough troubles around here without city slickers tryin' to bamboozle us with their fool contraptions. With the county full of murderers like those crazy miners, this place ain't fit to live in anymore. I hope they hang the lot of 'em."

And so it went. From farm to farm. Eventually almost everyone had something to say about the men on trial. Sometimes they betrayed their true feelings by only a word, only a fleeting expression in their eyes. As near as I could determine, the feeling seemed to run about fifty–fifty pro and con.

I spent the best part of two weeks going through all that area trying to sell my machines. Through Marion and Herrin and Carterville and Colp and along the shores of Crab Orchard Lake and along the Big Muddy and all through there. I actually sold four sewing machines. But the real gold was those little marks I had on my list.

At the end of the two weeks I putt–putted late one night up to the house of my contact to deliver my list. My hosts acted as if I were the Second Coming. After feeding and pampering me, they apologized for having to send me on my way before daybreak.

I drove back to St. Louis, my mission completed. In the following months, out West, I watched the newspapers closely for news of the trials. I didn't feel much hope. But one day in the spring, I read that the jury had found all the accused miners innocent. Incredible! I couldn't help thinking there was a great probability my information had made the difference. It gave me a great sense of worth and self-confidence.

From that day on, no matter what else happened in my life, I thought, my life had been a plus for humanity, having helped save the lives of those twenty-two men. It was a nourishing secret I carried around with me from then on. Later John L. Lewis gave me an inscribed watch for my part in the affair.

15

ALREADY IN HELL

I lounged around St. Louis a couple of days seeing the sights and then I headed out. When I headed the long way west I was still seething with anger against the mine owners and the railroad companies. As I rode the freights over the endless prairies, the boredom and the cold of approaching winter fed my thirst for revenge against the railroad bull who had tried to kill me. By god I would get at least one of the heartless louses.

Personal revenge could be immensely satisfying as well as a powerful deterrent to future acts of evil. It was fine to turn the other cheek in lesser matters, but when someone was crazy or evil enough to murder, then drastic measures were called for. I husbanded my hatred, my sweet fantasies of revenge, all the way out through Kansas City and up through Sioux City and Fargo and Minot, North Dakota.

At Minot I heard they were paying fifty cents an hour in the harvest so I decided to work a few days and replenish my dwindling bankroll. Perhaps also, subconsciously, I was delaying that moment of truth in Washington State. My first day in town I was approached by a farmer who needed an extra man to replace one who had left. He was a shifty-eyed galoot about fifty and I should have been suspicious of him, but he said he paid fifty cents an hour plus all the chuck you could shovel down.

His farm was a spread of about a hundred acres, ten miles from town. Strangely, all the men, including two or three Wobs, had been working there only a day or two. But the grub and the bunks were okay, so we pitched in and did our best.

We had all the grain in in about a week. We congregated around the back door of the farmhouse to get our pay. The farmer finally came out, looking uneasy. "Boys," he said, "I've had a few setbacks this year. The goddamn grain merchants haven't been paying up as promptly as usual for some reason. The best I can do right now is pay you off in I.O.U.s."

"I.O.U.s!" said one stiff. "We can't eat I.O.U.s."

The men began to grumble. "Why'n hell didn't you tell us this when you hired us?" another yelled out.

The men began to move closer to the farmer where he stood on the porch. One stiff wanted to beat him to a pulp on the spot. Another grabbed a shovel and started up the steps toward him.

"Hold your potato," I cautioned the hothead. "There are better ways to handle this."

Maybe because the others knew by now I was a Wobbly, they had confidence in me. The man with the shovel backed off. I stepped up to the front of the group. "Well, Mr. Kroll," I said, "if you can't pay us off in cash, then how about a few chickens and pigs? These men have to eat."

"I told you men I'd give you I.O.U.s," the farmer said. "Take it or leave it. If you men aren't gone by sundown I'm going to call the sheriff."

The other workers and I had a brief conference. It was decided that I should continue as their spokesman.

I went up to the farmer again. "Well, Mr. Kroll, I said, "the boys decided if you're not even going to give us a few chickens for all our hard work, we're going to camp right here until you come to your senses."

Kroll seemed furious. He turned to the open doorway to the house. "All right, boys, you know what to do," he said.

All of a sudden five or six husky men and teenage boys with pick handles came charging out of the house toward us. We tried to move back, tripping over one another in our haste. But we didn't move fast enough and the long pick handles came down on the heads and backs of several of our group. I caught a stinging blow to the ear. There were only about a dozen of us, so we were no match for the pick handles. Also I could now see one of the farmer's sons holding a shotgun on us from the porch.

We retreated out to the road, grabbing our bindles. One man had a bad gash across his forehead. When we were a hundred yards or so down the road we stopped to lick our wounds and have a powwow. The men were grumbling and cursing and vowing revenge.

"Look," I said when they had calmed down. "There's no sense in all of us getting in trouble over this. A big group of men moving around is going to cause suspicion. We Wobblies know how to handle these things. If you boys let me handle this, I guarantee I'll make that hoosier sorry he ever went into the farming business."

There was much grumbling and discussion. Most of the gang were anxious to catch a freight that came through every evening headed west. They finally agreed to let me settle the score with John Farmer.

I walked back into town with them to get some grub. Then, a little before dark, I told my grumbling fellow workers goodbye in the railyards. Then I walked out to the edge of town and waited for nightfall.

Fortunately it was as dark as a stack of sab cats that night. I bided my time walking alongside the country road, running into the fields to lie down every time a car or wagon came along. And all the way out to the farm I kept reciting over and over to myself the little poem about sabots* and sabotage that had become part of Wobbly lore:

> If freedom's road seems tough and hard
> and strewn with rocks and thorns,
> Just put your wooden shoes on, Pard,
> and you won't hurt your corns.

By some time before midnight I was at the farm. All was quiet. Then, as I got within about forty yards of the barn the farmer's dog began to yap. Fortunately I had befriended the mutt during the week I had worked there, so I called to him in a low voice and he stopped barking and came up wagging his tail.

Sabot is French for wooden shoe. One story of the origin of the word *sabotage* is that French peasants, driven off their land and compelled to work in factories, would throw their shoes into the machinery to halt production.

I didn't waste any time. I sneaked in the barn, shooed the cow and some pigs and chickens out, put bridles on the two big work-horses, and led them out and tied them to a tree about fifty yards away. Then I went back to the barn and lit a match and threw it in the hay. I ran back to the horses, hopped on the bigger of the two, and began galloping cross country toward the next town out across the prairie. Every couple of hundred yards I would turn and look back at the lovely sight of the barn going up in flames.

Next day at dawn I began stopping at farmhouses. Before eight o'clock I had sold the horses for thirty dollars each to another farmer. So much for I.O.U.s.

I didn't lose any time getting on a freight heading west. Next day I was in Montana, the day after that in Idaho.

Going into the Northwest, as usual in winter, everything was water. But after the long hot summer it was a watery world I liked. Every place on earth seems to have some special something about it, if you just look for it, some quality that grows on you, that gets in your blood. And the Northwest had a certain something that was unique and found nowhere else, a certain feel and smell to the air, a feeling of excitement in the atmosphere, as if each little drop of fresh-smelling rain were a vibrant universe of its own. In spite of my deadly earnest mission, it felt like coming home.

I crossed the Snake River through a drizzling rain and before many hours more we were nearing the great rushing Columbia. I began to get a choked-up ominous feeling as the train neared Pasco.

I got in to Pasco in the early afternoon. The rain had stopped. The first thing I did was go to a clothing store and buy a wide-brimmed hat I could pull down well over my eyes. Next I went to a grocery store and bought a large potato and some hot chili powder. I already had some supplies in my pack in case I had to hit the high lonesome and hide out for a spell.

I was ready. Now that I was prepared, I felt a relaxing calmness come over me. Strange to say, in my mental excitement I felt a tranquil reassurance, a self-convincing feeling I was going to pull it off.

I pulled my hat down over my eyes and ambled back toward the railyards. I figured I would wait around as long as it took, pretending I was waiting for a freight. My plan was to wait for my nemesis to appear and try to trail him until after dark or he was alone someplace and then lower the boom. Or if I caught him heading out on a freight I was ready for that possibility too. But this time I'd be on deck and not a sitting duck riding underneath.

I waited all afternoon, jawboning with a few other 'bos from time to time. The freights came and went, and I saw a few mean-looking shacks, but I never saw my man. No doubt he still worked the night shift...

About dark I went to a greasy spoon for some grub. Just as I was mopping up the last drops of gravy from my hot beef sandwich I looked down the counter and my blood froze. It was him. I could never forget those bloodthirsty sadist's eyes. I quickly picked up a paper and pretended to be reading.

A couple of minutes later my assailant got up to leave. I was in for another shock. His body came lurching down the aisle, passing within inches of me. When I dared to look at the retreating figure I saw that my would-be murderer had a peg leg. He went awkwardly out the door and it closed behind him.

I turned to the waitress, slipping a quarter under the edge of my plate. "Who was that one-legged guy?" I asked.

"Oh—that's Peg-leg Murphy, the ex-railroad bull," she said. "He was trying to push some kid off a freight a few months ago and slipped and fell under the wheels."

Something in my stomach tightened. Murphy—how weird! Maybe a distant relative. I hoped not. And talk about poetic justice, however grisly.

"Thanks," I said. I put on my wide-brimmed hat and followed my erstwhile assailant out the door. I felt my heart beating faster now.

I saw the lurching peg-legged figure half a block down the street. It had started to drizzle again. I followed him slowly, crossing to the opposite side of the street to make my pursuit less obvious. I felt my vengefulness flooding through me like good booze.

We passed into more run-down areas. The railroads weren't noted for taking good care of their cast-offs. Finally near the edge of town the peg-legged man entered a clapboard shanty.

I went through a vacant lot and crept up to a side window. Two figures were slumped at a table with what looked like a bottle of bootleg booze between them. The second figure was a fat tooth-less, obviously drunken woman who must have been his wife.

Then I saw another figure in the dimness of the room: a kid about my own age, a replica of the two hopeless-looking figures at the table. Except for the gaping mouth and eyes and the erratic jerky way of walking.

Suddenly I lost all desire to send my assailant to hell. He was there already.

16

THE PORTLAND REVOLUTION

I felt confused and lonely, yet excited to be in the Northwest again, where so many of the important events of my life had occurred. Life is seldom simple. Sometimes it seems like the more intelligence and imagination you have, the more active your brain is, the more ambivalent you are about life. My mind was seething with all kinds of conflicting feelings.

If only I had been able to find Emmett, I thought, maybe I could have gotten my thinking a little more straightened out. I wanted adventure and yet I wanted security, a good steady job and a wife and family. I wanted desperately to overthrow this crazy unjust system we were suffering under, and yet I wanted safety and stability and some fun out of life. I wanted to travel and yet I wanted to settle down. I wanted to play an important role in the labor and revolutionary movements, and yet I feared the immense responsibility that entailed.

I had intended on playing the woods for a while. But sitting around in the drizzle in a hobo camp next day on the outskirts of Pasco, drinking some jungle juice by the sputtering morning fire, I heard some fellow workers talking about a big new Wobbly longshore strike in Portland. "The Portland Revolution," they called it. In my restlessness and desire to throw my energy and discon-

134

tent into something constructive, I decided I had to go to Portland and find out what was going on.

But first I wanted to go to Seattle and try to track down a former girlfriend who lived there. I was lucky enough to find refuge from the rain in a fairly clean boxcar, and by nightfall I was walking along Second Avenue in Seattle.

It was exciting walking along the old Skid Road I had spent so much time on, and I stopped to exchange greetings with a number of Wobs I knew. Some of them had been in the recent action on the waterfront in Portland and urged me to go help out there, and I was getting more and more excited about this new IWW struggle. But at Mrs. Thompson's boardinghouse I got news that shattered my hopes: The former girlfriend I was seeking had gone off with some bloke to try homesteading in British Columbia. And the owner's daughter, now getting a reputation of her own as "Boxcar Bertha," was off on her adventures riding freights around the country.

Depressed, I went to the Wobbly hall, got some supplies, and prepared to sack out for the night. I had a bad case of the dismals. Would I ever find my own "rebel girl" to share my life and struggles with? But I always had the IWW, I consoled myself, like a religion, a healing balm, a home: the ideals, the comradeship, the activity, the love of life and humanity the IWW engendered, the sense of a purpose in life. To pass the time before I got sleepy I copied down a piece tacked up on the wall called "Definition of a Strikebreaker, by Jack London." Then I spread out my blankets along one wall and hit the hay.

Next morning I felt a little better. The IWW hall was a hive of activity. The Marine Transport Workers Union was growing rapidly, and a number of Wobbly seamen had news from all over the world. The IWW had printed up a mess of its literature in Chinese, and seamen in China had gone on strike and gotten a fifteen percent pay increase. Japanese seamen, using IWW methods, had organized industrially and gotten their pay increased from seven dollars a month in 1919 to fifty dollars a month now in 1922. The IWW was growing on all fronts.

But the big news was Portland. Sitting around the hall, I got a rundown on the situation. The waterfront there had been in ferment since April, when the shipowners and stevedore companies had started a new "fink hall" through which everyone working on the waterfront had to be hired. Roughly half of the

Portland longshoremen were in the ILA, the International Long-shoremen's Association of the AFL; two or three hundred were Wobs, and the rest were unorganized.

Under the new fink hall arrangement the employers were supposed to give half the jobs to the ILA members and half to the others, including the Wobblies. Actually it was a means of screening out the more militant unionists in both the IWW and ILA and destroying the power of the unions. The efforts of the master class to drive workers farther down into poverty and slavery seemed to be unrelenting—they didn't give up for a second in their mindless greed for profits, and the instant you beat them on one front the leeches were immediately looking for other ways to drive you down.

A strike had broken out in April in response to the new fink hall, and there had been excellent cooperation between the IWW and most of the rank and file of the ILA. But the only gains achieved were the ILA's right to have their own man stationed in the fink hall, and a rapid growth in the IWW's Marine Transport Workers Union.

In October the strike had broken out again. This time cooperation between the IWW and the ILA was even better, and a joint strike committee was set up. Soon hundreds of longshoremen were picketing the docks. Wobblies rode the freights in from all over to help out—harvest stiffs, loggers, sawmill workers, construction workers. The Portland waterfront was soon a scene of seething humanity, with huge crowds of workers lining the docks to keep out the scabs. Seventy-five new police were hired; the cops had blatantly sided with the shipowners, and there were many arrests. It came to be called "the Homemade Portland Revolution."

I was sitting on a bench in the Seattle hall reading a new tramp novel, *Emmett Lawler*, written by a friend of the Wobblies in L.A. named Jim Tully, when the secretary announced a group of Wobs was leaving by side-door Pullman for Portland. I jumped up, ready for action, and grabbed my pack. There were about a dozen of us. Soon we were hiking through the drizzle down to the railyards, singing "Hold the Fort." I felt a stab of reminiscence. It was like the bloody Centralia affair all over again, except this time for once the good guys seemed to have the upper hand.

We rode through the late autumn rain down through Tacoma and Olympia and on south, catching exciting glimpses now and

Members of the Marine Transport Workers union of the IWW gather near the Delaware River in Philadelphia.

then through the drizzle of the great inspiring snow-clad mountains to the east—Rainier, St. Helens, and finally resplendent Mount Hood in a sudden flash of sunlight as we crossed the Columbia at Vancouver. How could people help but aspire to greater things with those tremendous marvels of nature to inspire them? I thought.

It was a spirited bunch of stiffs I was with, all veterans of the class struggle, not unfamiliar with the goon's sap and the bull's club. A couple of them had seen me box, and I was glad to learn my reputation as a member of the flying squadron was still alive. We had a few rousing tales to tell one another as we rocked south.

After we left Olympia our rattler really began to split the wind, and we got into Portland by early afternoon. The whole city seemed to be in ferment. As we hopped off our boxcar in the chaotic yards a couple of railway workers took out their red cards and flashed them at us. I felt my spirits soar. Maybe here was where it would begin, John Reed's town, the great river port of the West.

We jumped on a streetcar and were pleasantly surprised when the conductor refused to take our money. I noticed an IWW Marine Transport Workers pin on his lapel. "Thanks, fellow worker," I grinned. "Take us to the Revolution."

"That's the only place this trolley goes!" he smiled back with a gleam in his eyes.

In a few minutes we were at the waterfront near the center of Portland. The whole area was seething with activity. Hundreds of people swept back and forth—union men, scabs, cops, and thousands of onlookers, most of whom seemed to be cheering the union men on. The whole riverfront was jammed with ships, some looking completely abandoned and some being slowly loaded by a handful of scabs. A vast confusion of unstowed cargo stood about. I could smell the odor of rotting fruit and saw thousands of sacks with green shoots of newly sprouted grain bursting up from them.

A husky Wobbly picket captain greeted us at the crowded entrance to one of the docks. He didn't have to be told we were Wobblies—something in our faces must have made it obvious. He reached in a pocket of his mackinaw. "Here, fellow workers— you're in the MTW now. Welcome to the battle!" And he pinned an IWW Marine Transport Workers pin on each of our coats.

Then he pointed over the heads of the hundreds of shouting pickets to where a motley group of ten or twelve worried-looking men were loading a tub called the *Rose City*. "See that disgusting sight down there?" he said. "That handful of lizards, snakes and scorpions crawled up out of the river mud and they're trying to steal our beautiful wheat harvest here! And can you imagine, the zookeepers want to protect those slimy things?" And he indicated a squad of police off to one side trying to elbow their way into the crowd.

I tried to take in the chaotic situation. We newcomers grabbed picket signs and joined in the revelry. Then I realized the police were trying to form a wedge to make a path for ten or fifteen more scabs to get down to the dock. The Wobblies had their usual policy of never initiating violence, but there was no law against standing side by side on a public sidewalk, and the harness bulls were having a hard time getting through. But they seemed determined to make it, and we were just as determined they wouldn't. The mass of humanity surged back and forth in a gigantic tug of war. Slowly, it seemed, the bulls and scabs were inching forward.

I noticed a large Luckenbach ship which had just pulled in at the next dock. There seemed to be a ruckus on board. The twenty or so seamen with their sea bags over their shoulders came trooping down the gangway, a few hurling epithets over their shoulders at the scowling captain on the bridge. Then I did a double take. Just below the deck, near the port bow, was painted in five-foot-high letters:

IWW — 100%

A cheer went up from the crowd as the Wobbly seamen came off the ship. The score of burly seamen edged their way through the crowd toward us. They looked angry and happy at the same time. "Can you imagine—that slavemaster creep wanted us to work cargo like a bunch of reptiles!" one seaman growled, indicating the disgruntled captain on the bridge. "So we all told him where to get off and signed off. Give me one of those picket signs!"

The group of Wobbly seamen was welcomed by more cheers and slaps on the back. The cops a few dozen yards away looked alarmed and disgusted. When the burly seamen pitched in eagerly and added their strength to the seesawing crowd the tide began to turn against the strikebreakers.

Seeing our side gaining the upper hand, I decided to get closer to the sweating scabs and see just what the miscreants looked like up close. They looked just like the petty crooks I had been told they were—mainly criminal riffraff forced by the authorities to choose between the rockpile and scabbing. But I was determined to find out if there weren't a few brain cells in some of those skulls that were receptive to reason.

When I was at the edge of the dock I jumped up on a pile of sprouting grain sacks and tried to reason in a friendly way with the sweating men loading cargo. I did my best to convince them that what we were doing was in the interests of all workers, including themselves. Two or three acted like they understood some of what I was saying and acted a bit sheepish, but they kept up their slow fumbling pace of loading.

Then I remembered the "Definition of a Strikebreaker" I had copied and stuffed in my pocket in the hall in Seattle the night before. Summoning up all my lung-power, I began to read it aloud to the scabs:

DEFINITION OF A STRIKEBREAKER, by Jack London*

After God had finished the rattlesnake, the toad and the vampire, he had some awful substance left with which he made a strikebreaker. A strikebreaker is a two-legged animal with a corkscrew soul, a waterlogged brain, and a combination back-bone made of jelly and glue. Where others have hearts, he carries a tumor of rotten principles.

When a strikebreaker comes down the street men turn their backs and angels weep in Heaven, and the devil shuts the gates of Hell to keep him out. No man has the right to be a strike-breaker, so long as there is a pool of water deep enough to drown his body in, or a rope long enough to hang his carcass with. Judas Iscariot was a gentleman...compared with a strike-breaker. For betraying his master, he had the character to hang himself...a strikebreaker hasn't.

---

*The late Tony Bubka, a labor historian, discovered that this document was falsely attributed to Jack London. He traced it as far back as a cordwainers' strike in nineteenth-century England.

Esau sold his birthright for a mess of pottage. Judas Iscariot sold his Savior for thirty pieces of silver. Benedict Arnold sold his country for a promise of a commission in the British Army. The modern strikebreaker sells his birthright, his country, his wife, his children, and his fellow men for an unfilled promise from his employer, trust or corporation.

Esau was a traitor to himself. Judas Iscariot was a traitor to his God. Benedict Arnold was a traitor to his country. A strikebreaker is a traitor to himself, a traitor to his God, a traitor to his country, a traitor to his family and a traitor to his class.

There is nothing lower than a strikebreaker.

I knew by their expressions that the poor excuses for men trooping back and forth before me heard my words. Some of them seemed to wince visibly. A few of my compatriots had gathered around to listen too, and they gave the royal razz to the scabs when I had finished reading. Just as I turned to go back to the massive tug-of-war still going on behind me, I saw one of the scabs suddenly sneak off behind a stack of rotting produce and I didn't see him again. I wondered if he had been shamed into quitting, had drowned himself like the river rat he was, or was taking a monumental leak.

As I prepared to jump down from my perch, something off to one side caught my eye. About half a block down the street a car jammed full of men suddenly revved up and headed directly for the hundreds of massed pickets. For a second I froze, then I let out a yell that must have been heard in Springfield. They must be going crazy to do something like this, flashed through my mind —the strike must be driving them to desperation.

The huge throng began to scatter, but it was so tightly packed that those in the center didn't have a chance. The car came on and on, gaining speed. In another instant it had ground to a halt in the center of the crowd, bodies lying across its hood, bodies lying everywhere.

I sprang down from my perch and began to elbow my way through the crowd, helping to lift some of our fallen comrades to their feet. Three of the men were seriously injured and were being carried off to the edge of the crowd. The driver of the car seemed frozen at the wheel, the look of a babbling idiot on his face. The five or six men crammed in with him looked terrified. One of our men reached in and grabbed the keys. Two more of our boys began to drag the driver out of the car, but I stepped in front of them. "Let the bulls handle this, fellow workers," I said. "The evidence is all on our side."

I looked around to see what was taking the cops so long. To my amazement the nearest bulls, three of them about thirty yards away, were just standing there. I saw our picket captain go in their direction, yelling at them, and I hightailed it after him.

All the goddamned bulls would tell us was that an ambulance had already been called.

"Aren't you going to arrest that maniac?" the picket captain asked.

The cops kept temporizing. "Fellow worker, take down their badge numbers," the picket captain told me.

I took out my copy of "Definition of a Strikebreaker" and wrote down the numbers on its back. More men rushed up demanding the driver of the scab car be arrested. The work of the scab stevedores had ground to a complete halt now and not a one was to be seen. Finally, as if ripped by the horns of a dilemma, the bulls leisurely approached the scab car and began to interrogate its occupants. They seemed more intent on escorting them to safety than finding out the truth of the affair. As we heard the siren of an approaching ambulance, they finally arrested the trembling driver and took him off through the crowd.

I was stunned. So it was going to be like Centralia all over again. Well, we were better prepared this time, and if they could dish it out we could give it back with interest. I sure had a talent for hitting the hot spots, I thought: Centralia, the railroad strike, Herrin, and now Portland.

It was late afternoon by now. There weren't any more scabs in sight. After the ambulance took away the injured men the crowd began to thin out. I spotted two of the Wobs I had ridden down from Seattle with on the freight, and we decided to vamoose to the Wobbly hall and put on the feed bag. On the way through the drizzly streets we exchanged comradely greetings almost every step with fellow strikers, and everybody seemed to be pumping adrenaline, talking excitedly.

The IWW hall was alive with activity. New Wobs were arriving from all over the West, eager to do their share. The hall was so crowded that the strike committee was giving out 25-cent meal tickets to the pickets to eat at one of the many cafes supporting the strike—at last report there were only two that would serve known strikebreakers. We skedaddled off to a greasy spoon and filled our bellies with some not–half–bad slum. Halfway through the meal I noticed a bloke who had been sitting there without being served; he had a growing look of consternation in his weasel eyes.

"What's with him?" I asked the man next to me.

"He's a lousy scab," I was told. "This is a union house and somebody spotted him. He could sit there till hell freezes over and they'll never wait on him."

"I'm surprised somebody hasn't slugged him," I said.

"It's more fun this way," my fellow diner said.

Sure enough, after a few minutes the alleged strikebreaker gave a grunt of disgust and got up and left. Probably a stoolie sent in to try to pick up some information, I thought, resisting an impulse to put out my foot and trip him as he went by.

That night we were having a potlatch and dance at the Wobbly hall. It was a heady feeling walking through the buzzing streets crowded with people on the way back to the hall. All everybody seemed to be talking about was the strike. The whole city seemed to be alive with it. The band was already playing some lively tunes as we went into the crowded place and I was excited at the sight of dozens of attractive women scattered through the crowd. Also I was surprised at the many ILA members there, as well as members of the local grain workers union who were supporting the strike.

As the night's activities got formally underway the local secretary gave a rundown on the condition of the men run down by the car, and a summary of the progress of the strike. A big cheer went up at the news that dock workers in Australia had refused to unload ships from Portland, and similar promises of support were coming in from all over the world.

I wasn't much of a dancer, but you couldn't really do what was properly called dancing in that jam–packed hall anyway, so I got up the courage to move around the floor a little with some fetching gals. One was an IWW waitress from Aberdeen, Washington, who told me all the waitresses in town had lined up in the One Big Union there. I told her I'd try to get up there and visit her after we won the strike.

At one point in the evening I found myself standing next to a Swede named P. J. Welinder who was chairman of the publicity committee for the strike. He was beaming with pride. "I have never seen a display of solidarity like this before," he gushed. "I was in the Swedish general strike of 300,000 workers back in 1909, but it was not half as good as this. If we can yust keep it up."

After a minute he went on: "Say—I heard you read that scabby definition on the docks today. You have a powerful voice, and I understand you were in Centralia in 1919. Some of us are going to speak on the anniversary of the Everett Massacre up in Seattle on the fifth—how would you like to say a few words about Centralia?"

I felt flattered as hell. Nobody had ever complimented me on my voice before. Well, I was going to have to decide if I was going to be a "leader" in the labor movement sometime, I thought—it might as well be now. My secret role in the Herrin miners' affair seemed to be propelling me in that direction, so why resist what seemed to be the inevitable? "I'm not much of a speaker," I said. "I'll let you know."

The highlight of the evening came during an intermission in the dancing when a clever fellow with a great gift of mimicry got up and sang a long and lilting song about the strike called "The Portland Revolution," by Dublin Dan. Dublin Dan Liston, born in Ireland, had run a bar in Butte, Montana frequented by union men before coming to Portland. The song was about the arrests of Wobblies in the strike on trumped-up charges so blatant that the judge had to find them not guilty. The large audience sat spell-bound as the Wobbly singer held forth:

The revolution started, so the judge informed the mayor, ·
Now Baker paces back and forth, and raves and pulls his hair,
The waterfront is tied up tight, the Portland newsboy howls,
And not a thing is moving, only mayor Baker's bowels.

A call went out for pickets, you should see the railroad yards,
Lined up with honest workers, all displaying Wobbly cards,
It made no difference to those boys, which industry was hit,
They all were fellow workers, and they meant to do their bit...

In the next stanza the defendants have the audacity to make out an IWW membership card for the judge, then they proceed to cavort about in a series of humorous antics describing their activities and proclaiming their innocence. In the end the judge throws up his hands, unable to find anything to charge the Wobblies with, and lets them go free.

Loud and prolonged applause greeted the performance. Then there was more dancing. It had been a full day. I couldn't remember when I'd ever had a better time. At the end of the evening everyone clasped hands and sang Ralph Chaplin's "Solidarity Forever." Then I helped give the dance floor a quick sweeping out and bedded down with scores of others at the back of the hall.

I dreamed that a mad motorist was trying to run me down, then I grabbed the hand of the waitress from Aberdeen and we ran up the gangplank of a beautiful big ship with "IWW 100%" painted on its side, and then we were sailing down the broad Columbia on our way to the sea.

17

THE DEHORN SQUAD

Early next morning I got my 25-cent meal ticket and traipsed off with five or six other Wobs for some java and flapjacks at a greasy spoon. The *Rose City* wasn't loading and we were sent to picket at another dock farther along the riverfront. Even at dawn the drizzling city was in ferment, with strikers rushing back and forth, exchanging warm greetings, cheering one another on.

Congestion and confusion were everywhere. Piles of rotting produce were jammed up all along the shoreline. Stacks of lumber stood about haphazardly. At one pier was a mass of shattered glass that had been broken by inept scabs. Cargoless or partly loaded ships were jammed together awkwardly, while one big vessel waited in mid-river, unable to find a mooring.

Halfway to our picket site we got the news from a group of jubilant passersby that the workers in a nearby lumber mill, ordered to load a ship, were staging a sympathy strike in protest. At another dock the flour mill workers had joined us in the strike and were picketing spiritedly. It was a great feeling just to be alive in that electric atmosphere of militant struggle.

We found our dock and relieved the half-dozen night shift pickets there. No attempt had been made to load the big tramp steamer moored there for three days, they told us with smiles of satisfaction. But with hundreds of pickets available and more flocking in on boxcars every day the IWW leadership wanted to keep all bases covered just in case. We sat on some sacks of sprouting wheat for the next five hours, shooting the bull. No scabs appeared.

As we prepared to leave for lunch, one of the pickets who had been around for a while said, "Whataya say we have a little fun before we put on the feed bag?"

We were game for it. He led us along the waterfront until we came to a dock where a few scabs were working. After a few minutes they left for lunch. We left with them. They didn't seem to notice us until they entered a small cafe a block or so away. As they sat at the long counter our guide yelled down to the waiter, "Hey Slim—since when do you serve reptiles in here?"

Slim got the hint and didn't go near the newcomers. After three or four minutes the scabs got the picture and scurried off to another place, casting worried looks behind them. We followed them. The union waiters at the second place gave them the same treatment. And those scabs had to go back to their dirty work without their lunch.

We went into the union hall for some java and sinkers just as a group of Wobs was leaving for Frisco and L.A. to organize picketing of scab-loaded ships from Portland. One of the IWW officials came up to me. "Hey, aren't you Kid Murphy?" he asked. "I seen you box in Seattle. Didn't you help close up the booze parlors there?"

"Yeah, me and a few hundred other Wobs," I admitted.

"Well if this strike is lost," he said, "it will be because the plutes are numbing the brains of the proles with that pisswater. It's sure the politicos and cops aren't going to enforce the law. How'd you like to do a little speakeasy work around here? You're built for it."

"Sure," I said. "I need to practice my left jab. Breaking bottles is good for toughening up your hands."

So I was assigned to the dehorn squad. I had been told that most of the Japanese and others who ran the pool halls and barbershops had been refusing to admit scabs. But many of the "soft drink establishments," as the big capitalist dailies hypocritically called them, were still running rampant.

I thought I was big at six feet four. But when I finished my java I was introduced to a few Paul Bunyans who made me feel like a midget. They were mostly big jovial loggers with arms as thick as small pines. A couple of them had a few minor bruises to show that a few bouncers had been foolish enough to tangle with them.

When one of them shook my hand I thought he was going to bust my knuckles.

"Now that we've got a professional boxer with us, let's tackle Swampwater Sam's," one of them said. "The kid can lead us into battle." And with that the crazy cuss, who must have stood six feet eight, picked me up and threw me over his shoulder and said, "Let's go get 'em, boys!"

The giant logger set me down on the sidewalk outside the hall. There were six of us. We made our way along the street, exchanging greetings with fellow workers. Occasionally we stopped in front of a blind pig to talk briefly with other dehorn squad members who were peacefully picketing outside. As far as we could see, none of the booze joints had more than half a dozen customers. But Swampwater Sam's was different, my new companions told me. Apparently their rotgut was more high-powered than that of most of the poison parlors, and one hoosier was said to have been blinded by it—but the rubes still kept coming.

"We've tried politeness so far and it hasn't worked," the Wob in charge of our group said, "so this time I think we're going to have to be more persuasive."

We came to the joint. It looked like a real dive. The front window was painted over and you had to go through a narrow L-shaped opening to get into the place. A pimply-looking guy about six feet six with a mouthful of gold teeth stood just inside the door. He didn't seem to see us.

Our picket captain reached into one big pocket and took out a small garden snake and set it down in the entrance. We flattened ourselves against the window. An instant later we heard a grunt of surprise and a leg came shooting out, kicking at the slithering snake. Gunnar, our picket captain, grabbed at the ankle, and a second later the hefty bouncer was flat on the sidewalk.

"Come on, Joe, let's go in and toss one down," Gunnar said, slipping rapidly inside the door as two of our compatriots waited outside to deal with the prostrate goon.

The four of us went in. It took me a couple of seconds to get used to the dim light. Ten or fifteen sleazy-looking guys sat drinking at tables, while a few more slouched at the bar. Gunnar and the others headed for the bar.

Before I could tell wet from windy I saw a big form hurtling toward me from the shadows. The goon butted me with his head and I went down against the wall with a crash. Then I felt something sting my cheek and realized he had kicked me in the face. So that's the way they played.

Out of the corner of my eye I could see Gunnar and the others battling some guys at the bar. I saw a spittoon flying through the air and a big mirror behind the bar shattered, and my assailant turned away for an instant to look. I was on my feet in a second. The goon rushed me again. But now I had my Irish up. I feinted with my left and laid a bunch of fives on his jaw and the goon crumpled like a rag doll. I grabbed a glass of dehorn off a nearby table and poured it onto the fly of his rumpled trousers.

My fellow workers were escorting the remaining patrons out of the joint now. Gunnar was having an earnest conversation with a big worried-looking gazabo behind the bar, with one hand emptying kegs of bootleg booze. "...And not till the strike is over, right?"—I caught a scrap of their conversation.

The owner nodded dyspeptically.

"Next time we won't be so gentle," Gunnar said with a malicious smile.

My attacker was just starting to come to. The floor was a stinking lake of booze and for the first time I noticed the front window had been broken out.

"All right, boys, let's amscray before mayor Baker comes and escorts us to his rockpile," Gunnar said with a big grin as we brushed ourselves off and left.

And in the next few weeks we closed every bootleg joint in Portland. We picketed the blind pigs or broke them up entirely, enforcing the law the elected officials refused to enforce. The ship owners and their political and police stooges got more and more desperate, sending more and more stoolpigeons and agents provocateurs among us, trying to incite us to violence, but we refused to be sucked in by their tricks. And little by little, seeing how dirty our opposition was playing and how just our demands were, public opinion shifted more and more to our side. Soon even the sin-busters were exhorting their congregations to support us, and organizations of all kinds were protesting to the mayor over our shoddy treatment. It gave a stiff a real faith in the perfectibility of man.

I gave much serious thought to fellow worker Welinder's invitation to me to speak at the Everett Massacre memorial meeting in Seattle. During idle moments on the picket line I found myself framing what I would say. Hell, if I would prance around half-naked in the boxing ring and expose myself to all kinds of punishment and humiliation, why couldn't I stand up in front of a sympathetic crowd and spout a few words in a constructive cause? If I was ever going to be a real leader of men I had to start somewhere. "Don't worry about stage fright, kid," the friendly Swede told me. "The secret is to yust imagine everyone in the audience is in their underwear and you won't have any trouble."

"Okay," I told him. "I'll do it."

On a rainy day in early November we rode the cushions in to Seattle's King Street station. It seemed strange riding in a passenger train. The last time I had done it was on my way to St. Louis to learn the sewing machine salesman trade, and before that when I had generated the rotten egg gas on that train between Kansas City and Slater. By god, I had pulled some doozies, I thought, trying to build up my self-confidence for my speech. I smiled to think what the "respectable" passengers sitting around us would think if they knew what a devil I was.

There was a packed hall in Seattle and I was shaking like a fifty-year-old boxcar on bad track at sixty per. But I finally got a handle on myself and settled down. The main speaker was Walker C. Smith, the Wobbly editor and father of Boxcar Bertha; he gave a dramatic recapitulation of that terrible day back in 1916 when five of our boys had been slaughtered in nearby Everett by the flunkies of the lumber barons. Welinder gave a history of the events in Portland that brought the audience to its feet cheering. Then Kate Sadler gave one of her excellent and stirring talks. They were tough acts to follow.

But when it came my turn to speak I galvanized myself into action and gave it all I had. I was pleasantly startled at the first burst of applause when I mentioned Wesley Everest. From that moment on it was downhill all the way. I just recounted in simple terms my experiences in Centralia and later in the courthouse in Montesano, then finished up with an appeal for both the Centralia prisoners and the strikers in Portland. The final applause was music in my ears. Perhaps it was at that moment when I decided seriously that I wanted to play a prominent role in the labor movement and that I had what it took to do it.

The struggle in Portland continued. The situation of the employers was getting more and more desperate. IWW longshoremen and other stevedores had stopped unloading ships from Portland in Los Angeles, in Australia and in other places. More and more merchandise was clogging the docks. Lumber and flour companies were suing the stevedore and shipping firms for not transporting their goods. Several sawmills and flour mills had closed down, and the biggest steamship companies were beginning to divert their ships to other ports. Many ships were badly loaded, and as a result some had run aground. One large vessel had rammed into a bridge, causing extensive damage. Soon much of the business community was pressuring our enemies to bargain with us, and a group of businessmen got together to provide Thanksgiving dinner for the pickets.

We had the town tied up tight. Scabs were becoming more and more unpopular. At one cafe the owner spotted a group of scabs and gave them the silent treatment. Some cops came and told him the law required they be waited on. So he served each of them one glass of water and one toothpick.

At one scab joint we pulled the same trick we had used in the cafe strike in Seattle: Scores of our men filled the place just before lunch, ordered a single cup of coffee, and dawdled over it for an hour. The cops arrested one Wob for refusing to abandon the cold coffee he was nursing. A dozen or so others demanded to be arrested too, and when they were not, they jumped into the paddy wagon and got a couple of free meals and a night's lodging in the jail.

But the hardheaded employers refused to budge. The smaller ones wanted to settle, but they were bulldozed by the big boys who could afford to divert their ships and cargoes to other harbors.

In San Pedro, L.A.'s port, more and more ships from Portland were being tied up, and the bulls were beginning to arrest our organizers for speaking on the waterfront. As a result a free speech fight had broken out. Wobblies were being arrested right and left and sentenced to one to fourteen years in prison under California's criminal syndicalism law.

The strike continued through the winter. One day I found myself picketing in the snow. It was a unique and beautiful experience to see the huge hulks of ships covered with snow like great white whales at their moorings. I began to fantasize about what it would be like to ship out on one of those behemoths, off to see the world.

We had a huge picket line of up to four and five thousand workers over the holidays and into the new year of 1923. Many of the employers were going broke. Now some of them, in last-stand desperation, were putting merchandise on small scows and rafts and transporting it haphazardly down the river to various small ports.

The scab crews were looking worse and worse. There were high-school kids now and workers wearing bits and pieces of army and navy uniforms. One day a group of army officers arrived and ordered six fully uniformed soldiers to stop working as scabs. But the big boys would not give in. Apparently they would rather go broke than acknowledge the right of workers to have a union and collective bargaining.

We often picketed in heavy rains in January of 1923, and a disastrous flood hit Portland. Some of our people went to work helping move endangered goods out of the rising river's path, but they would quit en masse if a scab was recognized among the crew. We had sent hundreds of dollars to help our beleaguered fellow workers in San Pedro, and now our own strike fund was going dry. We couldn't expect our people to starve, and some drifted off to find work in other industries. Portland was virtually closed as a major port.

But our adversaries still would not budge. We finally decided in desperation to transfer the strike to the job—those who wanted to could go back to work on the docks and ships and stage slow-downs and other job actions, working in accordance with how they were treated.

Seeing the decision coming, needing some work desperately, I went up to my Swedish friend Welinder in the Wobbly hall one day to ask his advice. He was in a dismal mood.

"It's like the Paterson textile strike of 1913 all over again," he sighed. "We won in Lawrence in 1912 because the owners had yust those mills in yust that one place. But the Paterson plutes owned other mills in other cities they could transfer their operations to, so we couldn't hurt them so much. The big boys here could transfer a lot of their operations to other ports. If we'd yust had the other ports organized like San Pedro, or gotten the kind of support the Aussies gave us, we would have won."

I told him of my plight and of my hankering to go to sea. His eyes lit up a little. "Sure, Yoe," he said. "We need organizers on the ships too. If we can organize all the ships, next time we'll take the whole works."

And he told me of an oiler friend, Arne, he had just been talking to who was on a Swedish ship loading in Seattle. They needed a couple of men in the engine room. They were going to Vladivostok and then down to Australia. Nobody was very crazy about going to Vladivostok in midwinter, and not many wanted to work in the heat of the engine room of a ship crossing the equator any time of year. He gave me a note of introduction to his Swedish friend and wished me luck.

I left the Wobbly hall with a new enthusiasm. Perhaps I would go to sea at last! The romance of foreign travel! The challenge of taking part in the IWW's snowballing campaign to organize all the sea toilers of the world, and with this mighty weapon gain control of all the industries for all the people.

Next day I spent some of my precious funds riding the cushions to Seattle. As the train crossed the great Columbia and I heard its screeching whistle, I took a copy of the *Industrial Worker* from my pocket and began to read. At the bottom of one of the pages was framed a short quotation from Bertrand Russell:

THOUGHT

Men fear thought as they fear nothing else on earth... Thought is subversive and revolutionary... Thought looks into the pit of Hell and is not afraid. It sees man, a feeble spark, surrounded by unfathomable depths of silence. Yet it bears itself proudly... Thought is great and swift and free, the light of the world and the chief glory of Man.

And as the train roared on into the darkening drizzle, I vowed never to stop thinking, never to stop seeking out the truth of life in order to solve mankind's problems, to follow the truth of thought wherever it led, and at whatever cost to myself.

18

TO SEA!

The sea. How it excited my imagination! I had dreamed of it, off and on, ever since I had read my first sea novel back in Springfield at the age of ten. The thrill of travel and adventure. Exotic women in picturesque foreign places. The beauty of the sea and ships. The excitement and mystery of the unknown. I wanted to see everything, do everything, know everything about the world — and at last I had the chance to do it.

As the train drew near Seattle through the misty drizzle I felt my mind coming more and more alive, the blood racing through my veins, and I strained my eyes for a glimpse of the distant harbor and the sight of ships. Soon I would be out there, immersed in the greatest adventure of my life, being swept along by the rhythmic motion of the sea.

Soon I was among the bustle of the waterfront itself, people rushing on and off ships, cargo stacked everywhere, sweating stevedores heaving heavy sacks about, the screech of gulls. A five-minute walk brought me to the pier I sought, and a new rush of excitement surged through me. There she was, the ship Welinder had told me of, the blue and gold Swedish flag fluttering beneath the stars and stripes, a huge-looking vessel five or six hundred feet long, the giant arms of her cargo booms swinging back and forth through the air.

Trembling a little, I showed my letter from Welinder to a stocky blond by the gangplank who spoke no English, and he waved me aboard. My first time on a ship! I climbed the steep planking and stood looking along the great expanse of alleyway and deck with the giant deckhouse rising above—a city in itself.

Another burly blond came lumbering by and I showed him the letter. He glanced at it hurriedly and motioned me through a hatchway that led to a large inner cabin. The room I was entering proved to be the mess room, where three men sat drinking coffee and talking in a strange-sounding language full of "ooos" and "uuus" and other voluptuous mucousy sounds.

"Arne?" I said. I showed my letter again and one of the men, a wiry slightly balding man of about forty, stood up with a big toothy grin and extended a huge paw.

"Oho—a friend of Velinder. I yust see him few days ago.
Any friend of Velinder a friend of me! Sit down, kamrat."

I was relieved to see that he spoke English—after a fashion. I shook hands with his two companions, who apparently spoke only Swedish.

"The job is...open?" I held my breath.

"Shure—come vith me!"

When we were out of earshot of the others in the companion-way, Arne halted. In a low voice he said: "You are...fellow vorker?"

I took out my card. Then he showed his, and it was the first time I had seen a Swedish IWW card. Then he patted me on the back and gave a big grin and said: "Kamrat fellow vorker! But no tell captain."

I swore I wouldn't. We climbed a ladder to the level above. Behind the bridge, near the great smokestack, was a row of cabins. Arne knocked at one. A large man of about fifty with reddish hair and a humorless face answered. Arne spoke to him in Swedish. The chief engineer looked me over. He finally spoke briefly, then turned his back on us and slammed the cabin door. My heart sank.

"He say you look strong enough," Arne said and slapped my back again. "You can be viper."

"Viper?" I said. "Oh—wiper!" I grinned.

"Ya—viper. You can sign name?"

"Sure," I said.

He led me to the officers' mess. An inscrutable-looking slightly graying man in his fifties sat studying charts. Arne seemed to speak to him with a grudging deference. The older man shook my hand without rising and seemed to look at me with a bemused expression. Arne said a few words to him, and captain Erikson reached for a sheaf of papers and handed me a pen. With trembling hand I signed the ship's articles, not having the faintest idea what I was signing. The only word I recognized was "Stockholm." When I finished signing the captain took back the papers and resumed studying his charts without another word. "Come on," said Arne, and we left the cabin.

Not exactly the world's warmest reception, I thought, as we went back out on deck, but I still felt elated. Then Arne led me down into the bowels of the ship to show me where the engine room gang bunked. We entered a hatchway and I saw a gleaming mass of tangled machinery yawning for fifty feet below me. I felt dizzy for a moment, fearing I would fall. Then I got a grip on myself and followed Arne down a ladder, hanging on for dear life, feeling the faint motion of the huge vessel as it rocked gently at the dock.

We went down ladder after ladder, along level grillwork, past huge boilers and cylinder heads, Arne nodding at a couple of members of the engine room crew, and finally we came to a hatchway that led into a narrow compartment filled with two-tiered bunks. Arne pointed out my bunk to me, then showed me the head. He explained that on most ships now the engine room gang slept in the foc's'le up in the bow, or at the stern, but that whoever designed this ship in the frozen north apparently thought the slaves would enjoy the heat from the engines—or get more work done when they bunked right next to their jobs.

Then Arne introduced me to the five or six other stiffs lying or sitting on their bunks—oilers, firemen, water-tenders, and Ole, a young Swede about my own age who was the other wiper and who spoke a halting English. Two of the others were Swedes, one a Norwegian, none of whom spoke English, an Englishman and a genial Sicilian who spoke a pidgin English about on a par with Arne. They seemed like fairly nice blokes and I shook hands all around. The two Swedes and the Englishman were playing poker in the crowded space on the deck. Two or three of them were chewing tobacco and would spit a big gob into a coffee can now and then.

I stowed my gear and then Arne motioned me over to his bunk, his back to the others. "These donkey's breakfasts aren't so hot," he said, patting his thin straw-filled mattress, "but at least it's a good place to hide things," and he withdrew five booklets with red covers and the familiar IWW symbol on them. I could see they were all in Swedish.

Arne smiled at my surprise. "Ya, the Vun Big Union is growing fast in Scandinavia now," he beamed. "I line up four of the boys on this tub already. Maybe ve take over the ship before this trip is over, eh Yoe?" he said with a wink. We talked a while more and then I went ashore to say goodbye to some friends and have my last shoreside meal.

I got back to the ship about eleven and climbed into my bunk. Most of the others were already asleep. The donkey's breakfast wasn't exactly the Ritz, but it was a little better than some of the vermin-infested mattresses I'd bedded down on in lumber camps, and the excitement in my brain at my new adventure finally died down enough for me to slip into four or five hours of sleep.

Next day was a Sunday and I didn't have to work. We were scheduled to sail in the early afternoon. I arose with the others, scraped the whiskers off my mug, and climbed up to the mess room. The cook was an old grizzled Swede and the mess boy was an alert and friendly young Filipino who was always smiling and seemed anxious to please everyone. It took me a moment to figure out why there was a ridge around the edge of the long table.

The breakfast was enormous, I couldn't believe it—huge stacks of flapjacks and heaps of eggs and sausage and strange brittle crackers I had never seen before. The coffee was passable. It was great to know I would be eating well on the trip.

The magic hour finally came. It was like being in a dream. The giant hatches were battened down, two tugs came alongside, the gangplank was hoisted and we began to edge out into the teeming harbor. It seemed like life was just beginning.

I stood out on the prow watching the great panoply of the Sound open before us, feeling gusts of spray against my face, looking back now and then toward the receding hills of Seattle, feeling the beat of my heart mingling with the great throbbing rhythm of the deck beneath me, catching occasional glimpses of the captain standing on the bridge, motionless and stone-faced and inscrutable as if he were part of the ship. What must he be thinking? I wondered. Did he with his immense responsibility still feel the thrill of it all as I did now?

We plowed steadily seaward, past Port Townsend with forested Vancouver Island off to our starboard, through Juan de Fuca Strait and out past Cape Flattery to the open sea. And just as we left land and I felt the heavy plunge and roll of the open Pacific, the westering sun sank before us like a great bursting pomegranate plummeting into the sea. I was beside myself with ecstasy. Everything I had ever read about the sea began to crowd upon my mind: passages from Jack London's *The Sea Wolf* and the novels of Conrad, John Masefield's "Sea Fever," and *Moby Dick*. And feeling myself suddenly part of some great moving human drama, I began to recite into the cold rising wind a few lines I remembered from Tennyson's "Ulysses":

I cannot rest from travel:
I will drink life to the lees...
There gloom the dark broad seas...
My purpose holds to sail beyond the sunset...
To strive, to seek, to find and not to yield!

Presently I heard the mess bell for evening chow. I clawed my way along the railing of the wildly gyrating ship to the midship superstructure. As I went into the mess room three or four of the others looked up and nodded. For the first time I saw most of the deck hands at the other end of the long gently pitching table. They seemed a motley group from five or six lands. Arne looked up with a grin and patted the bench beside him. The Filipino mess boy gave me a big smile.

I sat down and looked at the few platters of food the crew members kept sliding up and down the table. "Pass Lot's wife," one burly seaman said, and someone tossed a pinch of salt over his shoulder and threw the salt shaker down the table; the first speaker caught it and shook a huge amount over his food.

I was in for a rude surprise. After the great breakfast and lunch I guess I had expected T-bone steaks at least. But the entire fare consisted of salt fish, those jawbreaking Swedish crackers, some tasteless beans and leftover coffee from breakfast. The fish was so salty it almost made me gag to force it down. It suddenly dawned on me: maybe they fed us good in port for fear some of the new hands would change their minds and sign off; but now we were at sea we were helpless to protest. "A little different than breakfast and lunch," I said to Arne.

"Ya, them *cheapskates* feed us slop vonce ve be at sea."

"Ya, on vay over from Sverige they feed us barnacles from off the side of the ship," my young fellow wiper Ole said from across the table.

On my left was the middle-aged Sicilian, Giuseppe. Like the Filipino, he was always smiling. With a misty look in his eyes he began to tell me of his parents' little farm in Sicily, how he had been working on this ship for almost ten years and saving all his pay and how after one more voyage he was going to buy a little farm next to his parents' place and "swallow the anchor" forever. "I getta nice wife, hava bambinos, fucka the sea forever," he said with a big grin and a slashing motion with one hand. "I never wanna see the old widow-maker again."

After the meal Arne and I climbed down into the bowels of the ship to our bunks. Most of the others were there, playing poker. Standing next to my bunk, I suddenly became aware of something surprising: I still heard the sound of the nearby engine and felt its rhythmic throbbing, but the ship now was tossing about very little compared to how it had been behaving topside.

"We're not tossing around so much now," I said. "Are we stopping?"

Everyone looked up and grinned or laughed. The Englishman, Derek, glanced up from the poker game. "You just bloody flunked your first test for smarts, Irish," he guffawed. "Any bloody idiot should be able to figure out a ship don't sway as much at the bottom as at the top—the higher you go the more it sways. Let those blasted deck 'ands get seasick. Me for the warm stable life o' the bloody bilges."

I felt like my face must be getting red. "Oh yeah," I stammered. "I never thought of that." It was to be one of the reasons I preferred the engine room—on most ships.

Next morning was the big day. My first twelve-hour shift. With all the other crew members it was six on and six off, but the two wipers worked straight through from six in the morning till seven in the evening, six days a week, with an hour off for lunch.

I awoke to the pulse of the great engine, like a gigantic pumping heart separated from us by the thinnest of membranes. With the cramped quarters it was like being back in one of the worst of the lumber camps again, with a thousand buzz saws in the next room and the whole shebang constantly moving. The smell of oil and grease was thick and nauseating. I scraped my cheeks with my razor, slipped into my black dungarees and singlet, and hurried up after the others for a breath of fresh air.

At 5:15 AM the sea was a gently rolling slate color, the sun just beginning to thread through the gloom with faint rays of light off our stern. I breathed in the cold exhilarating salt air and followed the others into the mess room on my shaky landlubber's legs. It was like working as a cowboy and never being able to get off your horse, I thought, this continual rolling and plunging.

The food kept getting worse. This first full day at sea there were about half as many eggs as the day before in port, leftover salt fish from last night and the same belly-breaking crackers which were already starting to give me constipation. The Filipino mess boy seemed to serve the slum with an air of apology. The grizzled old Swedish beanmaster stared out at us from the galley as if relishing some peculiar sort of revenge for his own sufferings and shattered hopes in life.

A few moments before six, we climbed down into the heat of the engine room. The on-duty officers and engine room gang stood at their stations before gauges and gadgets, looking bleary-eyed. I followed young Ole to the rear of the huge room where we found the first assistant engineer, a stocky auburn-haired Swede of about thirty-five. He looked as humorless as most of the other officers I'd seen. He eyed me briefly and warily, then spoke in clipped tones to my fellow wiper.

Ole turned to me: "He say do not let me catch you loafing and ve get on okay." I tried to nod in a friendly way at my new boss. He ignored me, barked a few orders at Ole, and turned on his heel and walked off with a quick jaunty roll.

Ole grinned at me as if to reassure me it wasn't so bad after all. I followed him down a walkway past huge boilers to where a big bale of rags stood. We each took a handful and then he grabbed two buckets and filled them with what smelled like kerosene. "Come," he motioned me to follow him. "Each day ve clean all the ladders and gratings and floor plates and railings."

"*All* of them? Every day?"

"Ya."

We climbed up one of the ladders, the huge room swaying more and more and getting hotter and hotter the higher we went. It was a struggle to pull myself up with one hand and try to keep the bucket from spilling over with the other. I could imagine what one of those grim-faced officers below would do if I spilled a bucket of kerosene on his head.

Finally we were at the top of the immense room, just under the skylight. Ole started cleaning off one of the ladders leading to the alleyway above and motioned me to get another ladder a few yards away. I felt dizzy and unsteady on my feet and forced myself not to look down at the mass of men and machinery yawning below. The smell of the kerosene and all the other odors of the huge room made me a little nauseous. But seeing the dangers, I could well understand why it was important to remove every trace of oil or grease which might send me or my fellow workers slipping and plunging into that morass of hot churning machinery below.

I bent myself to my task. The oil and muck came off easily enough. Every few minutes I had to discard an oil-soaked rag and get a clean one. After half an hour I was already besieged by boredom. How rapidly elation and romance could turn to disillusion and misery! My god, were we going to do this same identical thing twelve hours a day, day after day after day? I soon began to sweat in the rising heat from the engines and every two or three minutes had to wipe my dripping face and neck with the sweat rag tucked into my dungaree tops.

We did the ladders and then went along the gratings and narrow walkways, cleaning every crevice. After a couple of hours I began to feel really woozy, but I was determined to keep up with my new workmate. Finally, incredibly, three hours were up and we had the first of our two ten-minute coffee breaks. It seemed I could barely climb up the ladder to the deck above.

Over coffee, I finally broke down and told Ole of my dizziness and of an incipient headache. "Oh—maybe you need the salt tablet. I show you."

Now he tells me! I thought. We climbed back down into the broiling engine room and he showed me the dispenser attached to a bulkhead. I popped a tablet in my mouth, took a quick drink of the foul-tasting water from the water hose, and slipped three more tablets in my dungarees for good measure. Then back to the grind.

The work went on. When it came to cleaning the steel deck plates my back soon began to feel the strain from squatting down or stooping over. Which was worse, I wondered, this or tossing around hundred-pound sacks of grain all day on the scorching plains of Kansas or Nebraska? I tried to console myself by thinking of the fantastic experiences I would have in exotic foreign ports.

A little before noon, when we were cleaning the gratings of a narrow walkway near the bottom deck, I heard someone yell something from somewhere toward the bow. The first engineer, who had been checking something a few yards astern of us, came rushing forward like a madman. When I didn't move fast enough on the narrow walkway he gave me a rude shove as he rushed past, almost sending me over the railing. He swung down a ladder and disappeared somewhere in the tangle of machinery.

"Sonofabitch!" I stood looking after him with burning eyes. I turned to Ole. "Is he crazy?"

Ole shrugged. "Cramped quarters," he said and went on with his work.

Noon finally came. I didn't see how I could make it through a whole day of this. Going along the main deck alleyway I looked out hopelessly at the endless gray sea. It wasn't like a job on land; there was no turning back now.

Lunch offered something new: watery soup and Swedish cheese and pickled herring. The cheese was all right, but I couldn't make up my mind whether I liked the herring. I bolted my food, drank some java, and climbed down to my bunk for some much-needed rest.

The afternoon was more of the same. By six o'clock I was totally exhausted. We carried our gear below and stowed it. Just as we were about to trudge to the showers, the first engineer appeared and barked some more orders. "He vant we should vash the oily rags," said Ole with a scowl when the First had turned and left.

"But our shift is over."

"Ya, but vhat can ve do?" said Ole, leading me to the drum where we had tossed our rags.

I staggered after him, almost out on my feet. We took the dozens of filthy rags to a crude washing machine and dumped them in. "If they are too bad, ve trow them overboard," said Ole. "Now ve prepare the soap." And we took two short knives and spent eight or ten minutes shaving slender splinters off the huge bars of pungent soap into the washer. Then Ole started it up and we waited while it shook and gurgled. Finally we took the rags out and hung them up to dry.

When we had finished it was all I could do to stagger to the washroom for a sticky saltwater shower. But afterward I felt a bit revived and managed to follow Ole on the long climb up to the mess room. So this was the romantic life of a sailor!

Except for Arne, the shipmate I came to like best was the genial Sicilian, Giuseppe. Everyone else called him what sounded like "Sis"—short for Sicilian, I guess—and he seemed to hate it. But I called him by his name and he seemed to like me for it. As we sat by the taffrail watching the ship's wake after the grinding days of work, he told me more in his halting English about his childhood in Sicily and his plans for his farm. I don't know what there was about me that made people trust and confide in me—maybe because I was still so young, or maybe because my honesty and idealism showed through.

One day when we were alone in our quarters, he said: "Looka, Joe. I trust you. I wanna show you something." And he turned over his straw mattress and showed me where he had hidden his money—almost ten years' pay. And then he gave me the address of his parents in Sicily and made me promise I would send them the money—except for a hundred dollars for myself—if anything happened to him. I promised him I would.

Two days later when I came topside for supper I saw a strange sight. It looked like the steward back near the stern throwing some kind of large objects into the water. "What in hell—?" I asked Arne who had just come up behind me.

He laughed. "Ve have a good surprise, Yoe," he said. "In Seattle the captain he buy some good mattress for us. Ve no longer have to sleep on straw. The steward he trow away the old donkeys."

I smiled. "Great," I said. It was about time we had some improvement. Then it hit me. "Jesus! Giuseppe's got his money in there!" I said.

Arne gave me a blank stare. Then he turned and rushed along the alleyway and across the open deck to where the steward stood, only three or four of the battered mattresses left beside him on the deck. I rushed after him. While Arne shouted and gesticulated at the steward, I turned over each mattress carefully and looked for the cleverly concealed slit where Giuseppe had inserted his money. His mattress was not there. And these were the last of the lot, the steward said, in a mild state of shock by now.

"Get Sis—I see the captain," Arne barked, and I rushed to do his bidding, throwing a brief glance back over the taffrail to where three or four of the battered mattresses bobbed around far behind in the wake.

I cast a brief look in the mess room and then plunged down into the engine room. Giuseppe was just entering our quarters. When he finally grasped what I was saying he gave a wild shriek and rushed to his bunk. There they were—the new mattresses. He sank his head on his bunk, sobbing. Then he let out another yell and darted for the nearest ladder leading topside.

There was a furor on the deck as the crew rushed aft to peer at the receding wake. Nothing was visible but water now. I rushed after Giuseppe up to the bridge. There, on one open wing, Arne stood confronting the captain. It seemed evident the stone-faced skipper had no intention of turning back. Besides, it was almost dark now and a faint mist had begun to hide the ocean's face. Giuseppe rushed up to the captain, grabbed his arm and pressed his face against it sobbing, muttering something in Italian I couldn't understand. The captain seemed faintly embarrassed but adamant. He gently took the Sicilian's hands and removed them from his coat sleeve. Then Arne pleaded with him again in Swedish but it did no good.

After a couple of minutes Arne and I took Giuseppe between us and led him slowly below. Arne got a bottle of akvavit he had stashed somewhere and made the Sicilian drink some of it. His bronzed skin seemed almost a deathly white now. Presently he lay down in his bunk on the new mattress and turned his face to the bulkhead.

Next day Giuseppe seemed almost back to normal. He said little but seemed ready to resume his work philosophically. But as Ole and I came up on deck for our noon meal we were confronted by a startling sight. Back toward the stern by the gangway stood Giuseppe, all decked out in his Sunday best, tie and polished high-top shoes and a funny little hat, and even more strangely, a neat little suitcase in one hand.

Before I could think or move, he turned toward the midship structure, gave a funny kind of salute, then turned toward the side of the ship, stepped out jauntily like some bozo taking the first step of the wedding march, and then he was gone.

I yelled and rushed back toward the stern, throwing out the first life buoy I came to. Someone back near the taffrail threw out another, and I heard what must have been "Man overboard!" in Swedish ring out. I kept on back toward the stern, but then swung around abruptly and headed up to the bridge instead. I saw Arne rushing in the same direction ahead of me.

When I got topside the first engineer suddenly stepped in my path, grabbed my arm and spat out something I didn't understand. This time I did the shoving—I pushed him back against a railing, saw him stumble with a look of outrage and incredulity on his face, and rushed on past.

On the bridge Arne stood shouting at the captain. I came up and joined in. Between the two of us it finally seemed to put a dent in the mentality of that wooden-faced patriarch. Seeming faintly shaken, he gave an order to the helmsman and the great ship slowly began to come about.

But by then our lost shipmate must have been a mile or two behind. To make things worse, a mist had begun to set in over the thrashing waters. It was like looking for a whisper in the wind.

We circled back and forth slowly for well over an hour but it was hopeless. And no doubt Giuseppe didn't want to be rescued anyway. Next day the captain conducted a brief memorial service. For days afterward there was a gloom about the ship, while puzzled crewmen speculated on why our lost shipmate had dressed up and taken his suitcase with him—perhaps he really believed he was going to a better place. Good old Giuseppe—I hope he found it.

19

FROM VLADIVOSTOK TO SYDNEY

Another Sunday came. For a while I thought I would never survive to see it. But hard and monotonous as the work was, and depressed as I was over the death of Giuseppe, my back and other pains slowly eased and I gradually swung into a sort of rhythm of subdued misery and mental deadness that made the long twelve-hour grinds bearable.

The first few days I was too exhausted to do anything but fall into my bunk at night, drifting off to sleep to the sounds of the unceasing engine and the everlasting poker game. But finally I had enough excess energy to spend a little time talking about the IWW and the "revolution" with Arne, or digging out the books I had brought and reading for an hour or two in the dim light of the cramped bunkroom. My shipmates teased me about my reading and sometimes called me "the professor" or "the college kid," but I didn't let it bother me too much.

First I read about the history of seamen's struggles, about the remarkable voyages of the Vikings, and of the Polynesians, who could navigate hundreds of miles just by the feel of the rhythm of the waves. Of the fifteenth-century "Law of Oleron" of the first known seamen to demand to be treated as humans instead of slaves, and who spoke of themselves as "companions of the vessel." Of the great Norwegian-American Andrew Furuseth, who had headed the Seamen's Union of the Pacific for nearly half a century. When threatened with jail in one strike the feisty Furuseth had said: "They can't put me in a smaller room than I've always lived in. They can't give me plainer food than I've always eaten. They can't make me lonelier than I've always been." With the help of Senator "Fighting Bob" LaFollette, Furuseth had finally gotten a Seamen's Act passed in 1915 that abolished the jailing of crew members for leaving a ship before their tour of duty was up, and helped end other abuses.

But in spite of this "Magna Carta of the Sea" of 1915 the seamen had lost a massive maritime strike in 1921 and wages had been slashed severely. Had Furuseth embraced the industrial unionism of the IWW whereby all marine workers would strike together, they might have won it. But the old Norwegian seemed fearful of sharing his power with other leaders (the longshoremen had far more members), and he fought the IWW and its concept of One Big Union more and more bitterly.

And so I came to see that it was far more than ideology that made the world turn—often human psychology, petty jealousies, personality conflicts called the tune. The marxists seemed to ignore the factor of human psychology, seeming to think that economic uniformity would mold everyone into think-alike, act-alike robots—but it seemed highly unlikely to me that that would happen. At least I hoped the world would never be that deadly dull and uniform.

Sometimes I would sit up by the taffrail watching the endlessly receding wake where Giuseppe had disappeared, at the blown spume and spindrift and sea bream, and be awed by the immensity of it all, and think with dazed humility of old Khayyam's lines: "And O but the long long time the world will last / That of our coming and our going heeds / As the sea's self should heed a pebble cast."

And then I began to delve into some of the literary works I had brought, the plays of Eugene O'Neill, *The Hairy Ape* with its great scene in the IWW hall, and the passage from *Bound East of Cardiff* in which a seaman is dying at the bottom of the hold after a fall from the deck above; he tells the comrades trying to console him:

This sailor life ain't much to cry about leavin'—just one ship after another; hard work, small pay and bum grub; and, when we get into port, just a drunk endin' up in a fight, and all your money gone, and then ship away again. Never meetin' no nice people, never gettin' outa sailor town, hardly, in any port; travellin' all over the world and never seein' none of it; without no one to care whether you're alive or dead...

We plowed on relentlessly into the cold northern Pacific. I began to have the nightmarish feeling the voyage would never end. The first engineer began to come down on us harder than ever. One day the bilge pumps stopped working and he had us standing almost knee-deep in slime scooping out the filthy sludge of the bilge with its dead rats and other putrid matter, working three hours overtime until we could clean out the clogged-up strainers and the pumps would work again.

And the food got worse and worse. One day, by coincidence apparently, all five of us who were IWW members found ourselves alone in our quarters — Arne, two other Swedes, and to my intense surprise, the Filipino messman. The complaints began to fly thick and fast, in Swedish, English, Spanish and Tagalog. "When are we going to let the cat loose?" I finally demanded.

Arne seemed to think deeply. "Not yust yet, Yoe," he finally pronounced. "The time is not ripe. Let us have our shore leave in Vladivostok first and collect some of our pay. Then vhen the ship is about to sail ve vill have more power." The others agreed.

I was getting bored to the point of madness by the exhausting monotony of the wiper's job. I vowed I would never ship as a wiper again — at least not with twelve-hour shifts. The second Sunday at sea I prevailed upon Arne to let me stand beside him for a couple of hours before the gauges and begin to learn something of an oiler's job. Again I asked him when we were going to let the cat loose and again he said, "Not yust yet — the time is not ripe."

Two days later at evening mess I picked up one of the horrendous gut-busting crackers and found a thin layer of green mold on it. Simultaneously a Swedish seaman did the same, gave a snort and sent his cracker sailing through the open hatchway into the galley. The men all began to grumble. Arne beside me picked up his cracker with dismay, turned to me and said: "The time is ripe."

After dinner I followed him out into the port alleyway. "What are we going to do?" I asked.

"Yust give me a vhile to think about it," he said.

Next day at lunch, to my amazement, we had steaks and delicious apple strudel for dessert. The old Swedish cook seemed to be looking at us with a forced smile from the galley, and the Filipino messman was smiling even more. Arne was all smiles too.

On the way back down to the engine room I asked Arne if he knew the reason for the abrupt change.

"Oh," he said, "I yust leave a little note in the galley last night to tell the cook if ve don't get better grub, it's overboard you go."

On and on. On and on. It seemed the trip would never end. But finally, after nineteen or twenty days we saw the first gray outline of land ahead, and by evening we were entering Golden Horn Bay and finally could see Vladivostok itself slowly taking shape in the distance, with low hills rising behind like a ghostly city out of some ancient fairy tale.

Tired as I was after my twelve-hour shift, I stood out in the gusty spray and freezing cold near the bow with three or four others, my heart beating fast. The nearness of land—any land— was tremendously exciting. Merely to walk on firm soil that was not constantly moving would be heaven. I could well understand now why many sailors who had been weeks or months at sea could get a little crazy when they finally reached a port. Except for Canada, this was my first foreign land.

And so much history here. As the strange buildings and smattering of Oriental cupolas drew near I thought back to 1918 when Britain, France and the United States had landed troops here to provide a support base for the Kolchak forces fighting Lenin. But Kolchak had been defeated anyway. I wondered how an American would be greeted so soon afterward—would they know or believe that my fellow Wobblies had refused to load ships for the invaders?

We drew into the port proper, on a peninsula between two bays, just as darkness came down. I strained my eyes to see the jumbled mass of the waterfront—a few huge ships, giant ware- houses, and the blinking lights of the strange-looking city beyond —how fascinating it must be!

As we slowed and a tug came out to meet us, Arne came and stood beside me at the bulwarks. "Vun of the Svede seamen tell me he vas here before," he said with an anticipatory grin. "They have a seamen's club, a cafeteria, vodka, music, girls to dance vith.

It is open till eleven. Ve get some girls, eh Yoe?" And he slapped me on the back.

The mere word sent shivers up and down my spine. I wondered if we could go ashore tonight. As the huge vessel finally was being shunted up against the pier we decided to go to the mess room to see if anyone knew anything about shore leave.

Ten or twelve crew members were sitting in the mess hall muttering angrily, sullen looks on their faces. It seemed the first mate had just come down and told them there would be no shore leave. Period. I felt my heart sink. Why? The mate said he didn't know. I felt like running up to the bridge and grabbing the captain by the collar and demanding an explanation, but I only sat and sulked with the others. Seven thousand miles of back-breaking work and loneliness and now a dirty trick like this.

Arne seemed almost as desolated as I was. "Maybe the Ruskies they vill not let us go ashore," he speculated sadly.

Later I sat for over an hour back by the taffrail, trying with straining eyes to penetrate the mystery of that dark enigmatic city, so near and yet so far, looking for a sign of life—but the only thing I saw moving was an occasional wharf rat.

Next day the men were still grumbling over breakfast. The fact we did not have to work only partially alleviated our anger and disappointment. As soon as it got light I rushed out to peer again at the strange city. There it was, big as life, with its strange dark buildings and an occasional colorful onion-like cupola, and a couple of bright red flags with the hammer and sickle on them flying from atop buildings.

It was a cold overcast day. Soon people began appearing on the docks, so heavily bundled up I could hardly see their faces. The great cranes and cargo booms began to move. I could hear voices below me chattering gruffly in a language I had never heard. I bent over the railing and looked down. A rather heavy form smiled and waved up to me and I waved back. The slightly pudgy but strangely attractive face kept peering at me before I snapped out of my early-morning daze and realized something surprising about it—a woman! To my incredulity and delight, she threw me a brief kiss. Then she turned abruptly and went off to join some others—about half of them also women—who were pushing a big cart closer to the side of the ship.

Arne suddenly appeared behind me. "The men they all get killed in the var," he commented philosophically.

I spent the day below reading. Next morning I took up my perch by the taffrail again. And the same female stevedore looked up at me. Her deep blue eyes had a strange dreamy quality. We stared into one another's eyes wistfully for a long moment, drinking deeply. Then she seemed to give a sigh, shrugged resignedly and trudged off to her work.

As I regretfully watched her walk away, I thought: That's what life is all about too—people looking warmly into one another's eyes, a blending of human spirits that transcends ideology, that so brief communion when soul meets soul with a kind of mating through the eyes. A woman in a strange land I would never see again, but with whom in a strange way I felt forever linked.

That night in my reading I found a new aphorism for my notebook: "At the back of every person's head there should be a tiny hammer continually tapping to remind him there are unhappy people in the world": Anton Chekhov.

The next day we were off again. Vladivostok had been like an interlude in a dream. It was back to the interminable steel plates and gratings again, and scrubbing the grime off the bulkheads with cotton waste. The first engineer and the other officers seemed meaner than ever—no doubt they too chafed from the absence of shore leave. It was back out into the Sea of Japan, south through the Korea Strait, on into the East China Sea.

The days got hotter and hotter now. We passed east of Formosa and crossed the Tropic of Cancer. I was continually overawed by the immensity of the sea. On the maps I pored over there were land masses and islands all over the place, and yet we plowed right through them day after dreary day without seeing the tiniest atoll, not a single other ship, nothing.

As we approached the Philippines the heat became unbearable. What dunderhead had ever decided to put sleeping quarters next to the engine room? And the deck crew complained too because the steam lines for the winches passed right through their bunkroom in the prow. The heat became so bad I couldn't sleep and it was all I could do to go through the thousand repetitive motions of my job without falling asleep or plunging to my death on the machinery-covered deck below.

One of the Swedish firemen fainted from the heat and the first engineer swore a blue streak and kicked him back to conscious-

ness. Arne and Ole and I started to go to his aid, but the First
backed off and we returned to our work.

Once I caught myself dozing off high on a scaffold and would
have fallen if Ole hadn't rushed to my aid. One of the wiper's jobs
was to go topside now and then and trim the ventilators, the big
funnels that rose from the deck like misshapen toadstools, to turn
their open scoops to the wind. But when there was no wind save
what was generated by the motion of the ship it did little good.

Finally the five of us who were Wobs got together to discuss the
situation. Arne said the trouble was there were not enough
ventilator fans—this ship had not been built for the tropics. Arne
volunteered to go to the captain to request that some more be
installed at our next port of call. He conveyed the captain's answer
to us the next day: "Out of the question."

As we plowed farther south under scorching skies the problem
became truly unbearable. The sweat rolled off us in buckets.
Everyone was either sleepwalking or grumbling. Arne told us one
of the deck crew who was thinking of joining the IWW had offered
to talk with the other seamen about it. We had a meeting. They
agreed to back us up in whatever we decided to do. It was a risky
business. Refusal to work at sea was dangerous and could be
construed as mutiny. But something had to be done.

The following morning after breakfast all of the off-duty men
marched up to the bridge to confront the captain. It was more
fans or no work.

It was the first time I had seen expression in the old man's face.
He looked from one to the other of us the way a parent might
react if his only son announced he was going to get a sex change
operation. He muttered a few words under his breath in Swedish.
Then he tilted his captain's cap back and wiped his brow. "Ya,
ya…" he said after a minute, and I heard a word that sounded like
"Manila."

Arne translated for me. "He say ve vill put into Manila for more
fans—but no shore leave." Just like that.

We all marched off to our jobs, a little amazed at our power.
Once we had decided to act it had all been over so fast.

Next evening we put into Manila. It was the first time I had
seen palm trees, and a certain alluring something that stirred the
blood seemed to pervade the air. I could see a few young women
far off through the shadows, and I felt the same maddening
frustration I had felt in Vladivostok—that seemed a hundred years

ago. What in hell was wrong with the skipper—did he think we'd jump ship and never return? Was he jealous of a few moments of pleasure we might snatch from some shoreside women? Did he think we'd all get drunk and land in the calaboose?

We were all pleasantly surprised when the new fans were installed in a day's time. They made a world of difference. After that successful job action Arne and I signed up several more of the crew in the IWW.

The rest of the passage on to Sydney passed uneventfully. We crossed the steaming equator somewhere south of Borneo and a few days later it began to get cooler again. Finally one afternoon we saw a huge land mass ahead, and by evening we were entering Sydney harbor.

It was a beautiful sight, Sydney, rising on its low undulating hills with the Blue Mountains rising against the sunset far to the west. We glided through Woolloomooloo Bay and along beside a huge park, and then we were at the wharf. The temperature was faintly balmy, as nearly perfect as you could ask. The city beyond the waterfront warehouses seemed to have a buzzing gaiety to it.

This time, there was no question about our going ashore—if it had been denied us again there would have been a riot. We were to be in the pleasant port for at least four days and everybody was planning on making the most of it. We got the half of our pay we were entitled to and practically ran over one another going down the gangplank. The feel of solid earth under my feet for the first time in over a month was almost intoxicating.

It wasn't long before we were through customs. I was in the tow of Arne and Ole and the Englishman, Derek, who had been here before, and we headed for the nearest pub. I still drank only rarely, but this was a time to celebrate and I had heard the Australian beer was good.

I had another reason for celebrating too—it was here that the IWW had had perhaps its greatest victory of all, when in 1916 it had organized a national referendum that got the draft law repealed—right smack-dab in the middle of World War I. Maybe those so-called criminals the English had sent to settle Australia were smarter and better people than their jailers.

I lived it up for three days and then I went back to the ship to do some serious thinking. I must have been crazy to sign on a ship whose final destination was Stockholm. We wouldn't be there for another two months. And Arne told me no one knew when or where the ship was going next. What in hell would I do in Stockholm?

I made some inquiries and learned there was a big English–speaking refrigerator ship leaving for Seattle in three days. They had one opening—wiper. Jesus. I had sworn I would never ship out as a wiper again, but I felt desperate to get home. Funny. A month ago I was crazy for adventure and travel and the sea. Now I longed for dry land and familiar faces. Maybe there is something about human nature that dooms it never to be satisfied.

It meant sacrificing the half of my pay I still had coming, but I made the big jump and signed on. Most of the crew were Aussies and they seemed like really nice guys—smart tough cookies who treated their friends right but who wouldn't stand for much pushing around. And as on the Swedish ship, I was told three or four of them were Wobblies.

Funny, I had grown to like glancing up at the bridge at the inscrutable face of the Swede captain—perhaps he had become, in a strange way, a sort of father figure for me. I felt a little shame-faced sneaking off the ship with my belongings. I met Arne and Ole and some of the others for a farewell drink at a nearby pub and we all patted one another's backs and gave a salute in parting to the IWW.

Each ship is a nation unto itself. This ship was as different from the last as a wombat from a kangaroo. It was a big refrigerator ship carrying beef and mutton to the States. The one good thing about it was that the engine room gang's foc's'le was right up in the prow, to port of the deck crew's, so there was no problem with unbearable heat. The bad thing was that this part of the ship pitched and plunged more than any other, so that bedding down was like trying to sleep on a bucking bronco.

But it was good to mingle more with the deck crew right next door, and I began to learn a little about seamanship. Of course the pay was lousy—only a dollar or two more a month than I'd made on the Swedish ship.

The work was as gruesome as ever. There were a few variations, such as having to chip old paint off the engine room bulkheads, but mainly it was the same. We weren't at sea for half a day before I realized I had jumped from the frying pan into the fire. If I thought the Swede first engineer was bad, my new one, a Dutch-

English guy from South Africa who stood about six feet five, was a holy terror. Just after my fellow wiper and I had cleaned the floor plates near the boilers, he came by, slipped or pretended to slip on something, let out a yell that could be heard in Capetown and pushed me viciously against the scorching side of the boiler. Then he threatened to put me on bread and water if he found any more spots of oil on the plates. I stood glaring at him, holding my burned arm. He turned and lurched off, scowling.

The food was atrocious. The beanmaster was a punchy old chowderhead who didn't know a flapjack from a seagull turd. The jungle juice I had swallowed in the worst hobo jungles was better than the unrecognizable swill he called coffee. The belly-breaking biscuits he served made me long for the good old corrugated iron Swedish crackers.

The deck crew had it as bad as we did, and were continually complaining about the mean old-time bucko mates who were forever making them do repetitive make-work jobs that didn't need doing.

It wasn't long before we and the deck crew got together in the foc's'le one night to discuss the situation. We decided to issue an ultimatum to the captain: better food, no make-work, and an end to violence against crew members, or we were going to take "job action."

The men delegated to take our demands to the captain reported back that he tore up the ultimatum without reading it. The grumbling became worse than ever. Somewhere near the equator one of the bucko mates badly beat a seaman for dropping a paint-scraper overboard, almost putting out one of his eyes. We held an emergency meeting. One of the older hands asked for some volunteers who were big and husky for a special assignment. Three or four of the men looked at me. Four of us offered our services.

That night we lay in wait behind a lifeboat near the offending mate's cabin. One of us unscrewed the light bulb from the bulkhead nearby and it was pitch black. The sadist finally appeared and we jumped him from behind and lowered the boom. I coldcocked him before he could let out a scream and the others got in their licks as well. Then we vanished before he could get a glimpse of us. Next day he was sporting a black eye, but he acted just as mean and cocky as ever.

Nothing we did on that ship seemed to work to win us better food or conditions. If anything, we were treated worse as the days wore on. A few of us finally decided to resort to desperate measures. Late one night when the engine room officer on watch was absent we got busy and, working according to a carefully rehearsed plan, connected one of the steam lines to the refrigeration lines filled with ammonia. We worked fast and had the job done before the engineer reappeared. We cooked that beef good.

It wasn't until the following day that our handiwork was detected. The captain was fit to be tied. When he couldn't prove who did it his attitude finally softened. We improved conditions on that goddamned ship in a hurry. They lost thousands of dollars worth of beef.

The ship plowed on through heavy seas toward Seattle. I couldn't believe I was really returning home. I felt as if I had lived several lifetimes in the five weeks I had been at sea. But one mild April day we spotted the tip of the Olympic peninsula and I gave a gigantic sigh of relief. I had become disillusioned with the sea in a hurry, and yet in a strange way I loved it, the way one might love an abrasive brother.

At the Seattle docks police swarmed all over the ship. But they couldn't find a clue as to who had cooked the beef. When they finally gave up, I got my belongings and hurried ashore. My first seagoing adventure was at an end.

20

'SUCH A LOT
OF DEVILS'

The great teeming city of Seattle towered above me on its hills. I rushed with my gear up the bustling streets that held so many memories for me. It was late April and a sun-washed freshness filled the air. I felt a surging energy coursing through my veins. I felt I was about to burst with the beauty of the earth. I suddenly realized I was ravenously hungry. I thought of the greasy spoon I had helped organize: real food; and *women*! And even better, *Wobbly* women.

A couple of blocks more and I was standing in front of the place. It was mid-afternoon and only a couple of customers sat vacant-eyed over coffee. I could see two familiar faces at the rear, near the entrance to the kitchen. It was Ann and Molly, two of the most gung-ho of the waitresses during the strike, women in their early or mid-twenties, both left with kids to raise by themselves. They were not raving beauties but damned sweet, smart, well built class-conscious rebel girls.

I went all the way to the rear of the counter—I always tried to sit close to the coffee urn to make it easy on the help—and ordered dinner and a cup of java. They both welcomed me warmly. Something inside me exploded with joy when I saw the tiny red Wobbly button pinned to Molly's uniform—so she was still true blue.

They wanted to know all about my first sea voyage. While my hamburger steak and spuds were sizzling on the grill I regaled them with the high points—and the low points—of my trip.

Some more customers came in and Ann went to wait on them. I watched Molly as she stood before the big black stove. Her hair was a mass of gold above the greasy grill. Her eyes and face and arching form seemed to have a plaintive something about them. She looked like she needed affection and a good loving—just like me.

We started exchanging moony looks as I shoveled down my grub. Would she be the one? Her hand touched mine as she brought me more coffee. I sat tongue-tied, staring at her like a callow lovesick twelve-year-old. This is life! I thought. What all the hard work and battles and brutal time in prison were for—act! Was the great "Kid Murphy" who had knocked down the first engineer and gotten away with it afraid to ask a fellow Wobbly for a date? I swallowed more coffee. Molly waited, her fingers tapping on the edge of the counter. I finally blurted out: "Would you like to go for a dock on the walks after work?"

I felt my face redden. We both laughed. "I mean—"

"Sure," she rescued me, and I couldn't believe what I was hearing. "Sure," she said, "I haven't gone for a dock in a long time, Joe." And we laughed some more.

She was getting off in half an hour. She said her mother was taking care of her four-year-old son and she could leave him there for a while. We walked and walked, all along the waterfront and up toward Lake Washington. Then we began taking streetcars all over town. At one stop I bought her a box of candy and we began stuffing chocolates into one another's mouth. As dark came down I finally got up the courage to take her hand and after a little while she lay her head on my shoulder.

At one point she pointed out a small duplex and "That's our little rat's nest," she said.

"Oh it's not so bad," I said. "In fact I think it's kind of cute—like you." God, was anyone ever so corny?

We got off at the next stop. I knew it was going to be one of those great days in my life. And it was pure heaven—a landlocked sailor's just deserts. Perhaps I had come home at last.

Next morning I awoke at dawn. She was beside me—all the glowing beauty of her, vibrantly alive even in sleep. I lay just looking at her in wonder for a while. Had I really become part of another beautiful fellow human being's soul?

Presently I got up and fixed myself some coffee. I went into the tiny living room cluttered with a few children's toys to drink it. Another gorgeous spring day was dawning. As soon as I sat down in the creaky overstuffed chair my eyes lit on the copy of the *Industrial Worker* on the rickety stand beside it. THE GENERAL STRIKE STARTS, the blaring headline read.

My god—I get back just when all hell is breaking loose! I remembered there had been talk of a general strike before I had shipped out, but still the reality hit me like a huge splash of sea-spray in the face. The world seemed to be changing so fast, to be so fluid and chaotic—you could be gone a week and come back and find a completely new ball of wax.

I devoured the long article greedily. The great May Day strike, to begin in some areas five days earlier, was to demand the release of IWW class war prisoners, the eight-hour day, and decent bedding in the migrant logging camps. As in the successful 1917 strike, loggers had already begun burning their bindles in some places in protest, and the biggest blanket bonfire in history was planned for International Labor Day on May First.

I read on in the IWW paper. The greatest explosion of new activity was in the Los Angeles area, where the continued repression of the IWW had resulted in a running battle between the IWW and the establishment. The waterfront strike which had begun in support of our Portland strike was turning into the biggest and longest free speech fight in IWW history. An international boycott of all goods from "barbarous California" had been launched because of the long prison sentences being meted out merely for being a member of the IWW. And now at last the general strike!

By the time I had finished the papers, my head was spinning. So much happening, so much I was needed for, and just when I had found a woman I really liked. But however brief, my time with Molly was a plus, I thought, for both her and me. And it didn't mean I'd never see her again. It was just what I needed to cap my arduous sea experiences—the finishing touch to completely recharge my batteries. I felt like a whole man. I was ready to do battle with the master class again. Damn the greedy cutthroats!

Why couldn't they see that we'd all be better off if they'd just come down off their high horses and we all joined together to run the industries democratically for the good of all?

Later, I sat beside Molly on the trolley on her way to work, holding her hand.

"I'd like to see you again, Joe," she said as we came to the cafe. Something seemed to catch slightly in her voice. "It was a wonderful dock on the walks."

"I'd like to see you too." Then I told her about being needed in the general strike. "I'll be back as soon as I can," I said. We kissed goodbye in a vacant storefront and then I hefted my pack and headed off to the Wobbly hall.

The hall was bursting with activity. Hundreds of members were working feverishly there. Plans for the great walkout were proceeding full blast. Committees were being formed to visit the various camps in the woods, to close up the gin mills, to raise funds, to picket the docks—for every conceivable activity that could make a mass demonstration of fifty or a hundred thousand workers a success. I exchanged smiles of greeting and pats on the back with boon companions and fellow rebels and cast about to see how I could help.

I soon joined a group of around a dozen Wobs who were to proceed to the Grays Harbor area west of Olympia, pull out as many lumber camps and mills as we could, and if we had any spare time and energy left, close up as many blind pigs as possible. We were only one of dozens of such groups that were to fan out all the way from the Columbia River to the Canadian border. We had our work cut out for us.

We loaded up with literature and supplies, hefted our packs, and headed for the railyards. There was an air of expectancy as we swept along with our Wobbly regalia. In the railyards workers greeted us with cheers and urged us on, giving us the latest information on the freights. We stood in the busy yards and waited beside the maze of tracks. A train whooshed north. Then a rattler began to take off going south and we hopped on. From the deep sea to the deep woods!

We got in a fairly clean boxcar and rocked south through a slight drizzle. We held her down past Tacoma and then Olympia and then off to the west. We sat exchanging tales of our experiences. Most of the fellow workers were young and seemed to cotton to my yarns. An older Wob suddenly said, "If our time is limited at some of these shebangs and we can't all rattle our teeth, I vote we elect Joe here to do the talking."

They took a vote and I was elected as the mouthpiece. I felt both excited and humbled. My first test by fire as a real organizer and I wondered if I could pull it off. We passed Montesano and the memory of the trial there was suddenly like a gallery of stark bigger–than–life pictures on the walls of my mind. I vowed to outdo myself in the struggle ahead.

About noon the train pulled into Grays Harbor. To our delight we saw a group of Wobbly pickets along the waterfront. It looked like most of the stevedores were out, and only one of the lumber schooners in the harbor seemed to be loading. We hit the grit and hoofed it over to where our fellow workers were picketing.

They were a spirited group and gave us a warm welcome as we ambled up. "We've got the lumber lords on the run!" one grizzled old Wobbly exulted as we came up to them on the old pier. And he did a little dance and finished it off by suddenly turning his rump toward the one working lumber schooner and breaking wind. What a character! I thought. But then the IWW was full of high–spirited characters like that.

We had a conference with our fellow Wobs. Some of the camps had come out already, they told us, but many more small operations were still working back in the woods. Most of the seamen had come off the few ships, but a few seemed undecided and were boozing in the local "soft drink establishments." They gave us directions to the blind pigs and working camps. We wished them luck and started on our rounds.

At the blind pigs we tacked up the flyers we had been given at Wobbly headquarters in Seattle. They read:

NOTICE TO ALL BOOTLEGGERS AND GAMBLING HOUSES:
You are hereby given notice to close up during the
strike or drastic action will be taken against you.
—Industrial Workers of the World

Also we spoke briefly to the men boozing inside. A few got up sheepishly and left. At one bar a big bouncer tore down the handbill as soon as I put it up. I decked him and put it up again.

Then we started out into the deep woods, splitting up into groups of six each. We hopped a ride on a short logging train to the first camp about four miles in. When we got to the logging road where the men were working, I jumped up on a donkey engine and blew the whistle. The stiff working the engine looked at me as if he'd seen a ghost. Off at the edge of the woods fourteen or fifteen men stopped working and stood gawking at us. I waved my arms at them and they put down their saws and axes and began to approach.

Up a little rise, a tough-looking bloke who must have been the foreman let out a string of curses and then rushed toward us like a rat with ten sab cats after it. Two of our biggest boys blocked his path and detained him in conversation.

The others followed me and the three other Wobs to the nearby bunkhouse. It was a typical jerry-built shack without any washroom or other amenities. They all sat around on bunks while I passed out literature and then began to speak. I began by discussing the gains the IWW had achieved already. Then I explained the strike and its purposes. Then I made a personal appeal to reason and conscience.

"What are you doing with your lives?" I asked them. "Are you going anywhere? Do you *know* where you're going? Do you think life was made just to work like an ox, then get drunk and sleep until you go to work again? Because you don't have brains or guts enough to try to improve things? Wouldn't any of you like to have a wife and family some day? I know I would. And wouldn't you like your kids to grow up and live better lives than you're living in this stinking pig sty? When you're ready to cash in your chips wouldn't you like to be able to say to yourself: 'I was one of those who had the gumption to fight back—I was one of those who made the world better'?"

When I had finished, the men began mumbling among themselves. Finally one said, "All right—I'll line up." Then four or five more lined up and we made out their cards.

Then one stiff said, "Well, I don't agree with all the principles of your organization, but you've got my sympathy."

"'Sympathy,'" I snorted. "I believe that's somewhere between 'shit' and 'syphilis' in the dictionary." Everyone laughed. "'Sympathy' didn't get you the shorter hours and better pay you enjoy already. And it won't get you a washroom or decent mattresses and blankets."

The man nodded. "I agree with all that there stuff," he said. "But what I don't see is how the workers can run the industries. It can't be done."

I thought a second. "Listen," I said. "You ever hear of Steinmetz, the electrical wizard of General Electric?"

He nodded again.

"Well he was a Wobbly," I said. "And if a genius like him thinks the workers can run things, I say they can too. Tell me something," I said. "You mean to tell me that without that lazy-assed foreman out there you stiffs couldn't run that logging operation? I don't believe it."

"Well, hell," the skeptical logger said. "Whaddo I have to lose— write me out a card."

And then the remaining men lined up too. Before the head muckamuck and a couple of his cronies had arrived to evict us, the whole shebang had agreed to come out and help picket the docks in town, and to burn their vermin-infested blankets on the First of May.

We went from camp to camp with varying degrees of success. A few days later even some of the newspapers admitted that over seventy-five percent of the woods and dock workers in the Grays Harbor area had joined the strike. Our enemies fought back with their usual hysteria when their power and profits were threatened. One striker picketing on public property near Aberdeen was killed by a mill guard and his murderer was later exonerated.

The last day of April we got a whole string of camps out along a single road through the woods. At each camp we waited until all the stiffs were packed up and ready to leave, and then we marched from camp to camp, our numbers growing as we went. By the time we reached the first little town there must have been three or four hundred of us. We gave out songbooks and as we marched into town we were all singing at the top of our lungs:

Fifty thousand lumberjacks, fifty thousand packs,
Fifty thousand dirty rolls of blankets on our backs,
Fifty thousand minds made up to strike and strike to win;
For fifty years we've packed a bed, but never will again.
'Such a lot of devils' — that's what the papers say —
'They've gone on strike for shorter hours and some
     increase in pay;
They left the camps, the lazy tramps, they all walked
     out as one;
They say they'll win the strike or put the bosses on the bum';
Fifty thousand wooden bunks full of things that crawl;
Fifty thousand restless men have left them once for all.

And then as darkness neared, we piled up all the dirty bindles, covered them with gasoline, and set them afire. Most of the gawking townspeople seemed to enjoy it as much as a Fourth of July celebration. It must have been one of the biggest bonfires in history. It was a stinking mess. But it was beautiful too. It was our own Declaration of Independence: independence from filth and vermin and sleepless nights and too-long hours of backbreaking labor.

Next day we spent holding down a series of slow drags for Seattle, fanning the flames of discontent all along the way. It was a stirring progression. In almost every little burg or camp we came to, pickets were out and the slaves were burning their bindles. We distributed literature and exchanged revolutionary greetings. Between towns we belted out all the Wobbly songs we knew at the top of our lungs, making the walls of the boxcars shake even more than they normally did. At Tacoma our fellow workers there had outdone us. All two dozen or so speakeasies were closed down, with black crepe draped over their doors.

We got into Renton Junction south of Seattle just as a huge IWW rally was beginning. There must have been ten thousand people there in spite of the cold wind and rain. We paused long enough to hear Elmer Smith give a stirring speech attacking capitalism and demanding the release of the IWW's class war prisoners. I wanted to stay on and say hello to Smith, but we had more work to do.

The IWW had volunteered its services to the Seattle mayor in closing down the speakeasies, and public opinion had finally persuaded "hizzoner" and the forces of "lawnorder" to accept our offer. So next we joined dozens of squads of fellow workers in shutting down almost every blind pig in Seattle.

We were sent on north. Coming off a train at Everett next day we saw that Wobbly longshoremen had tied up the waterfront. But we learned that a few blind pigs were still open and we skedaddled off to do our duty.

I had been told of the notorious speakeasy in Everett with a gigantic whale penis on display but I had to see it to believe it. The huge phallus seemed to stretch across one whole wall. The rest of my bunch had taken on two other bars and only I and a big logger named Sven entered the place. While Sven lumbered up to address the owner, I began to tack up one of our ultimatums on the wall.

Suddenly I saw two big bouncers coming for me. I looked around for a weapon, a chair or a bottle of booze. Then my eye lit on the grotesque whale penis. The two thugs closed in on me. Jerking the phallus from the wall by one end, I swung it toward them for all I was worth. I hit them both just right, on their Adam's apples just below the chin, and they went down in a heap. Then I swung the huge phallus again and busted out the big front window into a thousand flying pieces. It ended up knocking down a cop who had just arrived on the scene, then skidded into a milk wagon. Sven and I faded off down the street.

And so it went. We went north pulling out camp after camp, burning bindles, fanning the flames. And we learned that thousands of Wobbly stevedores and seamen were out all over the country—in New York harbor, Boston, Baltimore, Mobile, New Orleans—and of course San Pedro. And we went all through that country, up through Stanwood and Conway and Mount Vernon and Sedro Woolley and Bellingham, pulling out camp after camp.

On May 5th we found ourselves in the Wobbly hall in Bellingham. We talked to the branch secretary and a few others over coffee an'. Latest estimates were that at least 65% of the lumber workers had gone out in Oregon and Washington. Not as many as we had hoped but enough to send a clear signal to the Establishment. Many camps had already begun installing real mattresses and blankets, and some of the men had gone back to work.

In San Pedro the strike was almost one hundred percent effective, with over sixty ships tied up in the harbor and not a seaman or stevedore working. But in spite of it all, the plutes were still arresting Wobblies. Now twenty-seven of our members in L.A. faced one to fourteen years in prison under the criminal syndicalism act.

While we were gabbing the news came in that the strike was about to be transferred to the job. We all gathered around to read a bulletin that had just been issued:

TAKE THE STRIKE BACK ON THE JOB

Fellow Workers:

   The IWW does not believe in long drawn-out strikes off the job. These exhaust the workers and eventually end by the workers losing all they have gained. The strike for the release of all class war prisoners has been transferred to the job by the vote of the membership. This change of tactics will be carrying the fight into the bosses' territory and the boss will be forced to pay the expenses of the strike. Monday, May 7, is the date set for the strike to be transferred to the job.

—IWW Strike Committee

We all shrugged and agreed it was probably the best thing.

21

AND STILL THE WOBBLIES SANG

On May 7th I got on at a lumber mill up by Sedro Woolley. Several other Wobs were on the job. Of course everybody had either participated in the big strike or heard about it. And the workers in many camps had won improvements because of the walkout. But this camp was owned by a stubborn sawdust daddy whose ossified brain was still back in the Dark Ages. It still had the old muzzle-loading bunks you had to crawl into from one end, and you had to furnish your own blankets.

We called a meeting of the workers the next night out in the woods. Expectations were higher after the strike and almost everyone showed up. And the boys all agreed to try a slowdown. We put up these stickers or "silent agitators" that read: SLOW DOWN AND WATCH YOUR PAY GO UP.

Next day the fun began. We were even slower at eating breakfast. It took some of the boys a full minute to bring a forkful of flapjack up to their mouths. It was like watching a movie in slow motion. The cook was furious. When he berated one of the boys, even his answer was in slow motion: "What...did...you... say?" We walked slow, we talked slow, we worked slower.

The boss was fit to be tied. He flat out rejected our demands for blankets, a better bunkhouse and a nickel an hour raise. Instead he laid off one crew of about twenty men and went to the slave market in town for replacements. But we had a bunch of Wobs ready to take the jobs, and when they got out to the camp they worked even slower than the men they replaced. The boss finally threw up his hands and granted our demands.

But I was getting restless again. And we kept reading in the Wobbly papers about the situation at Los Angeles harbor, and the calls for footloose Wobs to go down there and help out. And I was curious to see "Barbarous California," the state of my birth. So one day another Wob named Boxcar Shorty and I decided to shake the sawdust off our overalls and hit the road south.

We rode the freights through Seattle and Olympia and Centralia (a lot of memories there) and into Portland. In Portland we tried to get hired on a ship headed for L.A., hoping to organize the crew to walk out when we hit L.A. harbor. But we didn't have any luck. So we rode the freights on south, down into northern California, Sacramento, Stockton and finally into Fresno in the middle of the farm belt.

In Fresno we ran out of dough and decided to work in the crops for a few days, then head on south. There was a pretty good little group of Wobs here too, and we soon got hired on as roustabouts on a ranch.

There were memories of Wobbly struggles here too. The IWW free speech fight of 1910-11 had been one of the biggest and most successful of all. It had erupted over the usual issue—the right to speak on the street to warn workers of the crooked employment sharks. When Wobbly speakers were arrested, hundreds of foot-loose Wobs flooded in from all over the West to take their places on the soapbox. And they were arrested too. Soon the jail was full to bursting. And in jail they would stage their "battleships": pounding on the walls and singing at the top of their lungs until they drove the jailers mad. The police doused them with high-pressure water hoses, and still the Wobblies sang. At one point the one-eyed, half-Indian Wobbly official Frank Little was threatened with lynching. "If you put a noose in front of me I'd just laugh at it," he said. And from Chicago, Vincent St. John sent a message to the mayor: "We will win the right to free speech in Fresno if it takes all summer." The authorities finally gave in.

Just about the time Shorty and I had gotten together a small stake to take us on to L.A., we got the news that the strike there had been transferred back to the job. Next day one of the participants in the strike arrived at our camp east of Fresno. That night about forty of us got together around a campfire to hear what he had to say.

He was a lean wiry guy about thirty who had been in some of the IWW's biggest fights. Like most Wobs in those days he had that peculiar combination of toughness and friendliness.

"It was the biggest and most beautiful thing I've ever been in," he began, sitting on a fruit crate near the fire. "The strike shut down everything along the whole L.A. waterfront. We must have at least a few Wobblies on every ship in the Pacific by now, and on every ship that came in almost the whole crew joined our strike. In a few days there were over ninety ships anchored out there with not a cargo boom working—a beautiful sight.

"Our pickets were stretched out all along the waterfront. You know, that's where Joe Hill was our secretary back around 1912 and that's where he wrote 'Casey Jones, the Union Scab' during a railroad strike they had back then. He musta done a good job of organizing, 'cause the Wobbly spirit was still there.

"The owners and the cops was mad as hell. They've got a special Wobbly detail of over fifty bulls on the L.A. force. The owners and the L.A. papers spread a rumor we were gonna start fires among the piles of lumber on the docks, and got everybody all edgy and excited. They sent a whole slew of cops down to the waterfront and they assigned a special cop to watch each of our pickets. And they raided our hall, and they wouldn't let us speak in public. And they arrested twenty-seven of our most active members on criminal syndicalism charges. Not for any crime, just for being members of the IWW. You know what that means—one to fourteen years in state prison.

"Then a woman offered her property up on Beacon Hill in San Pedro—we called it Liberty Hill—for us to have our rallies on. And what rallies! Hundreds of people came up to hear our speakers every night—some of the best speakers that ever stood on a soapbox—veterans of Missoula and Spokane and Fresno and San Diego. Pretty soon it seemed like the whole town of San Pedro was about to join the IWW.

"But the bulls soon started pulling their usual stuff—arresting one speaker after another for so-called 'inflammatory language.' One night a burly police captain jumped up on the speakers' platform and announced that anyone inciting disorder would be arrested at once. He was greeted by boos and catcalls—mainly, it seemed, by casual bystanders rather than us Wobblies.

"Well, the speeches began. 'Friends and fellow workers,' the first speaker said. 'This struggle—'

"'Arrest that man!' the police captain barked. 'The word "struggle" is an incitement to disorder!' And two cops mounted the stand and arrested our first speaker.

"Three more speakers were arrested almost before they could clear their throats. When our next member arose he began to recite in a girlish voice:

Mary had a little lamb;
Its fleece was white as snow...

"But before he could get any farther he was handcuffed and led off through the crowd."

The group around me and Shorty burst into laughter. "Maybe he was arrested for a crime against nature," a Wob near us observed sarcastically. When the laughter had died, the Wobbly from L.A. went on:

"One Wobbly after another was arrested, until dozens of our people had been led away to jail. At one point, when most of the cops were off herding the prisoners, a dock worker leapt up on the platform and suggested to the crowd that everyone at the rally march to the jail and form a continuous chain of marchers around it, continuing the rally there. The suggestion immediately caught fire, and the two or three thousand people at the rally began surging down the hill behind the cops and their prisoners. Another Wob and I began rushing along beside the marchers giving out song sheets.

"It seemed like everyone in San Pedro flocked to the jail to take part in that demonstration. And you could see the bulls looking out through the bars with fear in their eyes as we began to sing with a massive roar of voices that must have been heard as far away as San Diego. And from inside the jail we could hear our brothers singing in response, and I swear I could see the walls of that dungeon shake from the crescendo of sound. The parade went on and on, marching and singing. We chanted and sang for at least four or five hours until we must have sung every song in the *Little Red Songbook* five times over.

"After that, at our rallies, our boys began trying to get away from the bulls—jumping up on rooftops and continuing their speeches, while the cops climbed up after them. It was a sight—it was like a Mack Sennett comedy. And one of our boys led the cops on a chase across the rooftops and one of the bulls fell down plop in a big box of manure outside somebody's horse stall. I seen that with my own eyes.

"We had the harbor tied up tight. And now hundreds of IWW oil workers from Long Beach and a big bunch of Mexican Wobs from East L.A. began coming over to help us out too. We even had an IWW airplane distributing leaflets all over the south side of L.A.

"Upton Sinclair lived over in Pasadena about thirty miles away. And it was too much for him that the plutes wouldn't even allow us to speak. So he and a woman named Kate Crane Gartz and some others came down to Liberty Hill to speak. But the minute Sinclair began to read from the U.S. Bill of Rights he was hauled off too. Not only that, but the bulls actually *kidnapped* him. They drove him all over L.A. for half the night and held him incommunicado for over twenty-four hours. Even his wife didn't know what had happened to him.

"Well, it backfired. Even some of the most conservative rags in the country had banner headlines about Sinclair's kidnapping and the absence of law and order in L.A. And Sinclair belonged to an outfit called the American Civil Liberties Union, which Wobs and ex-Wobs helped set up after the Palmer raids. They got a big boost from their campaign to defend free speech at Liberty Hill.

"But the plutes weren't through with us yet. A few days ago they arrested around three hundred of us, just for picketing, and put us in a big stinking stockade over near downtown L.A. They finally released most of us for lack of evidence.

"In the meantime they'd been beating holy hell out of our twenty-seven boys in the L.A. jail on the criminal syndicalism charge. One poor stiff died there. I went to the trial of the others. The judge said he'd let them all off if they'd renounce membership in the IWW. Of course not one of them did."

The speaker's eyes misted up a little. "I left that courtroom knowing I'd been in the company of saints," he said in conclusion.

There was silence for a long moment. The firelight flickered on the speaker's lean thoughtful face.

Then, "Hell, we're all saints—ain't we, Shorty?" one of the other Wobblies said.

Shorty laughed. "Yeah, I reckon," he said. "But don't expec' me to perform no miracles."

And then the group around the speaker began to break up and drift off.

We worked on the farm a few days more. Later something truly amazing came out in the papers. Police captain Plummer, who had been in charge of the waterfront strike detail, made a statement repenting his role in the strike:

> Somebody has been making holy asses of us policemen... At the time of the harbor strike I went to see old man Hammond [owner of many of the lumber ships]. He told me to take a bunch of my men, arm them with clubs, go up on Liberty Hill and break the heads of the Wobblies. I replied that if we did that, they would burn down his lumber piles. 'They will do it anyway,' he answered. But they didn't. Not an overt act have they committed... We policemen have been made the tools of the big business interests who want to run things. I'm ashamed of myself for consenting to do their dirty work. The big fellows in this town can do anything they like and get away with it, but the workers can't even think what they want to think without being thrown in jail.

Hotdamn. So the truth came out sometimes after all. Even a few cops could tell the truth.

Shorty and I worked at the ranch another week. Then I began to feel like I'd been in "barbarous California" long enough. I began to long for the Northwest again. It wasn't much fun being in a state where you could be arrested at any time just for breathing.

22

'SHORT PAY–
SHORT SHOVEL'

Now that I had made up my mind to shake the dust of California off me, I couldn't get back to the Northwest fast enough. It had become more of a home to me than anywhere. And Molly was there. She was a gal I thought I might really get to like. Those few hours with her had been as close to bliss as anything I had known.

One hot summer day I rolled up my bindle, hoofed it down to the Fresno railyards, and caught a slow drag that jerked and bumped and rattled north toward Sacramento.

In Modesto several Wobblies got in my boxcar. President Harding had died a couple of days before, and a discussion arose as to how this might affect our hundreds of members in prison. Most seemed to feel that the new big honcho, Coolidge, was more apt to release them. There was talk of a new general strike in the Northwest in September to hurry the process along.

Then the discussion turned to the release from Leavenworth in June of Ralph Chaplin and several other prisoners from the big Chicago trial who had had their sentences commuted after signing a promise not to participate in any "illegal" activities. The deal had caused a huge uproar in the prison, an uproar that was still going on. James Rowan, leader of the lumber workers, along with the majority, had decided to stay in prison until a full pardon was granted, and felt bitterly toward Chaplin and the others who had "broken ranks." Chaplin was already engaged in a nationwide speaking campaign for the release of those still in prison, but many saw his defection as a breach of the purity of the Wobbly spirit. And for the next several months, I was to hear it argued over and over as to who was right in the Leavenworth commutation controversy.

As the train rattled north I got to talking with a tall carrot-topped bloke from the Midwest who was called Hoosier Red. We got into a long gabfest about our various experiences. He told me he was expecting to inherit a big wad of dough soon from some relative who had died back East. I dismissed it as so much bullshit, but he did seem like a nice guy and a dedicated Wobbly. He said he was going up into the Sierras east of Sacramento to work on a road construction gang for a while. It wasn't too far out of my way north and I needed the money, so I decided to go along with him.

By late next morning we were at the job site east of Sacramento. It was road-building out in the hot sun, but it paid fifty cents an hour so we took it. There were about forty of us working with picks and shovels, and there was a good sprinkling of Wobs in the bunch.

It was hard work but the grub and the bunks were okay, so I decided to stick with it a few days. Then the third day, the foreman came up to us after work and told us that because of some budgeting problem the pay was going to be cut to forty cents an hour.

When the foreman left we all sat around grumbling. Most of the men talked like they were going to quit and take off. A few wanted to strike. Red and I felt in an even meaner mood. "We ought to teach the lying slobs a lesson," Red said to the others. Then, "I've got it!" he said, jumping up like a rattler had bit him. "If they want to give us short pay, we'll give them short shovel. We'll cut off half our shovel handles and work half as fast and see how they like it!"

The suggestion brought a few guffaws. I jumped up and clapped my hands. "You're a bloody genius, Hoosier," I said. "I wish *I* had thought of the idea."

Of course the Wobblies in the group thought it would be great fun. We finally got the others to see the humor in it. As soon as it got dark some of us sneaked out to the tool shed, got a saw and cut about two feet off the handle of each of the forty or fifty shovels. Somebody else got a big board and made a crude sign that said: SHORT PAY—SHORT SHOVEL.

Next day we were on the job five or ten minutes before the foreman showed up. I never before or since saw such a look of surprise and consternation on a man's face—unless it was that of the farmer whose saplings we'd planted upside down. He just stood there for about two minutes looking flabbergasted.

"I thought I'd seen it all," he finally spluttered. "But you sons of bitches take the cake. Now clear out before I call the sheriff and have you all thrown in jail for destroying company property." And he strutted off.

We went back to the bunkhouse to get our gear. But we knew we had all been doing good work and that it would take them a while to get a new crew out from Sacramento.

Sure enough, after about fifteen minutes the big boss came out to talk to us. "All right, boys, you've had your fun and made your point," he said. "It's back to fifty cents. I'll have some new shovels sent out in a couple of hours."

We were jubilant. I heard later that the same stunt was pulled somewhere back East, and I've often wondered if someone from our crew instigated it.

After about a week Hoosier got a mysterious letter from Sacramento notifying him to pick up an important letter there. He cashed in, so I decided to quit too.

We got into Sacto late that afternoon. All the way into town Red had been mysterious about the letter. They had it for him at Wobbly headquarters. It was his inheritance. He showed me the check—$2,800. Boy are we going to eat tonight! I thought. And then, right before my eyes, before two minutes had passed, he stooped over and signed the entire check over to the General Defense Fund for IWW class war prisoners. I couldn't believe it. And that evening we went out and battered on the drag for our dinner.

But that's what real Wobblies were like. And a few, like Amos Orr, held up banks and sent the entire amount of their take to the *Industrial Worker*.

23

FLYING HIGH

It was already the end of August. I was anxious to see Molly, and I wanted to help out if there was going to be another general strike, so I didn't waste any time lollygagging along the way. I had fairly good luck on the freights and two days later I was boiling up beside the tracks in a Hotel de Hobo a few miles out of Seattle, getting ready for my grand entrance into the city.

I was trembling with eagerness and uncertainty as I approached the little greasy spoon near the skid road. It was about four in the afternoon of a lovely late summer day. Along the way I'd bought a little bouquet at a florist's stand and I felt a little foolish carrying it past the stiffs in their working duds. At last I was there and I stood just outside the entrance for a moment. I took a deep breath. Then I got a grip on myself and plunged on in.

I went to the back of the counter near the coffee urn. Ann was standing there stacking some plates. I sat down opposite her, holding the bouquet in my lap under the edge of the counter. "How about some java, fellow worker," I said.

"Oh Joe!" she said. Her eyes lit up, then looked a little sad. She brought the coffee. Her expression told it all.

"I'm sorry, Joe," she said. She patted my hand on the counter. "Molly took up with a logger and they moved to Spokane. I'm sorry, Joe."

I felt like something broke inside me. I didn't say anything for a minute. I fidgeted with my coffee cup. "What the hell," I said finally. "I had only one date with her. I couldn't expect her to wait for a bum like me. She was too old for me anyway."

"You're no bum, Joe," Ann said. "Hey—there's a dance at the Wobbly hall in a couple of days. Why don't you come?"

"You're a damn nice gal, Ann," I said. "Maybe I will."

I let the bouquet fall to the floor under the counter. I finished my coffee and left. I just wanted to walk, to get away from the city fast. I walked way up north along the shoreline toward Edmonds, hardly seeing anything, almost being hit a couple of times by speeding cars. To hell with the migrant life! I heard a voice in my brain say hundreds and hundreds of times.

A little before dark I came to a wide expanse of sand where a steep forested hillside dropped abruptly toward the water at Wind and Tide. I sat down and just thought and thought for several hours, staring out at the flat water of the Sound. I hit my fist several times against my forehead. What was wrong with me? I asked myself. Where was I going? Didn't I have brains enough to figure out what I wanted to do with my life? I wanted to fight the plutes and try to help bring about a better world. And yet: to hell with the goddamned fucking migrant life! I thought again.

It began to get cold. The lights of a few boats moved slowly far out over the water. Suddenly I remembered what several older Wobblies had advised me: Be an official, prepare yourself for some responsibility. That was it, I thought suddenly: If I could be a stationary delegate or get elected as a branch secretary somewhere I could stay put and carry on more of a normal life, maybe even have a steady girlfriend, maybe even get married.

Then I remembered the IWW's Work People's College in Duluth, Minnesota I had often heard about. Just a few hours ago, boiling up in the Wobbly jungle south of Seattle, I had seen an ad in the *Industrial Worker* for month-long courses they were offering: thirty dollars for board and room and a month's full-time intensive schooling. That was it—to hell with the migrant life. I had about fifty-five dollars on me. I would help for a few days with the upcoming general strike, then head for Duluth in time for the October semester. Thank you, Molly, for making me do some hard thinking.

Next day the Wobbly hall in Seattle was bustling with preparations for the new general strike to demand the release of our remaining class war prisoners. It was due to begin in a couple of days, on September 6th. The reasoning was simple: If our previous protest strikes had goaded president Harding into offering conditional commutation, another big strike might scare Coolidge into releasing the rest of our people.

I shot the bull for a while with dozens of high-spirited fellow Wobs I had met all over the West. At one point the secretary announced that one method the IWW planned to use to call the slaves out was dropping leaflets all over the timber country from an airplane. They needed someone to go along with the pilot to toss out the strike bulletins.

My brain was working again. "Hey," I said. "That was done just a few months ago in L.A. I hear it was damned effective."

"Well?"

"Well, hell. Sure, I'll do it." I had often wanted to go up in a plane. Now was my chance. It sounded like a great way to get my mind off Molly.

Next day at four AM I rode in an old Model T out to the airport with the pilot and two other Wobblies. We were loaded down with tens of thousands of leaflets fresh off the IWW presses. We pulled up beside the plane, an old dusting plane with a big rectangular compartment in front of the pilot's cockpit that was ordinarily used to hold insecticides. I climbed up on the wing and tossed the first bundle of leaflets into the yawning compartment. Jesus! Was I supposed to ride in *that*? There was no seat, no handles, nothing—only the bare slippery sides of the compartment to hang on to. I felt my resolve evaporating.

I climbed down for another bundle and turned to the pilot. "No safety belt, huh?" I heard myself croak.

"Nope. But you'll be okay, Joe. I'm not planning on doing any loops or barrel rolls until the stiffs in stir are released."

We finished loading and I jumped in among the hundreds of bundles. Someone spun the prop and we began to taxi down the runway. The wind rushed against my face. I bent down below the level of the fuselage, holding on for dear life. Jesus—what had I let myself in for?

Then we began to rush down the runway through the breaking dawn and the plane lifted off. It was an indescribable feeling, both thrilling and frightening. I finally got up the courage to lift my head into the rushing wind and peer over the fuselage. I saw the goggled pilot grin at me and yell something, but I couldn't hear a word he said. Then he rolled the old plane from side to side at what seemed about a forty-five degree angle, hurtling me against the bundles of leaflets, and I vowed to kill the clown if I ever got back to earth alive. I looked back again and the maniac was grinning. Then he gave a clenched fist salute.

I finally regained my composure and peered out again. Now that I was a little more relaxed I began to feel the thrill of it. We were going south at maybe five hundred feet up and I could see the shimmering surface of Puget Sound spread out to the west and south. Now, suddenly, it was the greatest experience of my life. Why would any dunderhead even remotely consider any other occupation when he could do this for a living?

Suddenly I heard the pilot thumping on the fuselage behind me. I looked back and he pointed down. I nodded. I bent and began to undo the wrapping of the first bundle.

We swooped low over a forest-enclosed lumber camp. I could see upturned faces of men on a logging road rush toward me. I sent the bundle of leaflets plummeting to earth and it exploded like a thousand white doves and then like a thousand miniature parachutes fluttering to earth. I turned and saw arms waving and running figures scrambling after the white flyers, hundreds of them caught now like Christmas ornaments in the branches of the trees. I saw three or four jacks raise their arms in salute.

We went from camp to camp, all down along the Sound and over Olympia with its capitol dome and then out toward Grays Harbor to the west. And every time we circled back over a camp dozens of arms raised to us in salute. Around mid-morning we refueled and started out again. Now I couldn't get enough of it. And then we covered the area all around Portland far to the south and all the way out to the sea at Astoria.

Next night, back in the Wobbly hall in Seattle, we began to get reports that the men were streaming out by the thousands. The IWW air force was a resounding success. The strike lasted for just a few days. But again we struck the fear of revolution into the capitalist class, and it was certain that Coolidge was made aware of our power.

24

HELEN KELLER: 'WHY I BECAME AN IWW'

I was off to Work People's College. I debated going east by way of Missouri so I could see my mom and dad and brothers and sisters, but I decided I had better not take a chance on being too late to enroll.

I rode Jim Hill's goat east to North Dakota, then rode blind baggage on an express all the way into Duluth. How many times I had crisscrossed this prairie, following the harvest. But now I had a new sense of purpose, a new life plan.

One cold morning, with the wind cutting like a scythe off Lake Superior, I pulled into Duluth. I took a streetcar out to the college, which had been started by Finnish Wobblies. There were about a hundred students there, around a third of them women. I signed up for courses in English, economics, sociology, labor history and public speaking. The professors were excellent, some of them run out of the best universities in America because of their democratic views. I plunged into my studies with a vengeance. And at the end of the grueling month of study I knew I was a thousand percent better prepared than before to take on the master class.

One of my fellow students, a young Finn named Niko, was planning to attend the IWW convention scheduled to begin on November 12th in Chicago and he urged me to come along. I had long wanted to visit IWW headquarters and the great city of Chicago so I decided to tag along. I had only a few dollars in my jeans but I figured maybe I could get some job for a few days to tide me over. If I was really going to make a career of the IWW I should meet some of the top officials. And a battle seemed to be shaping up between the centralists and decentralists at the convention, and I wanted to inform myself as well as possible on this crucial issue.

It was getting damn chilly in early November. Niko and I bought some long johns and canned heat and headed for the railyards. We damn near froze our asses off riding with some other 'bos in a boxcar, but next day we were sliding into the great Blue Island yards in Chicago. America's heartland. The proletarian capital of the world. I was actually in the city where it had all started, where Bill Haywood had picked up that piece of lumber in 1905 and called the first IWW convention to order. Where the Saint had led the organization for six history-making years. Where the Haymarket martyrs had struggled to the death. Where International Labor Day had begun.

After grabbing some grub in a railyard cafe we plunged into the great city. Even more than San Francisco or Seattle it had a vitality to it that stirred me. Thousands of people rushed to and fro through the blustery wind off Lake Michigan. Huge factories belched smoke, and shabby freezing men huddled in doorways or begged in the street.

We came to the big Wobbly hall on West Madison. I was here at last! As I had expected, it was a hub of activity, with preparations for the upcoming convention underway. Several dozen members and officials were at work in the various rooms, while a hundred or so more, many of them migrants with their packs or bindles, sat or lounged around the big meeting hall. IWW posters, photographs and stickers were everywhere.

Over java, Niko and I met a friendly fellow worker named Bill Chance who offered to take us on a tour of the building. I felt galvanized by some mystic force as we stood before an extremely realistic life-size painting of Joe Hill, then walked by Bill Haywood's desk. Chance, it developed, had been janitor at the hall for years, under both Haywood and St. John. I finally got up the courage to ask him the inevitable question: "Of all the Wobs you've known, who impressed you the most, fellow worker?"

He thought for a moment. "Well, Bill Haywood was no piker," he said. "But the Saint was extra special. When you met him you felt like he was a friend you'd known all your life." God how I hoped to meet him someday—if he ever got out of Leavenworth.

Then Chance introduced us to some of the top officials, Arthur Boose from Portland and a few others. I was mightily impressed by what friendly down-to-earth people they were, like anyone you would meet in a hobo jungle or along the skid road. And yet they were all stunningly sharp and alert in their off-the-cuff way. And I remembered how Emma Goldman's lover, Dr. Ben Reitman, on first visiting the Wobbly hall a few years before, expressed surprise that such a congregation of yokels and cracker barrel philosophers could strike such terror into the master class.

Bedding down in the IWW hall that night with several dozen other migrants, I began to pick up hints of divisiveness, mutterings of discontent. Circulating and gabbing among our fellow workers, I became aware of undertones of suspicion between the homeguards and the migrants. Some of the locals thought the migrants were abusing their right to stay in the hall, were sometimes too rowdy and not concerned enough with cleanliness. They also feared the farmworker cats and their leaders were trying to lead the IWW around by the nose. It was a complex situation and nobody was entirely in the right. I could see a massive struggle escalating between the pro-centralist farmworkers union and the decentralists of the lumber workers union.

Next day, not wanting to be a burden on the hall facilities, Niko and I were directed to a famous boardinghouse for hobos and sisters of the road run by a woman called "Red Martha" Biegler. She was a short fat woman with graying reddish hair. She welcomed us into her place with friendly gusto. The rooms were small but clean and comfortable and I got a good night's sleep.

Next day, my money running low, I was able to get a part-time job washing dishes at a greasy spoon down by the lake, and I breathed a sigh of relief. Like all real Wobblies, I liked to pay my own way whenever possible. I celebrated my birthday on November 7th by taking in a boxing match at a local gym. I was eighteen—a real man!

One day at the Wobbly hall Niko and I learned that Helen Keller was visiting Chicago. I remembered reading her brilliant essays on the IWW at the hall in Seattle. I found some free copies of them in the hall and stuck them in my pocket. Later I learned

Helen Keller "listening" to a radio by feeling its vibrations.

that the brilliant blind and deaf woman, the most famous person ever to become a Wobbly, was going to make a public appearance at a reception in a private home on the North Side. A minor official at the hall who had met her agreed to escort us to the affair. I blew some of my precious money on a secondhand tweed suit and we set out.

Several dozen people crowded into the huge parlor. And there she was, seated on a sofa, the most beatific look imaginable on her handsome middle-aged face. "It's a great honor," was all I could think of to say when I was introduced.

Being told there were some Wobblies present, Helen, to everyone's surprise, decided to recite from a long statement she had made a few years earlier entitled "Why I Became an IWW."* I had a copy in my pocket and took it out to follow along. An assistant repeated each sentence after she spoke it. Her speech was somewhat muddled, but I could understand most of the words without the help of her assistant or the printed copy. And to my amazement, Helen Keller spoke every single word from memory exactly as she had spoken them years before, without a single pause or mistake.

"I was religious to start with," she began, and her face seemed to glow as she spoke. "...Then I was appointed on a commission to investigate the conditions among the blind. For the first time I, who had thought blindness a misfortune beyond human control, found that too much of it was traceable to wrong industrial conditions, often caused by the selfishness and greed of employers. And the social evil contributed its share. I found that poverty drove women to the life of shame that ended in blindness...

"And now I am in the fight to change things. I may be a dreamer, but dreamers are necessary to make facts... Real happiness must come from within, from a fixed purpose and faith in one's fellow men...

"It is my nature to fight as soon as I see wrongs to be made right... I made up my mind to do something. And the best thing seemed to join a fighting party and help their propaganda... I became an IWW because I found out that the Socialist Party was too slow. It is sinking in the political bog...

"The true task is to unite and organize all workers on an economic basis, and it is the workers themselves who must secure freedom for themselves, who must grow strong. Nothing can be gained by political action. That is why I became an IWW... I discovered that the true idea of the IWW is not only to better conditions, to get them for all people, but to get them at once... We can't have education without revolution. We have tried peace

---

*Helen Keller joined the IWW in 1912 during the Wobbly textile strike in Lawrence, Massachusetts. She was introduced to IWW ideas in part by IWW member John Macy, the husband of her teacher and companion Anne Sullivan. See *Helen Keller: Her Socialist Years*, a collection of Keller's essays and speeches edited by Philip S. Foner (International Publishers, New York, 1967).

education for 1,900 years and it has failed. Let us try revolution and see what it will do now... I don't give a damn about semi-radicals!"

I was stunned by her brilliant performance—being there that night was perhaps the high point of my entire life.

The day of the convention came. All kinds of fascinating new Wobblies poured in to the hall. There were only twenty-six official delegates, but hundreds of others came and went over the next days as spectators or passionately interested rooters for the various factions and industrial unions.

The convention was carried on in a businesslike manner, with a recording secretary taking down everything and the delegates politely observing the rules of order. A few stirring Wobbly songs were sung, and letters of greeting read from all over the world. Emma Goldman sent a statement she called "Our Defiant Stand" attacking what she claimed to be an anti-worker dictatorship in the Soviet Union. Reports came in of dozens of new IWW branches all over the globe, and of the sharply increased membership in the United States.

Then the wrangling began. Semi-dormant hostilities between different factions and unions began to arise. I began to see some of those homey "cracker barrel philosophers" at their fiery thunderous best. The big hall rang with their colorful and stinging epithets, most uttered with good-natured sarcasm but gradually escalating to deadly earnestness. A number of bitter barbs were directed at one or another faction in the Leavenworth commutation fight.

There was a spirited discussion of strike tactics. There was the ongoing conflict between organizing homeguards versus migrants. But the chief and most bitter bone of contention was over how much autonomy the various industrial unions should have. The farmworkers union was for more centralization, while the lumber workers union and some others favored more autonomy. I leaned toward the latter view.

The wrangling went on for days. I attended the long sessions whenever my job did not prevent it. In the meantime snow flurries hit Chicago, converting it into a glistening icy wonder-land—except for those poor folks without a home who had to freeze in it.

It was getting along toward Thanksgiving. If I expected to get back to the Northwest without freezing to death I decided I had better be on my way. One cold gray day I said goodbye to my dozens of new friends and headed for the railyards.

Later I was to read of some of the main upshots of the convention. The administration had been completely reorganized. The convention voted to allow a sliding scale of initiation fees of one to five dollars and dues of fifty cents to a dollar. And a resolution was put out to referendum allowing the various industrial unions more autonomy in their organizing practices.

I rode the freezing freights west. But I had a new source of warmth and confidence within me: I had been to Work People's College and now was much better prepared to wage the class struggle. I had been to the pulsing heart of our great organization and seen the intricate mechanism at work. More than ever before I was part of the IWW's inmost heart.

25

'JESUS OF THE LUMBER WORKERS'

I got in to Spokane one bitter cold day in early December and rustled a job in a lumber camp. I was amazed at the improvements since the IWW had launched its last series of strikes. I figured I would work there just a few days and then head on west to Seattle. There I could confer with some of my higher-up friends in the organization about getting a position as a stationary delegate.

Around the middle of December blaring headlines announced that president Coolidge was going to release the rest of the IWW prisoners from the big trial in 1918. There was wild jubilation wherever Wobs congregated. But we still had members buried alive. And when I quit my job around December 20th I decided to pay a Christmas visit to the Centralia victims in prison at Walla Walla before going on to Seattle.

After over four years behind bars the Wobbly martyrs looked a bit older but as game as ever. Elmer Smith had been to see them recently and they were guardedly optimistic after the release of our top leaders. I assured them I would keep up my own efforts for their release.

I got in to Seattle on New Year's Eve. There was to be a gala entertainment that night at the New Finnish Hall out at Thirteenth and Washington. I rented a room in a nearby skid–road hotel, got cleaned up and rode the streetcar out with a bunch of other Wobs. The large hall was jammed and everybody was having a good time. I made a special hit with some of the Finnish gals when I told them about being at Work People's College.

The high point of the evening was the presentation of a skit about the Everett massacre called "Kangaroo Court," by Walker C. Smith, Boxcar Bertha's father. The role of the "Persecutor" was played by the famous Dublin Dan Liston, whose long poem–song "The Portland Revolution" had played such an important role in that historic strike. Some of the scenes went:

> COURT CLERK: Hear ye! Hear ye! The Dishonorable Court of Snohomish County is now in secession. (To jury) Do you solemnly swear to hear no evidence in this case favorable to the accused and to render a verdict of Guilty? Before this Dishonorable Court comes now the case of the City of Everett, State of Degradation, plaintiff, versus A. Wise Wobbly, defendant...

> COURT CLERK (to prosecuting attorney): Do you solemnly swear to tell the truth, the whole truth, and nothing but the truth, so help you God?

> PROSECUTING ATTORNEY: Certainly not! Why, I'm the prosecuting attorney in this case!

> CLERK: My mistake. Of course you won't...

> PROSECUTOR: Mr. Wobbly, by the testimony of two unimpeachable witnesses I have proven that you were singing two different songs at the same time. What have you to say on this point?

> A. WISE WOBBLY: I was not singing at all, Mr. Prostituting Attorney, I was merely reciting the Declaration of Independence.

> PROSECUTOR: Nonsense! I don't believe you know the Declaration of Independence. How does it start?

> WOBBLY: 'The working class and the employing class have nothing in common. There can be no peace so long as hunger and want are found among the millions of working people, and the few who make up the employing class have all the good things of life. Between these two classes a struggle must go on until the workers of the world organize as a class, take possession of the earth and the machinery of production, and abolish the wage system. We find—'

PROSECUTOR: That's enough. You know it all right...

PROSECUTOR: Mr. Wobbly, what is your nationality?

WOBBLY: I.W.W.

PROSECUTOR: Then you are not a patriot? Wouldn't you fight for the country?

WOBBLY: Certainly not! I live in the city.

PROSECUTOR: I mean to ask whether you would fight for your native land.

WOBBLY: I don't own any land. The IWW is fighting all the landlords for all the land and all the employers for all the machinery of production. If you own any land I'll fight you for it!...

JUDGE: My instruction to the jury, gentlemen, is that you disregard all evidence favorable to the accused and remain faithful to your trust—the Lumber Trust...

(A messenger brings a telegram in; the prosecutor reads it.)

PROSECUTOR (in trembling voice): Judge, your honor, read this telegram!

JUDGE (reading telegram aloud): 'The IWW, strongly organized in the lumber camps and mills and allied industries, will inaugurate an immediate general strike in case a verdict of Guilty is rendered in the Everett trial.' (Turning to jury) As I was saying, gentlemen, it is your duty to bring in a verdict of—NOT GUILTY!

The standing-room-only crowd roared its approval. The next night there was a Wobbly dance at the same hall, and I had a good time afterward with one of the Finnish fellow workers who had also been to Work People's College.

Next day I sat around the Wobbly hall reading the papers and wondering what to do next. I finally got to talk to the busy hall secretary and told him of my hopes of leading a less nomadic life and perhaps becoming a stationary delegate somewhere. He checked his files and told me there were no openings for the position at present. Disappointed, I played the woods for a while, working in various camps near Seattle.

Along in the late spring the *Industrial Worker* got a new editor, Mortimer Downing. I had first met him with Walker C. Smith back in 1920. In his early sixties, Downing was one of the earliest Wobblies and a remarkable man. By profession a chemist and assayer, he had been one of the leaders of the famous "silent defenders" trial in Sacramento in 1918 when fifty-four top Wobblies, seeing how their co-defendants had been railroaded in the big Chicago trial, refused to say a single word in their own defense and accepted their long sentences in silence. A rich heiress who had joined the IWW through them got a lesser sentence. The unprecedented trial had had a tremendous propaganda effect. All fifty-four defendants had been imprisoned for sixty-three days during the trial in a twenty-by-twenty-foot cell, and five had died from sleeping on the cold cement floor.

I ran into Downing this second time while delivering a poem I had written to the *Industrial Worker* office. He remembered my boxing as "Kid Murphy" and had heard of some of my other exploits. He seemed to take an immediate liking to me and invited me out to dinner. A mutual "friend" hinted later that he liked to have me around because I was big and strong and handy with my fists and made a good bodyguard. But when the great editor began sharing his ideas with me, I knew he gave me credit for having some brainpower too.

Downing was completely devoted to democracy, freedom and equality in all aspects of life. He had been one of the first Wobblies to become aware of the growing dictatorship and bureaucracy in the Soviet Union, and he spoke and wrote his views openly and eloquently. He told me how after only three months in Russia, Bill Haywood had already become disillusioned with the despotic regime and offered to return to prison in the U.S. if the government would return the forfeited bail money. But the Harding administration had refused. Downing also told me he had positive proof that some Wobblies such as George Hardy and Harrison George, who had joined the Communists, were still in the IWW only to wreck it.

More than any major figure in the IWW, Downing stressed the importance of rank-and-file control. Not complete decentralization, but a balanced structure in which local IWW bodies had a strong voice in local and regional matters that concerned them. The present administration in Chicago led by Doyle and Fisher of the farmworkers, he contended, had been trying to run the organization in a heavy-handed manner. The lumber workers union, on the other hand—led again by James Rowan, recently released from Leavenworth—called for more autonomy for the separate industrial unions.

Downing also stressed the importance of putting more effort into organizing the homeguards. With the combine and the tin flivver fewer workers were becoming migrants. A stable enduring organization could be built only by organizing the more settled workers. A growing crisis was developing over these different ideas and tendencies in the IWW, he told me, and he was sorely troubled over how to settle these problems before they became insurmountable. I felt flattered that such a brilliant man would share his thoughts and feelings with me.

Sometimes on my days off Downing would ask me to run errands or to chauffeur my old friend Elmer Smith around the state on his speaking tours on behalf of the Centralia defendants. These were some of my happiest hours. I had never met a man as dedicated to a cause as Elmer Smith or a more decent human being. He spent the rest of his life campaigning for the release of the brave men whom he had told had the right to defend their hall. Yet he was not a fanatic, but an easygoing friendly down-to-earth fellow you would never guess from his manner was a lawyer.

Early in May a strike broke out at four sawmills in Raymond, south of Grays Harbor. Around five hundred workers, about ninety percent of the work force, including all of the women working in the box factories, had gone out in response to a wage cut from four dollars to three-forty a day. James Rowan, the head of the lumber workers union, was taking a personal hand in the strike.

Rowan had been born in Ireland. In my experience the old-country Irish usually did not make very good union men, but Rowan was an exception. He had been on the steamer *Verona* when the five Wobblies were killed as it pulled into Everett in 1916. He had led the massive lumber strike of 1917 which had won the eight-hour day, one if the IWW's two or three greatest victories. He had been one of the leaders of the Leavenworth prisoners who had refused to accept parole. And he had written a brilliant book on the Northwest lumber industry, advocating not only humanity toward the workers but also responsible forestry practices.

Due to a temporary shutdown at my mill, I was hanging around Seattle for a few days. On May 6th I went up to Mortimer Downing's office for a chat. As I went in the door I saw facing him a ruggedly handsome middle-aged man whose large intelligent eyes were so bright and alive they seemed almost to jump out of his head. And yet they had a quiet depth of compassion to them too. I could see why James Rowan was sometimes called "the Jesus of Nazareth of the Northwest lumber workers." When Mortimer Downing introduced us he leaped up and shook my hand with warm alacrity. "With *two* Irishmen in this fight I know we can win," he joked, slapping me on the back.

It seemed Rowan was on his way south to Centralia, and then to a speaking engagement at Montesano and on to the strike area at Raymond, and he needed a chauffeur and road companion. Mortimer Downing recommended me for the job.

Soon I was maneuvering Rowan's Ford south toward Olympia. The great man sat beside me regaling me with mountains of information about the towns and areas we passed through. At the same time he leafed through sheaves of reports he had to attend to. We got in to Centralia in the early afternoon. I felt queasy with fear and loathing at entering this outpost of Legionnaire violence, where I had seen Wesley Everest's mutilated body and heard his choked-out words: "You don't have the guts to lynch a man in broad daylight," and "Tell the boys I died for my class."

In Centralia a fellow worker named Brown and another named Simmons joined us. As a precaution we decided to go in two cars. Brown went ahead with Rowan while Simmons and I followed in his old Model T.

Rowan's speaking appearance on the streets of Montesano that night had been widely advertised. But when we got to the infamous site of the Centralia defendants' trial a city marshal informed us there was an ordinance against street speaking. They must have just passed it when they saw us coming, I mused. Then we went to the mayor and he told us the same thing. So we got permission from a private citizen to speak in a vacant lot he owned. But the bought politicians of the lumber trust would not allow that either. We were all fuming.

Finally, about dark, we threw up our hands and decided to drive on west to Aberdeen. Rowan and Brown went first. But when I cranked up the old Model T nothing happened. I tried again. Nothing. Simmons jumped down and looked under the hood. Some wires had been disconnected—sabotaging the so-called saboteurs! Perhaps they had thought it was Rowan's car. After three or four minutes Simmons got everything connected up. We roared off.

As we got out west of town we saw a disturbing sight: Ahead in the darkness of the narrow road there was not just one car but the lights of seven or eight. As we drew nearer the cars ahead went faster, seeming to veer crazily from side to side. "What in hell is going on?" I wondered aloud.

Simmons poured on the gas and as we drew near the last car his brow flushed sweaty. Several car lengths ahead a big touring car was trying to run what must have been Rowan's car off the road.

Our first instinct was to try to pass the other cars and go to Rowan's aid. But then we noticed that rifles were protruding from the windows of a couple of the cars ahead and we decided to keep following along behind—no doubt those in the car just ahead thought we were part of the mob.

Far ahead, the two racing cars swerved back and forth toward one another. Then we suddenly saw Rowan's car swerve off the road and shoot into what looked like the front yard of a farm-house. A slender figure that must have been Brown leaped out of the car and rushed up to the door of the house.

The other cars shot into the farmyard, surrounding Rowan's car. Dozens of dark figures jumped out, rushing up to the vehicle. He's dead, I thought with an empty feeling in my stomach.

Simmons slowed and switched off his headlights. How I wished I still had the .38 I had used in the flying squadron.

"Look," I said, "why don't you pull up in the shadows back under those trees? Turn this buggy around and be ready for a quick escape. I'll sneak up there and see what's going on."

We pulled off the road about seventy yards short of the farmhouse. I picked up a couple of big rocks and began to creep through the shadows a ways back from the road. I could hear the mob up ahead yelling and cursing, rocking Rowan's car back and forth. When I stopped behind a hayrick about thirty yards away I could make out some of what they were yelling.

"Where's that literature?" demanded one of the hoodlums.

"Where's that black page of American history?" another screamed.

There were twenty-five or thirty of them. I could see now that they were for the most part well dressed, probably businessmen.

Another man leaped up as if to drag the figure inside from the car. "We'll stop you s.o.b.s from spreading your lies around here," he yelled, "or you'll go out of here with the nicest coat of tar and feathers you ever heard of."

I could see Rowan now in the car. It looked as if he had his hand on a gun in his overcoat pocket. He seemed cool as a cucumber. When the shouting died for a moment I heard him tell his attackers with perfect calmness that he was not spreading lies but the truth.

Then a gray-haired guy of about fifty with a stubby mustache who seemed to be the leader of the mob stepped up and said, "You're not spreading the truth, but a pack of damned lies. I sat in the courtroom and listened to the evidence in that case, and if I'd had my way those s.o.b.s would never have gone to jail at all—we would have taken 'em out and strung 'em up."

There were more threats and wild gestures, and then several of the mob started yelling, "Lynch 'em! Lynch 'em!"

Rowan moved his hand in his overcoat pocket.

Then I saw sheriff Foss, whom we had seen back in Montesano, step through the mob. He took out his gun and stuck it in Rowan's ribs. I expected shots to ring out at any moment.

But just then the front door of the farmhouse opened, throwing a long shaft of light over the mob. I saw Brown and the farmer and his wife standing in the doorway. The fury of the mob suddenly subsided. Brown began to walk slowly down from the farmhouse, while the farmer and his wife remained silhouetted in the light of the open doorway.

"I'm placing you under arrest for carrying a concealed weapon," I heard the sheriff say to Rowan.

Apparently Rowan considered it unwise to protest under the circumstances. I saw him hand his gun to Foss.

The crowd had quieted now. The men parted as Brown came up to the sheriff. Seeing things were apparently under control I tried to swallow my fear and slowly sauntered up to see if I could be of any help. When they found out who I was some of the men gave me dirty looks but didn't bother me. As Foss put the handcuffs on Rowan, Rowan winked at me. He still seemed the calmest person present. I heard Brown tell him in a low voice he would go in search of legal help. I told the two of them that Simmons and I would go back to the jail with Rowan to see if we could help out. But Rowan, apparently fearing for our safety, insisted we go with Brown instead.

When we saw that Rowan was out of the hands of the mob and in the sheriff's car, Brown and I got in the Ford. After the other cars had headed back to Montesano, we coasted down the road to where Simmons was parked. We filled Simmons in on what had occurred. "Well, maybe they're satisfied for a while," I said. "They had a good show—some great entertainment for adult infants."

The three of us had a conference. We decided it was too dangerous to spend the night in Montesano. And Brown said he knew of a pretty good shyster in Aberdeen who had defended a few Wobs. So, leaving the lights of the two cars off for a while, we drove slowly on west toward Aberdeen.

We found a flop in the home of a friend of Brown's and reported the news to the local Wobblies. Next morning, while Brown went in search of the lawyer, Simmons and I drove back to Montesano to see what we could do.

Rowan was brought out to see us. He seemed in good spirits and gave us a big grin. He told us he had spent the night in the same tank the Centralia defendants had been in. "The dungeon walls still bear witness that it was once inhabited by the pioneers of the coming civilization," he joked. I took it he referred to IWW slogans etched with loving care.

The sheriff came in. Foss was extremely conciliatory now. He didn't have his mob with him. They were planning to take Rowan to court that morning.

"Sorry about last night," the sheriff joked. "I think the boys had a little too much dehorn. I think the judge will let you off with a nominal fine. Just to show you there's no hard feelings, if it's over five bucks I'll pay the rest out of my own pocket."

Rowan suddenly got serious. "Fine hell," he snapped. "I know the laws in this state. It's not against any law to carry a gun in a car. There were plenty of guns in the cars of that mob of hood-lums—why didn't you arrest them?"

The sheriff shrugged.

"Cat got your tongue, eh? Well, I'm demanding a trial and I'm demanding it not be held until I can get my lawyer, Elmer Smith, out here. Ever hear of 'im?"

The sheriff nodded a bit grimly. He excused himself and went into another room for a few minutes. When he came back, "Sorry Rowan," he said. "But the powers that be say you go to court today."

The court proceedings began a couple of hours later. The judge seemed to know he had a hot Irish potato in the person of Rowan and seemed anxious to hurry and get things over with. Rowan was urged to pay a small fine so the officials could save face.

At the last moment, just as the judge was about to pronounce sentence, Brown arrived from Aberdeen with the lawyer. The shyster managed to convince the judge that a man had a right to carry a gun while traveling in a car. He dismissed the case and Rowan's gun was returned to him. We all gave a sigh of relief. I could see that Rowan wasn't a man to fool with.

A few days after the Montesano episode I went to hear Rowan speak to a crowd of several thousand at Renton Junction. He didn't have quite the force or charisma of a Haywood or Debs, but still he held the cheering crowd spellbound. His chief message was that the corporations were even stronger than the government now in America, were utterly ruthless in their methods, and that a countervailing force was needed—the democratic power of the workers.

26

THE GLORY HOLE

In July the call to duty came again. The huge Stone and Webster Corporation was building a gigantic hydroelectric plant and dam and tunnel system near the small Cascades town of Concrete around a hundred miles north of Seattle, to furnish more water and electricity to that metropolis. It was the largest power project ever undertaken in the area, and thousands of men would be employed. Experienced organizers were needed immediately to line up the slaves in the One Big Union of the IWW.

I packed my gear and headed north with two other Wobblies who had a tin lizzie. It always felt like the sheerest luxury to ride in an automobile instead of my accustomed mode of travel on a dirty gut-shaking freight train. I had loaded up on new supplies and now I was a delegate in the General Construction Workers Union.

We chugged north a few miles in from the Sound and turned east at Sedro Woolley. Far to the north, near the Canadian border, was the snow-clad peak of Mount Baker, with other lesser peaks in the distance. As we climbed higher into the Cascades the forest-covered slopes took on an ethereal beauty.

Bumping along higher and higher beside a rushing river, we finally came to the first part of the construction site near Concrete. In process was the construction of a 480-foot dam, all in solid granite, which would create a lake twenty-three miles long. Part of the project involved blasting out miles-long pressure tunnels to carry the water. Much of the work would have to be done in narrow rock canyons with nearly perpendicular sides. It was a construction and engineering feat of the first magnitude.

Concrete was a pleasant little town of around fifteen hundred people, wedged in among high mountains. It had an air of boom and bustle about it. We found the Stone and Webster hiring office and got hired on in short order as muckers—shovel men who clear away the debris the miners blast loose with dynamite. The pay was under four dollars a day.

Conditions were atrocious. In the crummy bunkhouse we were handed blankets that hadn't been washed in months. The food was unfit for human or animal consumption. Already several dozen new members had been lined up because of the lousy pay and terrible conditions.

Next day my two buddies and I were put to work drilling one of the tunnels into solid granite. It was hard sweaty work. First the miners would go in and drill their holes, put in their sticks of dynamite and blow holy hell out of the rock. Then it was our job to go in and clean up the mess they had made. But the worst part was that the foremen would order us into that potential death trap before the gas from the explosions had completely dispersed. It gave many of us headaches and did who knows what other damage to our inner workings. But all our complaints were to no avail. Something had to be done, and soon.

The few dozen Wobblies on the job had a general membership meeting on July 31st. A propaganda committee of seven members was elected. I was one of them. Our job was to send news to the IWW press, circulate IWW literature and periodicals, and arrange a series of meetings on Sunday nights featuring experienced IWW speakers talking on organization.

A few days later, on August 3rd, we had our first public meeting, in a vacant lot. A fellow worker named Henry Clark gave a rousing two-hour palaver that kept the attention of the two or three hundred workers riveted. He knew his biscuits and he went into all the whys, hows, wherefores and pitfalls of organizing the job. I and some others passed out the mental dynamite—IWW literature. A lot of it was aimed at reaching the home guard, as quite a few of the workers were local stiffs. We had a rare advantage in that the local newspaper was pro-worker. A group of local "rebel girls" enlivened the affair singing IWW songs. Later

we gave out literature from house to house. Within a couple of days we had almost doubled IWW membership. Seeing our growing strength, the bosses eased off a little at ordering us into the gas–filled tunnels.

Meanwhile, disturbing news began to reach us from Chicago. James Rowan had gone back to Chicago to take up his duties on the General Executive Board. Rowan, as chief exponent of the decentralist faction, had come quickly into conflict with general secretary–treasurer Tom Doyle, general organizer Joe Fisher, and those members of the executive board who supported their more centralist approach. Three of the executive board supported Rowan. They asked that the board be called into session to discuss the conflict between the two factions and other serious problems facing the IWW. The centralists, apparently fearing disruption, refused. Frustrated, Rowan and his three supporters decided to declare the board in session, even though they didn't have an official quorum.

Hostilities increased. A few days later Rowan and his group went to court and tied up the funds of the organization. They continued meeting at IWW headquarters. On July 31st Doyle and Fisher and twenty or thirty others ejected them from the head-quarters building. Later a fistfight broke out between six or eight of the members outside the building; Rowan was slugged and put out of action. Now all kinds of vindictive and disturbing accounts were coming through the mails from both sides, the Rowan faction claiming they had been ejected at gunpoint, the Doyle-Fisher faction denying it. The whole IWW was in a state of shock, uproar and depression over the whole affair.

I sank my head in my hands, sitting on my bunk, when I first heard of the debacle. Jesus! Were these the great men I had been idolizing? Why had they refused to call a board meeting? Why had Rowan, whom I had thought so brilliant, called one unconstitutionally? But most baffling and agonizing of all, why had he gone to the capitalist courts, the IWW's traditional enemies, to tie up our funds? And why had Doyle and Fisher, if the accounts were true, risked a scandal in the plute press by forcibly evicting Rowan and his followers? It sounded like they all were crazy.

The whole brouhaha was obviously much more complex than we could decipher from a few hasty accusations. We all sat around discussing it glumly for the next several days, waiting for more information. It all upset me so much I began feeling sick at my stomach, and one night I woke up in a cold sweat after a night-mare. To make matters even more confusing, both sides soon called for separate IWW conventions to convene in Chicago early in October. It looked like a godawful mess. But we gritted our teeth and continued with our organization work.

But the malaise that had afflicted my beloved IWW would not go away. Mortimer Downing wrote a somber worried editorial in the *Industrial Worker* warning of the need to guard against any disruptive tendencies in the organization. And on August 16th he printed a purported letter from Harrison George, the prominent IWW who had also become a Communist, advising other Communist members how to disrupt the IWW and use it for their own purposes.

In the same issue appeared one of those rare gems that made the IWW paper unique, an eloquent appeal for solidarity:

JEALOUSY

If intelligence antagonizes ignorance then, verily, ignorance antagonizes intelligence. To prevent frictions in any group requires the utmost caution of its members... It behooves every sincere worker to look at the facts as they really are. Who amongst us has not at some time felt a keen sense of inferiority in the presence of a superior intellect? Instinctively the human passion is aroused and nothing short of pure reason can prevent us from showing our antagonism. On the other hand, for individuals to parade their superiority before others invariably breeds jealousy, and jealousy ultimately spells ruin.

Fellow workers, to maintain a spirit of solidarity in any group requires the utmost tolerance for each other's views. Let us beware of this pitfall which organized labor has through all ages fallen into... Let us guard against this human impulse...and prove to the world that our idea of a labor organization is something different, something new, something big.

Along in early October we were switched from tunnel work to work in the "glory hole"—the deep pit carved out of solid rock which would hold the foundation of the dam. It was backbreaking work. But the worst part was that there was a defective flume high overhead in the steep-walled canyon that kept jamming and dumping rocks and cement onto the heads of us workers far below. Repeated complaints had been made, but the bosses refused to do anything about it. Who cared if there were a few more broken heads or a few more graves for the workers?

That was too much. On October 17th, after several men had been hit by falling rocks, we decided to pull the pin. We presented management with our list of demands:

Release of all class war prisoners
Overhead flumes to be made safe
25 percent wage increase
Clean sheets once a week
Better food
No overtime
A boycott of California products

Our demands were contemptuously rejected by the company puppets. Twenty-five of us walked out. We were soon joined by fifteen more who had been ordered to take our places. Soon over seven hundred were out, leaving only a handful of scabs. Even many of the engineers rallied to our cause. Work ground to a halt. We had done our organizational work well.

It was a beautifully run strike. There was absolutely no violence. We strike organizers and speakers always stressed that. Even the editor of the local paper commended us, although some of the big city papers printed the usual lies about violence and sabotage. We set up large orderly picket lines and not a scab crossed them. The company set up a hiring hall in Seattle and didn't bother to tell the new hires about the strike. When the first bus-load arrived in Concrete there was a solid wall of Wobblies across the main street blocking its progress. A committee of ours easily persuaded the scabs on the bus to return to Seattle.

In the meantime the two divergent conventions had begun in Chicago. Each report of what was going on was more confusing than the last. One day as I was finishing up my stint of picketing a distraught Mortimer Downing came up to me—he had just driven up from Seattle. We went to a greasy spoon on the main drag of Concrete. I had never seen him look so worried.

"My whole world's falling apart, fellow worker," he told me over coffee. "You've got to help me—to help all of us. Suddenly I feel I can't trust anyone anymore."

It seemed he was almost as much in the dark about what was going on in Chicago as everyone else. He was tired of printing Pollyanna wishful thinking in the paper. He wanted the truth. He wanted to send me to Chicago to find out what was really going on and report back to him personally.

I felt honored that he would trust me with such an important assignment. I wanted to learn the truth as much as he did—and perhaps be able to help ease the situation.

He took out his wallet and handed me a sheaf of bills. "Oh no," I said. "I couldn't take any money from the organization. I've got a few bucks saved, and I could teach a college course in hopping freights."

"Damn it Joe, this is *my* money," he said, "and I've got deadlines to meet. I want that information *fast*. I don't want you stranded on some siding in Nowhere, North Dakota."

Somebody opened the door of the cafe at that moment and a gust of freezing air blew in. That convinced me.

In a few hours I was on an express riding the cushions to Chicago.

27

IT WAS MY CAMELOT

As the train roared east through a strange darkness whitened by snow flurries, I lay my head back in the dimly lighted car and had long long thoughts. Of one thing I was certain: If the IWW fell apart I would be lost, devastated. It was my Camelot, my reason for being.

Could all that power and drama and struggle and human sacrifice and gains for the workers come to nothing? Joe Hill and Wesley Everest and Frank Little and the Everett martyrs being shot full of holes led to this? What of the thousands of women who stood in the snow at Lawrence and sang "Bread and Roses"? All the Saint's brilliant efforts? Gurley Flynn chaining herself to the lamppost? The Centralia victims' years in prison? Hoosier Red giving his entire inheritance to the cause? And all my own hard-fought efforts?

And yet as we swept through the Idaho pines I felt a surging power in myself, a sense of delicious destiny. And, half-asleep in the rocking traincar: How ambiguous the human mind is, I thought, how full of ambivalence. For all my worry, my sense of horror and impending doom, underlying everything I felt a sharp thrill of exhilaration and self-importance at being sent on such a vital mission, at sitting here in comfort, at being a kind of "big shot."

And I felt the undeniable thrill of travel, for whatever reason, the sense of compacted drama at shooting by the little lost towns in the night, the feeling of importance and purpose that always comes with going somewhere. Travel—I had spent so much of my life in travel. I had read somewhere that the only life and reality were in movement—movement of people through space, movement of the particles of the brain. By that definition I must be one of the most real and alive people who had ever lived, I thought. This was *life*. It was real. It was the sort of vivid life I had always hungered for. History was in the balance. Perhaps the whole history of the world.

As the train swept along, I thought of other trains and other trips, of Lincoln writing the Gettysburg Address on his way to that civil war battleground, and of the train that took his body to rest; of the special sealed train that took kidnapped Bill Haywood and two other miners' union leaders from Denver to Idaho to stand trial on trumped-up murder charges; of the railroad owners having all the locomotive whistles blown to drown out Eugene Debs when he spoke in the Terre Haute railyards, and of his "Red Special" he rode around in on his presidential campaign; of the armored train Ralph Chaplin had written about, sent out to attack the striking miners at Paint Creek, West Virginia; of the train that, in 1917, had dumped twelve hundred Wobbly strikers from Bisbee in the middle of the New Mexico desert, stranded and starving; and of my own many trips back and forth across the face of America, searching for work and a better life.

Toward dawn, sweeping into vast Montana, my mind slipping into sleep, I became overwhelmed again by the vital importance of my mission. I must think and act better in this crisis than I have ever thought and acted before, I knew, I must outdo myself. Dozing off as the first faint light appeared in the east, I tried to conjure up the spirits of Bill Haywood and the Saint. What would *they* do? My head tossing on the headrest, I pleaded with their spirits to send me some faintest message, some guideline to hope.

But they would not answer me. All I heard was the interminable clacking of the long train's wheels on the tracks, and I felt a dim gratitude that I was not freezing in a boxcar somewhere. Then I was asleep.

When I awoke we were near the Dakota border, plowing eastward past little lonely prairie towns. The vast expanse of America. I had passed through it so many times. The long rolling hills. The vast quiet prairie without sight of a single person or structure for mile upon mile. You would think there would be enough for everyone to have a piece of it and be able to lead a decent life. If the IWW was destroyed the chance might be gone forever.

The third day the long journey began drawing to a close. Reality would soon be getting more real, and I felt a little panicky and yet strangely excited that I must be prepared to meet it. The great city began to assemble itself in little bits and pieces, slowly congealing like a gigantic jigsaw puzzle into a coherent whole. I sat up and prepared to meet reality. Was it really less than a year ago I had been here, had sat at the feet of the great Helen Keller? It seemed so long ago, so much had happened in the interim. The train ground to a stop, and I grabbed my gear and made my way through the crowds in the station.

A cold wind blew through the long city canyons leading up from the lake. I felt the two letters in my pocket like small cleverly designed bombs that Mortimer Downing had given me—one for Rowan, one for Doyle and Fisher. Which to deliver first? I stood feeling helpless for a moment, standing outside the train depot. Perhaps something within me was stalling for fear of what I would find. Finally I asked directions of a passerby. Finding Rowan's headquarters closer, on North LaSalle, I decided to go there first.

Each step I took through the cold crowded streets sent a stab of pain into my feet. What would I find? It seemed I almost had to force myself to go the last half-block.

The minute I turned the corner I knew this was the place. Half a block ahead of me was one of the strangest sights I had ever seen. Leave it to the Wobblies to be dramatic. For a long moment I thought I was back in the deep woods of Washington or Oregon. On the sidewalk up ahead was a mountain of a man of about forty, decked out in logger's duds, complete with mackinaw and caulked boots. And he was doing something I never thought I would see a Wobbly do—praying. He was down on his knees facing a doorway, his hands clasped together, his head bent solemnly, with as sincere a look of tormented supplication as on the faces of those religious paintings I had been forced to look at as a child. Beside him was a small sign that read simply SOLIDARITY.

I went up to him hesitantly. His face looked vaguely familiar. I saw he had a Lumber Workers Union 120 button pinned to his mackinaw.

"Fellow worker," I said self-consciously.

His eyes revolved in his head painfully, it seemed. As he looked into my eyes and then seemingly beyond them I could see he was intelligent, perhaps extremely intelligent.

"Fellow worker," he repeated my words.

"I just arrived from out West," I said. "I guess it's bad."

"Very bad, fellow worker."

"Is there any hope?"

"A smidgen. I wouldn't be here if I thought there wasn't *any*."

"How long have you been out here like this?"

"Five days."

"Have the bulls given you any guff?"

"They ran off four stiffs here before me. Why they haven't bothered me I don't know."

"What's at the bottom of it all?" I asked.

"Got any easy questions?"

He seemed friendly but not over-anxious to talk. I told him I had a letter from the editor of the *Industrial Worker* for Rowan. "Give him my regards," he said. Did I just imagine there was a tear at the corner of the rugged timber beast's eye as I turned to the doorway?

"Good luck, fellow worker," I said. "Don't give up. Maybe I can spell you for a while before I leave this burg."

I went in the door. It suddenly occurred to me where I had seen him before—in the boxcar from Seattle to Centralia five years ago.

Two solemn-faced stiffs stood at the entrance to the offices of Rowan and his group. They were as big as the lumberjack out front and looked like they would brook no nonsense. I pulled out the letter to Rowan and put my credentials over it. "Howdy, fellow workers," I said. "I just came from Washington with an important letter from Mortimer Downing for Rowan." I added a little hesitantly: "I had the pleasure of chauffeuring fellow worker Rowan from Seattle to Centralia last May"—hoping I might be able to deliver the letter in person.

The two men shook my hand. "I've heard of you, Joe," one of them, whose name was Matt, said. "Jimmy's not here right now. We'll give him the letter the minute he returns."

I felt a reluctance to pull myself away. I felt a little as if I were a drowning man grasping for life. "Things look pretty bad, I guess," I said, temporizing. I couldn't decide if I should tell them I was trying to get information for Downing. "I'd like to help out if I can," I said. "Naturally I'd like to know what in hell's going on."

"My stint's over at five," the fellow worker named Matt said. "Come on back then if you want an' we can have some java and shoot the bull."

"It's a deal," I said. "Thanks for getting the letter to Rowan. It's important."

I shook their hands and left. The lumberjack was still on his knees praying out front. I gave him a friendly smile and a wave and walked on down the street.

It was early afternoon. Chicago was full of its usual din and bustle but in my disturbed state of mind I hardly seemed to hear it. From Mortimer Downing's brief description of affairs I knew this much: Initially the Rowan and Doyle groups had called separate conventions. But the confused delegates on arrival here had set up a third convention, at Emmet Memorial Hall over on Ogden Avenue. Most of the IWW, except for Rowan and his followers, had accepted that as the official convention. Since IWW headquarters on West Madison was closer, I decided to go by there first to deliver the other letter to Doyle and Fisher.

I approached the large familiar hall I had visited so many times last year—the center of my universe—with trepidation. A group of sullen-looking workers stood in front of it. But what first caught my eye was a startling replica of what I had just seen in front of Rowan's headquarters: another kneeling man praying, a SOLIDARITY sign beside him, this Wob with an Agricultural Workers Union 110 button on his coat. His face seemed as genuinely distraught and plaintive as that of the logger at Rowan's headquarters. I gave him a friendly wave and approached the men by the door. They were as glum and hopeless-looking a bunch as I had ever laid eyes on.

Just as I approached, two other Wobs came down the street with sad-eyed looks.

"Anything new?" one of the men standing by the wall said.

"Naw—they're still palavering, rehashing the same old stuff over and over." The two newcomers went on into the hall.

I went up to the man nearest the door. "Howdy, fellow worker," I said. "I've got a letter for general secretary-treasurer Doyle."

"Where you been?" The tall Wobbly seemed to eye me half-humorously. "Doyle and Fisher ain't ridin' herd on this outfit no more. We got a whole new shebang."

"I just got in from out West," I said with surprise. "Where can I deliver the letter?"

"Go on in—first door to your left."

I thanked him and went on in to the familiar old hall. Only it wasn't so familiar anymore. Now it had more the air of a funeral parlor than the headquarters of a dynamic labor organization. Groups of disconsolate-looking members sat about talking in low voices, a scattering of women among them. A few sat alone staring into space. Sounds of arguing erupted here and there. As I watched, a wiry middle-aged man cursed at someone else in his group, slammed a newspaper to the floor and stalked off. Others sat talking politely and earnestly, as if mapping out some plan of action.

I found the office I wanted and presented the letter. "Is it possible to see Doyle or Fisher?" I asked. My idea was to suggest to them, since they apparently were no longer officials, that they might want to share Downing's letter with whoever was in charge now.

"They're over at the convention," the busy man behind the desk said. "I'll see they get the letter."

I hesitated. "I'd like to help any way I can to get the two groups together," I said.

"We all would, fellow worker." The man before me smiled rather grimly. "Stick around. We might pull this thing together yet."

"The letter's important," I said. I thanked him and went out into the murmurous hall.

Back by the coffee urn I struck up a conversation with a friendly harvest hand, about thirty-five, from Spokane. I told him of my mission and of my ignorance of affairs. In somber tones he filled me in on things.

When the delegates began arriving, they were in a state of shock. The funds had been tied up by Rowan's injunction and two separate conventions had been called. A few gravitated to the Rowan or Doyle factions. But the vast majority quickly pulled themselves together, organized their own convention, and sent telegrams to all branches summarizing affairs and asking to be recognized as the legitimate convention. Sixty-one out of sixty-five branches had backed them up—the other four backing Rowan. It had been a miracle of rapid-fire organization in the true Wobbly democratic spirit.

Elected chairman was my old friend P. J. Welinder, chairman of the Portland strike publicity committee who had gotten me the job on the Swedish ship. Pending an investigation of the charges and counter-charges against both factions, the convention had temporarily suspended from office both Doyle and Fisher and the entire general executive board, with trials of the officials to be held later. A temporary administration of three was elected; in the interests of harmony between the Agricultural Workers Union and the Lumber Workers Union, it included one member from each. Now the convention was trying to unravel the reasons for the split, restore harmony, and get the Rowan faction to lift the injunction.

Paradoxically, amidst all the chaos—the harvest stiff told me— other aspects of the convention had hummed along smoothly: letters of support had come in from Emma Goldman, Roger Baldwin of the ACLU, and dozens of other prominent people. It was announced the IWW now had sixteen administrations in foreign nations. Labor bodies in Hungary and Czechoslovakia had just applied for affiliation, and an IWW strike had just been won in Mexico.

There had been rumors that high levels of the IWW had been infiltrated by the Communist Party. But when Harrison George, a prominent Wobbly turned Communist, was refused permission to address the convention, such worries were allayed. But other threatening rumors persisted. My informant lowered his voice. In conspiratorial tones he told me that two of Rowan's followers on the ousted general executive board, Bowerman and Raddock, were suspected of being *agents provocateurs* employed by the U.S. Department of Justice.

All he had told me suddenly took on a somewhat different aspect in my mind. My impulse was to jump up and tell him that I knew Rowan and that if he thought he was deliberately conspiring with federal agents he was out of his gourd. But I remembered in time that my mission here was to remain calm and get at the truth—and my own personal mission to try to help restore harmony—and I held myself in check.

I shook my head sadly and thanked the harvest stiff for his help. I looked around the cluttered hall. "One thing I can't understand," I said, "is why all these fellow workers aren't at the convention?"

The man beside me laughed ironically. "Probably for the same reason I'm not there just now," he said. "Oh we've all been over there off and on. But some of these people came hundreds or thousands of miles for this great event. Some of them have invested their whole winter stake in it, and will be freezing out in the breadline before the winter's through. It's just too depressing to them to sit and hear this whole farce being rehashed over and over by the delegates. I guess we're all sticking around to see how it all comes out. If it looks like there's a breakthrough we'll all be over there cheering the IWW on."

I shook hands with the friendly harvest stiff. I suddenly felt choked up with emotion. "The IWW will never go under," I said. "It can't. We won't let it."

I began to mill around the big hall, exchanging bits of conversation here and there with glum-faced members, recognizing a few I had met or had pointed out to me. And there was another face I kept looking for in the milling throng: Emmett, my long-lost brother Emmett, who had gotten me involved in all this in the first place and who had helped me out so often in my childhood; where was he? Why couldn't he magically appear and explain all this to me and point out the correct path to me as he had done so many times in the past?

I felt a little dazed by it all. It was past four. I decided to go in search of a greasy spoon to try to replenish my energy and brainpower before my appointment with Rowan's man Matt at five. I wandered down the busy street with my head spinning. So much to absorb. All so complex. How much of what the farmworker cat had told me was true? I dodged into a hamburger joint for a snack and some java and tried to go over it all in my mind.

I was in front of the Rowan headquarters a few minutes before five. The lumberjack was still on his knees praying. I smiled at him. For once in my life I had a few extra dollars in my pocket and I decided to slip him a frogskin—I felt sure Mortimer Downing would approve. He refused to take it so I slipped it under one corner of his SOLIDARITY sign.

The big lumberjack Matt came out exactly at five. From the look on his face I couldn't tell how he felt toward the solitary suppliant. "Come on, fellow worker Joe," he said, taking me by the arm, and we went off down the street. A cold wind blew. We went into a little joint half a block down and sat at a booth in the back.

Matt ordered coffee, then leaned toward me earnestly across the scarred tabletop: "What do you want to know?" I could see by his manner and speech that the man opposite me was a couple of notches above the usual timber beast in brains and education.

"Everything," I said. "Did you give Downing's letter to Rowan?"

"Sure 'nuf," he said.

"Did he read it?"

"Immediately."

"Any reaction?"

"Jimmy seemed very concerned about it. You probably know he has great respect for Mortimer Downing."

"And the reverse is true too," I said.

The waiter brought the coffee. When he was out of earshot I said, "So what brought all this on? What's been going on? We've read some of the bulletins from both sides, but Downing wanted me to get it from the horse's mouth."

Matt sat back in his seat. He looked at me levelly. "It's a tough world, Joe," he said. "We're all playing hardball for big stakes—the future of the labor movement—the future of the world. In any big movement there are different schools of thought. You've probably been around the Wobblies long enough to know that at least since 1913 there's been a struggle going on between people like Jimmy and the lumber workers who want more local autonomy for the unions, and the power-hungry tyrants who want to run everything from Chicago.

"It wasn't so bad when the centralists were men like the Saint and Bill Haywood who had enough brains to interpret the rules with some selective leeway and who had the confidence of the whole membership. But now we've got third-raters like Doyle and Fisher who've built up a self-serving political machine of power-hungry grafters, incompetents, Communists and probably a few government agents. A political machine—that's all you can call it. The issue is whether the IWW is going to be an organization of real functioning industrial unions organizing the workers for revolution, or a watered-down bunch of spittoon philosophers and labor fakirs playing footsies with the politicians.

"Look at the record," Matt went on. "Has the headquarters clique run any big strikes? Just this year they squandered eight hundred dollars sending one of their pets, Jack Leheny, out to organize and what did he accomplish?—exactly nothing. They've wasted the workers' money on political issues like defense of class war prisoners instead of organization at the point of production. Look at the publications—since 1920 they've been outdoing one another trying to be respectable to try to get sympathy from the bourgeoisie. They've stifled free speech in the IWW press. They've meddled in the Philadelphia dock workers union so much they've almost driven them out of the IWW.

"Fisher went back there to investigate fraudulent Marine Transport Workers ballots, and he whitewashed and mucked up the whole affair. Doyle wasted a pile of money on a useless junket to Washington. They and their ilk are trying to make all the unions mere appendages of their rotten machine. Dry rot has set in, Joe, and it has to be reamed out. Have you been down in the basement at the hall? Have you seen what the spittoon philosophers and hall cats are reading nowadays?—the *Racing Form*! And now the headquarters clique wants to spend the entire treasury of the IWW on a huge new headquarters building to further solidify its hold on the organization—a building that will probably be taken by the capitalists as soon as some agent provocateur manages to sprain his ankle on a freshly mopped floor. Why don't they ever have conventions out West where the action is?"

Matt paused for a moment to sip his coffee. My head was whirling from the nonstop blast.

"The whole matter in a nutshell is *organization*," Matt went on. "Headquarters, the way things are set up now, has been hamstringing organization. What were Joe Hill's last words? 'Don't waste any time mourning—*organize!*' Organize! Organize! Organize!" He pounded his fist on the table. "That's what Rowan and the rest of us want to do. Organize for the revolution! For a *workers'* revolution."

I nodded. I felt a little cowed by the barrage of words. Finally I got up the courage to mutter: "The injunction?"

Matt's face changed. "You've maybe hit our Achilles' heel, Joe," he said. "I'm not sure how I feel about the injunction myself. Maybe it was a mistake. Jimmy felt he had to protect the funds of the organization. They were being squandered by Doyle and Fisher's machine. And they refused to call an executive board meeting to discuss the situation." He looked thoughtful.

"Everyone makes deals in certain unavoidable crises," Matt said softly. "Welcome to the world of *realpolitik*, Joe. Lenin made a deal with the Germans. Lincoln made deals in Congress. The whole U.S. Constitution was a deal. It's not nice, but sometimes it's necessary."

He paused. "Tell me," he said, "who is the Wobbly you admire most of all?"

I thought. "Well, I met Haywood on two occasions and he impressed mightily," I said, "but since he went to Russia I don't quite know how I feel about him. The Saint I suppose," I said.

Matt smiled conspiratorially. "Mine too," he said. "Did you know that at the second IWW convention of 1906, when that piecard president Sherman wouldn't abide by the convention's vote to oust him, the Saint went to the hated capitalist courts to get headquarters turned over to the newly elected officers?"

"No, I didn't know that," I said.

"It was either that or a shootout on the streets of Chicago," Matt said.

I sipped my coffee. "Isn't there any chance for compromise?" I asked.

"Rowan has been expelled," he said. "The convention is stacked against us. Why don't you go over there and see for yourself?"

I nodded. "So what is Rowan going to do?"

Matt looked disturbed.

"That's what we're trying to decide now," he said.

My head was spinning. I walked through the darkness in the bitter cold wind off the lake. What should I do now? I wondered. There was so much to digest, to be evaluated, so much I still didn't know. Turning down Madison, I finally decided not to call Downing until I had taken in at least one session of the convention tomorrow and talked to a few more of the fellow workers. The longer I was here in Chicago, the more aware I was becoming of the immensity of the task Mortimer Downing had given me.

Dead tired after my almost sleepless trip and my long perplexing day in Chicago, I decided to take the El out to "Red Martha" Biegler's boardinghouse, where I had bunked the year before. Soon I was pounding my ear in the comforting proximity of fellow nomads and rebels.

Next day I had a good breakfast and headed for the convention. My head was still spinning with the widely divergent accounts of things I had heard. So I was being initiated into the brutal world of realpolitik. Lenin had made a deal with the Germans. St. John had dealt with the capitalist courts. Even so, I was still in a mild state of shock at the inconsistency of it: that the hard-fighting revolutionist Rowan, who had stridently refused commutation from Leavenworth and bitterly attacked those who did, should go crawling to the courts that had persecuted us so savagely. But I still didn't know all the facts.

Yes, there was a third fellow worker on his knees praying outside the convention hall. As I watched, a dead leaf blew against his face and he reached up and brushed it away, then bent his head again in supplication. Crowds of anxious members stood around waiting for the session to begin. Their faces were a pastiche of every emotion known to man: anger, hatred, hope, despair, love—and a grinding resignation. Some seemed on the verge of tears.

I began to circulate among them, meeting a few workers I had known out West, exchanging scraps of information. I heard at least five different versions of what had happened when Rowan and his group had been expelled from headquarters—with and without guns and blackjacks. One stiff speculated: "When Rowan was punched out, that was the end of it—that hard-headed Irishman will never forget or forgive—mark my words."

A little before nine the crowd began filing into the convention hall. There were only twenty-nine delegates, but there were two or three hundred spectators, fellow workers from all over the country. The mood was tense and solemn. It was as if a decision whether to close down the human race or keep it going were hanging in the balance. I thought of the first convention just a few blocks from here nineteen years ago, when Big Bill Haywood had gotten up and proclaimed: "This is the Continental Congress of the working class!"

The convention was called to order. And there was the chairman, my old friend P. J. Welinder, appearing as cool and calm and in control of the situation as if it were a gathering of bird watchers. Everyone was silent, poised to catch every word. The recording secretary sat in readiness. Things proceeded more seriously and somberly than on the floor of the U.S. Congress. The first few speakers were subdued and matter-of-fact, reciting their versions of events in what seemed an honest and businesslike manner, some favorable to Doyle and Fisher, some leaning toward Rowan, some critical of both factions, and most offering constructive suggestions for the settlement of the dispute and the improvement of the IWW.

Before long, however, things began to escalate. Along about eleven a worker named Thomas Smith began a long catalogue of grievances against conditions he claimed to have discovered at headquarters:

> "...Regarding the problem of providing speakers... The parties selected...did not appear to me that they were the right parties, to send either to the West Coast or the East Coast. I believed at the time and do still believe that they are nothing but leeches, trying to foist themselves on the organization. In my opinion the only loyalty they had or have was the loyalty for self-gain, in that they might be able to secure a meal ticket, at the expense of those still confined in the various jails throughout the country, and for the reason that they are always hanging around the headquarters. I have already mentioned there was no money in the treasury, yet there was always enough to furnish or finance transportation for such, which goes to show that as long as you stand well with the element in control of your finances, there will always be found a way to finance you... You see it all depends on how you stand with the gang at headquarters...
>
> "I also find that the basement is the gathering place for a lot of philosophers, whose philosophy for the most part consists of the merits and the demerits of horse racing. This matter should be looked into and ways and means provided to put a stop to such..."

A mild uproar greeted the conclusion of fellow worker Smith's remarks. On one side of me a man in farmworker duds made a grimace of disgust, while on my other side a big logger murmured, "You tell 'em, Tommy."

After a few moments the uproar died. An air of special attentiveness settled over the throng as chairman Welinder introduced the next speaker, suspended general executive board member Arthur Linn of the farmworkers union.

"Fellow workers," Linn began:

> "Having been elected chairman of the general organizing committee of Industrial Union 110, I took office February 1, 1924, and according to the new form of the General Executive Board I automatically became a GEB member.
>
> "About the first part of March I was notified by the chairman of the board that there would be a meeting of the newly installed GEB, which lasted for a period of seventeen days. Nothing very constructive was accomplished by this session, as most of the time was taken up in wrangling over personalities... There were some individuals around headquarters who, as far as

I can see, have never done anything in the organization but cause dissension and disruption wherever they have been in the organization, and at the present time were trying to disrupt the general headquarters. These individuals are M. Raddock, Fred Bowerman and John Grady, and they were just awaiting the cooperation of some tin Jesus who had the backing of the membership in the field. When James Rowan arrived in Chicago with a chip on his shoulder over the Leavenworth controversy he naturally fell in with this tribe.

"...A ballot was put out to vote upon the question of holding a board session, which did not carry by a two-thirds majority as provided by the constitution... I voted no on this ballot, and my reasons for doing so were that I did not consider the reasons given as sufficient grounds for a session... However, the Rowan faction decided to hold a session anyhow, as they told Doyle and Fisher, 'To hell with you people! We will hold one anyhow.' As this session was not called to order through the proper channels...I did not attend same and ignored it completely. They immediately set to work and sent out disruptive leaflets and minutes to the field, getting the membership in an uproar and hampering the work of the organization...

"Rowan and Company then proceeded to tie up all the funds of the general organization... The members around Chicago got disgusted with their dirty and underhanded tactics and proceeded to take action themselves, and politely notified them that if they were going to continue their meeting and carry on their disruptive work they would have to get out of headquarters. As they refused to adjourn their meeting and go back to their respective desks to function as officials of their I.U.'s they were told to leave the building, which they did. They put up a great holler about gunmen and hijacks throwing them out. But there were no guns or clubs used and not even a fight occurred in headquarters...

"Hoping for a clear-cut decision by this convention, I remain yours for a bigger and better IWW."

Another uproar followed Linn's presentation. There were moans and groans and muted threats and pleas for moderation in the crowd about me. Down the aisle it looked like two fellow workers were about to break out in fisticuffs. Up on the podium chairman Welinder, although it was not yet noon, suddenly announced a break for lunch. The combatants calmed down and the crowd began pouring out into the street. Everyone was distraught, heads shaking, fingers wagging, looks of anger or distress or sullen gloom on their faces.

As I started down the street with another Wob for a greasy spoon, a grimly smiling member thrust two flyers into our hands. A few minutes later, waiting for our lunch, we began to read them. It turned out to be a mimeographed poem written a few days before by a fellow worker in San Quentin Prison "to fan the flames of Court respect." It went:

JAMES ROWAN FOREVER

I must save the proletariat from the tactics of the stools;
The officials, Doyle and Fisher, they have broken all the rules;
And the fifty thousand Wobblies are a pack of ____- ____ fools;
But the Injunction makes us strong.

Second Jesus Jimmy Rowan,
Second Jesus Jimmy Rowan,
Second Jesus Jimmy Rowan,
And Injunctions make him strong…

We both laughed self–consciously. "I must admit it's clever," I allowed, sipping my java. And as an afterthought: "But cleverness doesn't make it right."

The stiff beside me shook his head. "It's a Chinese puzzle," he said, staring glumly in his coffee mug. "If you can figure it all out, 'you're a better man than I am, Gunga Din.'"

We sat gloomily feeding our faces, discussing the pros and cons of it all. The food seemed tasteless, superfluous. Some Wobblies took an adjoining booth and sat arguing in low voices. At one point I heard one say: "I've had enough. I'm going back to Schenectady and recommend we go independent." The others stared daggers at him.

We shambled back for the afternoon session. The wrangling and accusations went on. I could understand now why so many fellow workers had lost hope and gone back to mope at the hall. It was the most painful thing I had ever experienced, watching the IWW being torn apart. It was almost as if my own body were being torn apart. I knew that my life would be totally pointless and despairing if the IWW fell to pieces.

In the late afternoon a logger named Pat Cantwell got up and read a statement from himself and another delegate to the convention:

"Fellow workers:

"We are duly elected delegates, elected at the annual convention of Lumber Workers Industrial Union 120, held in Spokane, Washington... We wish to make the following statement: We came here for the purpose of settling the present controversy within the organization. After sitting in this so-called convention...we find that over one-third of the delegates present have taken a direct part on the side of Doyle and Fisher in the present controversy. The stenographer that was working for Doyle and Fisher while they were in office is also the official recording secretary. We have also seen Tom Doyle pass notes to the delegates while in session. Under these circumstances we do not feel justified in further participating in this so-called convention. We hereby notify the membership that we are withdrawing."

The two delegates got up and walked up the aisle and out the door, to the dumbfounded looks of the other delegates and spectators. Cries of "No! No!" "Don't go, fellow workers!" "Come back, fellow workers!" and "Solidarity!" rang out in the hall. I saw grown men crying at the defection of the two delegates. Several men got up and rushed after them and out into the street. But the two disgruntled woods workers did not return.

"Rowan ordered them to make that statement!" I heard one worker yell. "That means a split for sure," said another sorrowfully.

The day wound down. All was anticlimax after the exit of the two delegates. The long day's session broke up in grumbling and despair. I walked out into the cold windy street. Someone had turned the lone supplicant's SOLIDARITY sign upside down.

28

THE SPLIT

I got on the El and headed for Martha Biegler's boardinghouse to call Downing. How I dreaded the call. How could I tell him how bad it was? I sank into a blue funk, my eyes closed, my head leaning against the rattling window of the traincar.

Random phrases from the convention floor rang in my ears. Centralist. Decentralist. Industrial unionist. Anarcho-syndicalist. Revolutionary. What did they all really mean? The Doyle faction called themselves the industrial unionists, yet it was Rowan's concept of strong semi-autonomous unions that was really closer to industrial unionism. And each side claimed it was more revolutionary than the other.

I arranged to use the phone at the boardinghouse and finally got Mortimer Downing on the line. He had already gotten a few more bits of information since my departure, and he sounded as despairing as I was. I gave him my long report and he questioned me sharply on a number of points. Before signing off he said, "Don't give up hope, Joe. The struggle of the workers for emancipation will continue whether it's called the IWW or Jimmy Rowan's Tin Jesus Singing Society." He told me to hang in and phone him again when I had some more important news. I said, "For the One Big Union," and hung up.

I went to my bunk and lay down. I didn't feel like seeing anybody. I just wanted to sleep and shut it all out of my mind.

But I couldn't sleep. The invective of the convention kept banging around inside my head.

About ten I got up and put on my mackinaw and went out into the cold windy street. Winter had come already to Chicago. I just wanted to walk and walk and try to purge myself of all the clanging emotions I felt warring inside me. I don't know when the idea of going to Waldheim Cemetery entered my head. But suddenly I felt I wanted to throw myself down on the graves of the Haymarket martyrs, the ground where ashes of Joe Hill were buried, and cry my heart out, and sink down into that sacred earth and join them.

I caught a streetcar, my eyes unseeing, and soon I was in their exalted presence. The great statue rose above me, with August Spies' immortal words from the scaffold engraved below it: "There will come a time when our silence will be more powerful than the voices you strangle today." I knelt before it, feeling the freezing wind lash my neck and eyes. If only those great leaders and workers were with us today—*they* would know what to do! I bent my head against the granite pedestal, imploring them to send some message, to come back from the dead and make their powerful presence felt. They did not respond. For all their brilliance and moral rectitude they had been crushed. They were mute. A light snow began to fall—the winding sheet of the defeated.

Then I knelt before the ashes of Joe Hill, tears streaming down my cheeks. O Joe, where are you now that you are needed more than ever before? O Joe, come back and rescue this great union you gave your life to. Sing your immortal songs again. Send me some message to carry to the embattled delegates, some plea for sanity and unity that will carry us through this crisis. He did not respond.

I began to shiver. The snow covered my head, my coat, my shoes. Finally, in a final paroxysm of my despair, I decided to invoke the Saint. O Vint, where are you in this our most desperate hour? Come back with your brilliant mind and unconquerable spirit, come back and save us as you have so many times before. And then it struck me like a thunderbolt that St. John was not here—he was *alive*! A real living Wobbly saint somewhere on this earth. *He* was the one who could save us! And I remembered hearing how, when St. John was released from Leavenworth, James P. Cannon, a prominent Wobbly turned Communist, had sat up all night with the Saint trying to persuade him to Communism. But the Saint had not been taken in, and he had gone west to start a cooperative mine somewhere in the wilds of New Mexico.

The Saint was alive! And an idea began to form in my head.

I remained a few minutes longer in the softly falling snow, trying to conjure up the labor saints of times past, but all I managed to conjure up was a cold and a hacking cough.

Next morning I made my way back to the convention. There weren't as many spectators as the day before. It is slowly disintegrating, I thought with a sick feeling in my stomach.

The wrangling, the accusations and the half-despairing calls for unity went on. First on the agenda was a telegram from a lumber workers' branch in Vancouver, British Columbia. Chairman Welinder read it with an upbeat tone in his faint Swedish accent: "Convention: Your action in refusing to recognize either concurred in by this branch." There was a burst of applause from the delegates and visitors as he finished.

Next came a statement from J. A. Griffith, suspended chairman of the General Executive Board. I was particularly interested in what he had to say, since reports were that he had vacillated between one faction and the other in the controversy, and I hoped he might therefore present a more objective and balanced view of things.

"Fellow workers," Griffith began:

"I was called into headquarters by a telegram dated July 21st, signed by five board members: James Rowan, Charles Anderson, P. D. Ryan, Fred W. Bowerman and H. E. Trotter. Upon arriving here I did not assume office until the GEB was forced out of headquarters. I decided that the GEB was right and since that time I have performed the duties which I was called in for... It is not my intention to dwell on internal troubles in this report, but I wish to bring the following suggestions to the attention of the delegates to the convention.

"During the war we became a highly centralized organization. But the war is over. In my opinion...we should put all our energy toward building up our organization on the job, on strictly industrial union lines. Some may say that we are becoming less revolutionary—far from it. When we are organizing on the line of industrial unionism, having for our sole object and aim the abolition of the wage system and when we accomplish that and labor gets what it produces, we have then accomplished everything we started out for...

"I would suggest that we lay down a policy and follow it out... We will have to give...more local autonomy. In other words, we must let the rank and file rule and guide the affairs of the organization... There are two ideas in the organization at the present time. One that believes in organization on the job ...looking for job control. The other deals with revolutionary theories. Which do you want—theories or something that is practical?... My suggestion is clean headquarters from top to bottom.

"In closing I will state that in my opinion we should follow strictly on lines of industrial unionism.

"Yours for the IWW."

The next speaker was ousted secretary-treasurer Tom Doyle. As he rose to speak the convention was more quiet and attentive than ever. Observing him carefully, I reflected on how so often people exaggerate in one direction or another. The sincere and well-meaning-looking man standing at the front of the hall was obviously no Haywood or even a James Rowan, but neither did he seem to be the "third-rater" that Rowan's colleague Matt had called him.

"Fellow workers: Greetings!" Doyle began on an enthusiastic and serious upbeat note.

"...In the controversy that has just shaken the organization to its very foundation, we find that industrial union patriotism was to an alarming degree prevalent in many of the industrial unions. Industrial union patriotism must be destroyed root and branch, by a campaign of education which will replace it with revolutionary consciousness. When we joined this organization we all signed an application for membership and agreed to abide by the constitution and regulations of the IWW... If we, the members, would live up to our pledge, there would be no industrial union patriotism in the IWW. The patriotism of the IWW is to the working class, not to a small section of it. When a wageworker joins our ranks he does not and cannot join any industrial union as such, he must first join the IWW..."

Doyle went on to give a long detailed account of events in his administration and suggestions for improvements, and I was surprised that he seemed to support some of the reforms the Rowan faction was calling for. Maybe there is hope yet, I thought.

But the next speaker quickly filled me with doubts again. It was Charles Gray of the farmworkers union, who had just been at the court in regard to the upcoming hearing on Rowan's injunction. He rose with a somber and worried look on his sunburned harvest worker's face.

"I wish to give you fellows here a warning," he pronounced ominously. "I have a tip that what the Rowan forces are expecting to happen if this convention goes on much longer—they expect a split. If you do that and they can keep the court action stalled off until you do that, they will come forward with a claim that this convention is illegal; that it broke up and was altogether illegal. I got this as a pretty good tip, so I advise you to see to it that you keep as cool as possible during the convention, and remember that you are all members of the IWW. That is all I have to report on the case..."

An uproar of voices followed the brief report. Gray's warning seemed to throw those present into a deeper mood of despair than ever. I felt too depressed to sit and listen to any more. I got up and left and began walking at random through the city streets. I walked for hours until I wore myself out.

It was while I was drifting off to sleep that night that the idea took final form in my head. I remembered going out to Waldheim, trying to invoke the spirits of the dead, suddenly realizing that the Saint was still among the living. Did he know what was going on here? Did he know his beloved IWW was being torn apart? Had anyone bothered to notify him, to summon him? Well by god if nobody else would then *I* would. There might still be time.

It was about eleven. I leapt out of bed, dressed and caught a streetcar down to the hall. A few weary Wobs still sat up talking or arguing in low tones in the big meeting room. But I could find no one who could enlighten me as to the whereabouts of St. John. "Somewhere down in New Mexico, I think," one man said. "Come back tomorrow—they should have his address in the office," another said.

I hardly slept that night. Next morning I was down at the office the minute it opened. A harried-looking clerk gave me a friendly welcome, then did a double take when he noticed how agitated I was. "Come back this afternoon after the convention adjourns and I think I can have his address for you," he said. But there was something about his look that made me suspicious.

I calmed myself enough to gulp down some breakfast and made my way out to the convention. The trials of the general administration officials were in progress, and a more somber air than ever had settled over the large assembly. The murmuring crowd was suddenly galvanized when suspended general organizer Joe Fisher was called up to be interrogated.

"Is Fisher in the house? If there is no objection, fellow worker Fisher will be the next victim," chairman Welinder announced, and I questioned the taste of his attempt at tension-alleviating humor. The former general organizer arose. Strangely, he seemed to have a slightly cocky air about him today, and I wondered if it reflected some secret knowledge of events we of the rank and file were not privy to.

"Well, fellow worker chairman and fellow worker delegates," Fisher began. "Before we proceed any further I will state that there have been a lot of charges, recharges and accusations made, but if those who have made these charges do not appear here, why should I defend myself? Should I make the charges against myself and turn around and defend myself? It looks to me rather peculiar. None of these people are here. I want to see those people that make accusations or charges against me state their reasons so I can defend my position. Otherwise I have nothing to defend."

Some of the delegates laughed. I had to admit Fisher had a certain ingratiating spunk about him.

"Are you ready for the questions?" chairman Welinder asked.

"Now are we supposed to ask questions?" a delegate named Leonard of the construction workers union asked.

"You can ask all the questions you want," said Fisher.

"Well, I will start by asking if there has been a controversy."

"I should say, yes, and a big one," Fisher said.

"What caused it?" asked Leonard.

Fisher answered forcefully: "It was caused first of all by no system in the organization, conflicting opinions in the organization, one maintaining it was syndicalist, another maintaining it was something else. I maintain it is a labor organization with revolutionary aims and I defend from anybody the position I take."

LEONARD: "When the GEB was put out of headquarters, did you use any violence or force in evicting them from headquarters?"

FISHER: "I was not there. I was sitting in my office and performing my duties as general organizer."

LEONARD: "You had nothing to do with that?"

FISHER: "I had nothing to do with it..."

The questioning went on interminably, seeming to wear down not only Fisher but everyone else in the large hall. Most of it was a bunch of mumbo jumbo to me.

At one point Fisher said in exasperation: "I say, this controversy was enough to make a man cuckoo. It was too much of a strain on the men to overlook everything. One bunch said, 'Get out or we will run you out,' and the other bunch said, 'Stay in.' No human can stand that..."

Now a delegate named Jordan from the farmworkers union began to question Fisher: "I would like to ask you if you are willing to stand up for all your actions since you have been in office," he asked pointedly.

Fisher seemed to get a trifle flustered. After over an hour on the stand his caution and aplomb and good sense seemed to be wearing thin.

"I will state this," he said curtly. "I never compromise. I stand on it or fall down. Even if you expel me, I tell you I will still remain your friend. This is going to disappear if you don't take a positive stand here, remember that. Perhaps I will no longer be a member. It is up to you to determine whether Fisher or Griffith are guilty, and if you live up to the IWW that is what you must determine. I never compromise, I never apologize, I stand on my policy while in office..."

So he never compromises, I thought. Maybe that is a big part of the problem right there.

JORDAN: "Did you stand the 'acid test' while in office?"

FISHER: "Why certainly, I am here as strong as ever."

JORDAN: "You believe also that all members should stand the 'acid test' when they become members?"

FISHER: "Why certainly. When a man joins the organization he changes his life, he tries to establish a better society, it sure is a test, the biggest in the world."

JORDAN: "Did you ever violate the principles of the Industrial Workers of the World?"

FISHER: "I never did."

JORDAN: "Did you at any time since you became a member of the IWW ever take the witness stand in any courtroom testifying against other members of the IWW?"

FISHER: "I never did and I never will. We testify in their behalf, but not against them."

JORDAN: "Do you believe all the affairs of the organization should be settled by the IWW either at a convention or by the membership?"

FISHER: "Why certainly. Nobody except the organization, the membership or the convention. The convention should settle this, and they should go into the field and say what they did, tell the membership..."

"What do you think of the injunction?" another interrogator asked.

FISHER: "I maintain that the injunction is a compromising with the master class to go to the courts. It has been the policy since I have been a member of the IWW that nothing could be settled in regard to the organization in the courts. Of course we go there to defend our members, but that is another thing. If the IWW go into the courts at any time to decide a question, right there they deny the fundamental principle when you say these two classes shall have nothing in common..."

In summing up after the long interrogation, Fisher began to get more emotional, a bit overwrought. The words seemed to come out of his throat with difficulty:

"...I did my part for the IWW. I sacrificed for my duty. The IWW must get down to the base and study the different opinions. I say the IWW is nothing more nor less than a labor organization with revolutionary aims... If I say I don't understand the IWW I have no business in it... I am willing to leave it to your judgment whether or not you are going to expel me. I leave it to you. You have all the evidence here. I won't plead for mercy. I remember you people as my friends, and if you expel me, right on this floor I will say, 'Thank you'..."

CHAIRMAN WELINDER: "Are you finished?"

FISHER: "I am done."

Called on the stand next was former executive board chairman J. A. Griffith. His general mien seemed similar to that of Fisher before him.

"...If I am guilty, expel me," he said. "I want nothing of my past activities in this organization to count. It would be the same if you broke the laws, no matter how well you have lived up to them, you must be punished. Punish me, I want no sympathy, I don't need it. I never gave any sympathy, so why should I ask for any..."

The questioning went on. At one point a delegate said: "In your opening statement you spoke of the cause, and that the real cause of this controversy never has been named or mentioned, but you never gave any explanation of what, according to your idea, was the real cause of this controversy. Can you give us some definite statement what, according to your idea, is the cause?"

GRIFFITH: "I cannot. There are a great many causes leading up to it. The mere fact that an injunction was granted, and fellow worker Fisher refused to call a meeting, and they were put out of general headquarters at 1001 Madison Street is in about the same category as [the notion that] Mrs. Leary's cow that kicked over the lamp set Chicago afire. The causes are already there, and it needed very little to start it.

"In one respect you might say the organization for the last three or four years, in my opinion you understand, has been somewhat divided into two groups. Now, it is my opinion that part of the membership was more for job control, more for the organization on the job. There was another group which believed in the revolutionary theory. Don't misunderstand me to say those two groups couldn't get along. Far from that. The IWW is broad enough and large enough to take them all in, but I believe one and all must admit that as long as two absolutely stand on rigid lines, you might state there is bound to be a clash..."

The final speaker was Herbert Mahler, an impressive hulk of a man who had been one of the Leavenworth prisoners and one of the IWW's most successful organizers.

MAHLER: "On July 29th, when the former executive board members, Rowan, Trotter, Bowerman and Anderson were ejected from 1001 West Madison Street, I acted as spokesman for the men who put them out. There were five in number. We put them out without the use of guns, and without the use of physical force. About twenty minutes later a battle occurred on the street, and I took part in that also.

"The reasons for putting them out I suppose have been pretty well covered... First, I asked them if they were willing to meet with the other executive board members...in an effort to settle the controversy and they refused to answer my question. I told them if they refused to answer my question we were going to put them out on the street and keep them there. They refused to answer that also.

"So, giving them plenty of time, I told them we were going to put them out, that we were not going to hit them or beat them or anything, but were just going to put them out peaceably, that if they would not walk out quietly we could pick them up and carry them out. None of us carried a gun, and the other four men with me were well-known members of the organization. They walked out. There was no resistance offered on their part...

"I was not present when the street battle started. Five of them jumped on E. W. Latchem. This was probably twenty or thirty minutes after we put them on the street. Hearing of it, I went down. When I got there Ryan and Rowan were pounding Latchem on one side of the newsstand on the corner and the other three were after Edwards. I went over to help Latchem and called to Rowan and Ryan to come one at a time. Rowan turned toward me and I hit him. That ended the fight as far as he was concerned. Ryan ran across Morgan Street. Seeing the battle was over, I turned and walked back.

"When I got to the door of headquarters, I turned around and saw Trotter hit Fisher over the head with an iron bar. I started back, and in the meantime Latchem had gone over there. That settled that end of it, so I walked back into the building... As far as any guns or hijacks are concerned, it is plain bunk!"

My ears were ringing with the mountains of words. With no one from Rowan's faction here to testify, who could guess what the real truth was?

When the day's session was over I rushed back to the hall on Madison to get the Saint's address. A cold wind was blowing through the long streets. But to my intense disappointment the clerk I had talked with earlier was not there. Frustrated, angry, determined, I went from desk to desk in the big hall, but no one seemed able to help me out. I finally began to announce the reason for my urgent request. A few of the office workers perked up at that. One even said, "Great idea! Why didn't someone send for him before?" But no one could seem to find his address.

As I went out into the hallway a sympathetic-looking woman of about thirty, a rather attractive brunette with soulful idealistic eyes, followed me out the doorway.

"Wait." She put a hand on my arm. "I know his mine is somewhere around Jicarilla, New Mexico," she said. "I think if I look around a little I can find his mailing address."

"Thanks ever so much, fellow worker," I said. "In the meantime, look, here's a five spot I don't need. When you find it, please wire him about the urgency of the situation and tell him he's needed here immediately."

"Will do," she said. "But keep your five dollars."

"I want that wire to go through," I said, pressing the bill into her hand. I looked into her eyes. "You're a real IWW angel," I said. "I'll be back for that address."

I grabbed a quick meal and went back out to the boarding-house to call Mortimer Downing and give him the latest news. After about an hour I got him on the line. He sounded as depressed as I was about how things were going. Then I told him about my scheme to go in search of the Saint.

A sadness came into his voice. "It's a great idea, Joe," he said. "But prison hit the Saint awfully hard. I heard just recently his bronchitis is much worse. And anyway, I doubt if he could get to the convention in time. It's up to you if you want to try." He paused. "I was about to ask you to undertake a chore of a perhaps more practical nature..."

He told me the strike in Concrete was going well, but they had just learned the company had plans to recruit strikebreakers through an employment agency in Minneapolis. They planned to ship them out by train. "We thought if you could just get together a few of our gung-ho boys and ride out with them, you might just change the thinking and save the souls of those potential Judases," he said.

I had to make a quick decision. The IWW couldn't afford to spend much money on long-distance phone calls. "All right, it's as good as done," I said. He gave me the name of the employment agency.

"Thanks Joe," Downing said. "Yours for the IWW."

"Yours for the OBU." I hung up.

I thought things over for a while. Would I ever meet the Saint? I wondered. I went to my room and lay down, staring at the ceiling. I felt a little crushed that my plan had been shot down.

But I supposed Downing was right. It would probably be at least a week before I could locate St. John, and by then the convention would be over—or the IWW hopelessly split. And it might well be that the Saint wasn't in good enough health to confront such a momentous and difficult undertaking. I sighed. After a while I began to feel a surge of optimism at this new chance to help the beleaguered organization in its hour of greatest need. If the IWW ever needed a strike victory it was now.

I remembered meeting a Wobbly farmworker from Minneapolis named Carl Keller a couple of days before. I seemed to recall that he was an official of the farmworkers union. I gathered up my gear and rushed down to the hall. I was in luck, and I found Keller talking with a small group of fellow workers. When I told him about our plan his eyes lit up. "Always willing to help out some fellow workers in need," he said.

He took me across the hall and introduced me to another harvest stiff called Fargo Shorty who was planning to hop a freight home to the Twin Cities that night—and he was anxious to go along on my scab-educating mission back to Concrete. "I'm sure we can rustle up a few other handy boys in Minnie to help us out," he grinned at me.

And by midnight Shorty and I were in a boxcar headed for Minneapolis. Farewell to the easy life of the conventioneer—back to the rugged life of a real proletarian in a freezing boxcar!

29

HOLD THE FORT

Gliding slowly north out of Chicago, Shorty and I talked long and earnestly about the dramatic and painful events of the convention. Like me, he was confused, disheartened, desolated. "That's why I jumped at this chance at some action, fellow worker," he confided to me over the noise of the train. "I've got to do somepin' to shut the whole godawful mess out of my mind."

After Shorty drifted off, I lay looking out at the lights of farmhouses off through the darkness. How strange life was! A few days ago picketing two thousand miles away, then the hubbub of the convention—and now this lonely freight. Sometimes life seemed like an endless meaningless nightmare to me, some huge practical joke played by a sadistic god. Where was it all leading to? Was any of it really real at all? You came into this world battling tremendous odds and you fought like crazy and at last you found a dream, a glimmer of hope, and then before you could grasp it, it all went up in smoke. Well at least no one could accuse me of being a disrupter, of not doing my share for the organization. I had done my best in Chicago and now I was going to do my best for the boys in Concrete. Clack–clack went the wheels on the track. In another ten minutes I was asleep.

Minneapolis was cold and clear. It seemed it took all morning for the long train to crawl across the Mississippi from St. Paul. We hopped off the slow-moving train near downtown and found a greasy spoon. The coffee felt good going down. It never felt so good as after a freezing night in a boxcar.

After breakfast Shorty took me down to the IWW hall. A few glum-looking harvest workers sat about. Shorty knew several of them. When they found out we had just come up from Chicago they crowded around and wanted to hear the latest news. Shorty and I spent half an hour filling them in on things and their momentarily hopeful expressions turned to frowns. But when we told them about our plans to derail the scabs their eyes lit up again.

"Hey, I could stand a vacation in the Golden West!" one stiff said. "Nothin' like wintering in Barbarous California. It's only a hop, skip and a jump from Seattle."

"Hey, I saw those ads that slave market put up for jobs in Concrete," another harvest worker said. "I hear they're waitin' till they have a couple of boxcar loads—eighty or a hundred men. An' you get free grub all the way."

We had a strategy conference. Seven of the boys agreed to go with us. At least four of them looked like they'd be good in a fight. From the way they talked they all sounded like dyed-in-the-wool Wobblies who knew what the score was. We decided to go to the employment agency in ones and twos to avoid suspicion. Shorty and I went first.

Sure enough, they had a sign up for workers to do dam and tunnel work in Concrete. There was no mention of a strike. We ambled in and hoosiered up. A few stiffs who didn't look any too well-fed sat around the dingy place. Sure we'd done construction work, we told the rat-faced guy behind the counter. Sure, $3.60 a day sounded more than fair to us.

The employment shark took down our names. His eyes lit up a little. "You know any other guys what needs a job? We're not shippin' you guys out till we have a crew of at least fifty. We only got about forty lined up now."

Sure, we knew a few stiffs looking for work, we told him. He told us to be back by five that afternoon, that if there were enough men by then we'd take a night train out.

We hightailed it back to the hall. Things seemed to be shaping up fine. The next two guys went out. In the meantime Shorty and I loaded up on literature and songbooks, and I laid in a good supply of stamps and blank membership cards. Before the

afternoon was out, seven or eight more Wobs had decided to join
our group and we sent them down to sign up.

,   The train was to leave at eight that night. The employment
shark gave us vouchers to eat in a local greasy spoon. Then, just
before we boarded the two rickety old boxcars, a company agent
gave us all bag lunches with sandwiches in them to tide us over
until next day. The company agent got into the first boxcar with
a couple of boxes of food supplies, and all the Wobblies got in the
one behind it.

After a long delay we headed out. The long train creaked and
clanked out onto the prairie. It got as cold as a glacier's belly. As
per our plan, all us Wobblies just played it cool for a while, sizing
up the other men. There were all kinds: young and old, smart and
stupid, friendly and sullen. None of them seemed to have heard
of the strike. From keeping my ears open I figured, after an hour
or so, that at least half of them might be open to persuasion.

After a couple of hours we stopped on a siding in some tiny
town on the prairie. I winked at Shorty. He began to sing in a low
scratchy voice:

O, why don't you work like other men do?
How the hell can I work when there's no work to do?
Hallelujah, I'm a bum! Hallelujah, bum again;
Hallelujah, give us a handout
To revive us again!...

Some of the others began to take up the song.

O, I like my boss,
He's a good friend of mine,
That's why I am starving
Out in the breadline...

"Hey, that's a Wobbly song!" one of the stiffs said. "You guys
Wobblies?" He seemed so delighted at the prospect we felt obliged
to admit it.

"Hell, I've had a card for a while," another stiff said. "If I could
find a delegate I'd get my card stamped up."

I reached in my pack and obliged him. Shorty lit some canned
heat to see by. To my surprise, three or four others in the car
produced cards and bought a few dues stamps too. To celebrate,
I gave out songbooks to everyone.

The train started up again. We built a little fire with some scrap
lumber in one end of the car for heat and light, and soon over

half the stiffs were joining us in rousing renditions of "The Popular Wobbly" and half a dozen other IWW songs.

Eight or ten of the men had been Wobblies at one time or another. We told everyone about the strike and what our plan was. Several of the men expressed indignation at not being told about the strike. A few others remained silent or seemed indifferent. We gradually hinted that we would not feel very friendly toward anyone who intended to break the strike. Most seemed to go along with us, but three or four dumb-looking oafs said they didn't give a damn about any union or strike.

Next day we were rolling over frost-covered prairie in North Dakota. At our first stop just outside some little burg the men got down to stretch and relieve themselves and the company agent gave out more of the crummy sandwiches.

When we boarded the train again five or six of our original Wobbly group managed to get in the other boxcar. As the train rolled on west again we sat quietly sizing up the men in this car too, not wanting to tip our hand prematurely to the company agent. By late afternoon we had a pretty good idea the situation was about the same here too—a few Wobs or former Wobs, most of the others open to persuasion, and a handful of hard-core scabs.

At a division point where we stopped about noon, Shorty and I ambled up to speak to the new train crew waiting to take over. To our delight, the engineer and fireman both carried red cards. The engineer, a big friendly German of about sixty, had been a member of Eugene Debs' American Railway Union as a kid, and had been involved in the Great Northern strike. We palavered with them for a few minutes, explaining the situation, and when it came time to leave they wished us luck and climbed up into the engine cab.

Our problem now was how to organize the stiffs in this second car without the company agent getting wind of it. Lucky for us, the solution was dumped in our laps. Along about mid-afternoon we stopped to take on water at a little pokehole out in the middle of nowhere. The company agent announced he was going to walk back two or three blocks to the station house to call in a progress report to the big muckamucks in Concrete. As soon as he got there Shorty and I climbed over to the other side of the train and began running for all we were worth, yelling and waving our arms frantically, up to the engine.

"Hey! Hey! There's an old guy back in our boxcar having a heart attack!" I yelled, running up.

"We just asked the station master an' there ain't a doctor in this burg," gasped Shorty, out of breath.

The big Wobbly engineer turned to the fireman. "Stoke 'er up, Blackie," he said. "I reckon we got enough water for a short run." From his look I had a hunch he knew we were pulling a fast one, and without our little skit probably would have moved the train anyway.

We ran back to our car and clambered aboard. The second we were on, the train began to move. We hung out of the boxcar, looking back. After about thirty seconds the company agent shot out of the station building, waving his hands frantically. He had about the goofiest look on his face I've ever seen. Finally, as the train pulled well away, it looked like he was kneeling down in the center of the tracks pounding his fists on the crossties.

At the next watering hole we ambled up to the engineer. "Thanks Fritz," I said. "Our patient has made a miraculous recovery. For the last fifteen miles he's been running along behind the train for exercise. If you want, we'll invite him up here to dance a jig for you."

We were about twenty minutes taking on water. To get things rolling properly, we took a vote among all the men to see how the food in the two big containers should be divided up. We suggested to the men that they elect a committee to distribute it. Most of them seemed to be pleasantly surprised at our democratic procedures.

When the train got ready to leave, most of the original Wobs got in the new car. There were ten of us. We began to make our pitch. There were four other men with cards in the car, and as the train began to roll westward into the sunset I signed up seven or eight more. Several more wanted to line up, but said they were down to their last nickel and would line up as soon as they got a job. Only three or four seemed to be real recalcitrants.

We gave out more songbooks and sang some rousing songs, "All Hell Can't Stop Us" and "Workingmen Unite" and "Hold the Fort" (Shorty kept singing "hold the *fart*"). As darkness came down and we whooshed on west we went in twos to talk to the deadheads. We convinced two of them, and two seemed beyond the pale of reason so we finally gave up and left them alone.

Next day we were chugging through snow-covered ground in eastern Montana. We made another stab at the recalcitrants. There were two in each car that were determined to scab. As we started up into the Rockies and the long train was straining along at about ten per, Shorty and I went to stand in the door of the boxcar.

"Hey, look at the elk!" I yelled.

One of the scabs came to peer out. Shorty got behind him. "I don't see no—"

His voice trailed away in the cold air. We saw him plummet upside down into a snowbank. "Now how in the hell did that happen?" said Shorty.

The disembarked passenger got up, covered with snow, and shook his fist at us. I went to get his bindle and threw it out. He probably could have caught a car at the rear of the train if he'd really tried, but I guess he realized he wouldn't get far.

All the Wobblies in the car turned to look at the other stubborn scab. He flattened himself against the side of the car. "I been doin' a lot of thinkin'," he said. "I think you boys are right about things."

At our next watering stop high in the Rockies Shorty and I walked back to the next car. The boys were just finishing a chorus of "Dump the Bosses Off Your Back."

"How's it goin'?" I asked.

"Well, the food situation's improved," one of the Minneapolis Wobs said. "Two of the boys decided to jump off back there a ways to hunt grizzly bars."

Late afternoon of the next day we pulled into Town Creek, Washington, and were loaded onto buses. "Where's the company agent?" one of the bus drivers wanted to know. We all gave him blank looks.

It was a short ride to Concrete. Every worker had a look on his face like the cat who ate the canary.

We went winding up through the mountains. The huge construction project hove into sight, with the little town of Concrete nearby. As we got off the buses we could see dozens of our fellow workers picketing on the bridge up ahead that our scabherder masters planned to run us through on the way to the bunkhouse.

As we began to march toward the bridge a group of foremen and company gunmen pushed their way through the pickets to escort us.

"All right, men, hit it!" I yelled. And we all began singing:

We meet today in freedom's cause and raise our voices high;
We'll join our hands in union strong to battle or to die;
Hold the fort, for we are coming;
Union men be strong;
Side by side we battle onward;
Victory will come.
Look my comrades, see the union, banners waving high,
Reinforcements now appearing—victory is nigh...

The jaws of our "protectors" dropped as we marched singing at the tops of our lungs through and past them. The Wobblies on the bridge began clapping and cheering, rushing up to welcome us.

A singing industrial army, we marched up to the picket camp nearby. Now other Wobblies from Concrete and the surrounding area began streaming out to join us. Soon there were three or four hundred of us. We sang several more Wobbly songs, and our thunderous voices made the granite walls of the canyons shake.

The fellow workers began urging me to get up and make a speech. I finally got up and gave an account of our trip, and a little pep talk about winning the strike. I didn't want to discuss the convention yet. I got a good round of applause. Later some musicians and some members of the Concrete girls' singing society came out and we had a real hoedown. I felt a little better about the split now.

Later I sat on a big log in the twilight with some of the local Wobs watching the last rays of the sun rebound off the surrounding mountainsides. I turned to the Wob beside me. "You know, something important just occurred to me," I said.

"What, Joe?"

"That the IWW will never die."

"Hey Joe—you've got the straight dope," he said. And he jumped up, raised his arm in clenched fist salute and yelled to the other men:

"The IWW will live forever!"

30

KEEP ON TRAMPIN'

The dream was still alive. It was great to be back with the boys on the firing line again. Mortimer Downing was right: The struggle for the emancipation of the workers would go on whether it was called the IWW or Jimmy Rowan's Tin Jesus Singing Society. Seeing the great spirit of the embattled fellow workers at Concrete— where news of the split had apparently not penetrated very deeply yet—I felt my sullen mood disperse.

Moreover, Concrete probably came the closest of any place to being an all-Wobbly town since the Saint had organized Goldfield, Nevada back in 1906. The town newspaper and all the local merchants were with us, there was the terrific IWW girls' singing club, and the strike had been a model of orderliness and totally devoid of violence.

Had all that ruckus back in Chicago been just a nightmare, a figment of my imagination? Let the ideologues in Chicago leap at each other's throats—here it was still the same fighting, singing, high-spirited clan it had always been. I had just turned nineteen, and I felt more capable of carrying on the class struggle than I ever had.

Tall shadows climbed the walls of the steep canyon. After it got cold and the great bonfire died, a bunch of us hoofed it into town to our favorite greasy spoon. We sat around a big table over hamburger steaks and spuds, jawboning about all that had happened in my absence. The strike was solid, the boys told me with elation — the only slaves up in the company compound were three or four tame apes who did the hashing and dishwashing for the bigwigs. Now that the company's rescuing scabs had all turned out to be true-blue Wobbly rebels, it looked like we had it won hands down. Then Shorty and I filled in the others with more details on the trip out from Minnie. They all busted their guts laughing at the story of the nonexistent elk and the stranded company agent left tearing his hair out in the middle of the tracks.

Through it all, though, in spite of my elation and the good vittles and the heady camaraderie, there was gnawing at me an uneasiness about the inevitable question: What was going on in Chicago?

I felt a stab of heartache inside when it was finally asked. It was late now and I was dead tired. The boisterous voices were suddenly hushed and every eye in the place was on me. I took a deep breath. "Ain't you gazabos got any easy questions?" I said. "Hell it would take me all night to even start to try to explain that brouhaha. I'm out on my feet from that long trip, fellow workers. Tell you what — let's get together tomorrow night and I'll give you a blow-by-blow account. But don't worry — the IWW's survived worse things than this and we'll survive this too."

That seemed to hold them, and we broke up the little powwow with slaps on the back and vows to continue the fight. One of the Wobbly homeguards offered to put me up in his cabin nearby and we trudged off into the chilly night. The moon was up and I could see the soft gleam of snow on the nearby mountain peaks.

The next morning it was back into the trenches of the class war. I slept like a log and was up at dawn. My partner was still sawing wood, so I got dressed, tiptoed out and vamoosed down to the nearest greasy spoon for some chow. It was cold now in early November, but it was an invigorating cold that sent the blood racing through the veins, not the deadly wind-lashed chill of Chicago that ripped through you like a stiletto. There was much rain now, and far off down the street I could see a few of our boys marching off to the picket line with their slickers on, expecting the worst.

Two or three other early risers nodded their greetings as I entered the little cafe. A friendly waitress wearing an IWW button waited on me. I still had some of the money Mortimer Downing had given me, so I ordered some java, a big stack of flapjacks covered with honey, some eggs and a side of hash browns.

While I fed my face I glanced over the papers lying nearby on the counter. I hadn't seen a rag in days. A lot had happened. Mussolini was rampaging around in Italy, and here at home there had been a national election. COOLIDGE HAS SWEEPING VICTORY, one headline blared. Hell, I'll bet he never used a broom in his life, I thought. LAFOLLETTE CARRIES ONLY WISCONSIN. Too bad, but Wisconsin was enough of a load for any man—what did they expect of you anyway? MA FERGUSON WINS IN TEXAS. Now maybe *there* was a smidgen of hope—the male politicos had made a mess of things, maybe the women could do better—and I had heard she was more or less a socialist. WALL STREET BOOM SETS NEW RECORD. Bully for them—more leeches and parasites living off other people's sweat. NEW BATTLESHIP 'WASHINGTON' TO BE SUNK UNDER NAVAL DISARMAMENT TREATY. Now there was *news*. It showed what could be done for peace, even by the bumbling politicians. By gum, maybe there was some hope for the world after all.

Then, hiding under the plute sheets, I found the real stuff, the Wobbly paper, like a ray of light in a thunderstorm: IWW GENERAL STRIKE ON NATRON CUTOFF—3,000 OUT. Now there *was* news. And I sat devouring the long account of the mass walkout of underpaid workers on the new rail line being built in southern Oregon.

It was too early to phone Mortimer Downing, so I decided to mosey out to the picket camp and volunteer for some picket duty. Already in the early dawn we had a spirited bunch walking back and forth, clapping their hands together for the cold, and letting loose with a few old-time favorites: "It's a Long Way Down to the Soup Line," "There is Power in a Union" and "Workingmen Unite." I joined in at the top of my lungs and we made the canyon walls ring. We had a marching line of singing pickets all up and down the street and across the bridge that led to the work site. We were determined that nobody was going through.

About eight, with the gray sky threatening rain, I excused myself and went to phone Downing. On my way into town I met some members of the publicity committee and stopped to jaw-bone with them for a minute. I told them I expected to be leaving soon to make a full report on my trip to the *Industrial Worker* editor in Seattle.

"Hold on a minute, Joe," the head of the publicity committee told me. "We just got word from our informant up at the company office. The bosses are mad as hell about how you boys infiltrated that scab contingent. They were up half the night boozing and ranting and raving about how to get their revenge. He says they've got some new card up their sleeve now but he's not sure just what it is. Can't you stick around just a couple more days? We may need all the brawn and brains we can muster."

"Well—" I hesitated. "I'll see what Downing says," I said. "He's got deadlines to meet. But I'll see if I can stay a while."

I went on into town and finally got Downing on the line. He seemed half gloomy and half cheerful—cheerful about the Concrete situation and the big new strike at Natron, but gloomy about the situation in Chicago. "Get on down here and give me a full report, Joe," he said. "I'm going half crazy trying to figure out what to put in the paper."

I told him about the rumors of new troubles at Concrete, and he grudgingly gave me permission to stay a day or two longer.

I hung up, grabbed a cup of java and headed back out to the picket line. Now there were several dozen more pickets all along the line. The sky looked gloomy and ominous. The mood of the pickets seemed more high-spirited and serious than on most days. This was November 10*th*, and we all remembered the significance of November 11*th*: the day the Haymarket martyrs had been hung, the day the Legionnaires had broken into our hall in Centralia and lynched Wesley Everest. Our employer, Stone and Webster, was now claiming the job had been closed down for the winter, but we knew it was a trick and a lie. There was a look of fiery determination in every fellow worker's eye.

It was around eight-thirty in the morning and we had just finished singing "The Commonwealth of Toil." Suddenly six or eight big auto-trucks roared into town, loaded down with armed men. There must have been fifty of them, brandishing rifles and shotguns. As they screeched to a halt near our picket camp, about twenty-five more gunmen came strutting down to meet them from the company compound. We couldn't believe our eyes.

They came charging up towards us, swinging their guns around wildly, as if they thought they were charging San Juan Hill. At their head was sheriff Tip Conn himself, the Grand High Skeezix of the local law, swaggering towards us as if he owned the county and the dam site too.

"Keep cool, boys, keep cool," I heard the picket captain saying as he walked swiftly along the line. "No violence."

It all happened so fast we didn't have time to decide what to do. My first impulse was to run for it and try to save my bacon, especially since I had important information to get to Mortimer Downing. But when I looked up towards the nearby hillside I saw that there were sharpshooters spaced all along it slavering at the mouth for a chance to pick one of us off.

The plug-uglies were suddenly next to us, prodding us with the muzzles of their guns.

"All right, you bozos, all get in a column and start marching into town," sheriff Conn barked. Back behind him, apparently as advisers, I could see two uniformed officers of the state militia, strutting around like they thought they were taking on the German army.

"Are we being arrested?" one man asked. "What are the charges?"

"I'll show you all the charges we need," one of the deputies snorted, and he raised the butt of his rifle and clubbed our fellow worker to the ground. I could see blood gush out on the frosty earth. I felt like grabbing the s.o.b. and beating his head to a pulp, but what could we do? One gesture of defiance and we all would have been candidates for the meat wagon.

We grudgingly got in line. Were they out of their minds? I wondered. What could they possibly charge us with? When we were finally lined up, the command came to march. The gunmen on each side of us began prodding those they didn't think were moving fast enough with their guns. The long line of over two hundred men began moving slowly into town.

On my left was a dumb-looking boob who must have been about my age, carrying a shotgun. "Aren't you ashamed of yourself," I said to him. "A big boy like you being a toy soldier? I'm sure your mother's proud of you. Too lazy to do real work for a living?"

He stared daggers at me and looked like he'd like to stuff the shotgun down my throat, but he didn't say anything.

We kept on walking. Another young gun thug came abreast of me on my right. "Hey buddy," I whispered to him in a confidential tone, "your fly's open."

He blushed, looked swiftly to left and right, then sneaked a quick glance at his pants top. His face got redder. He looked like he wanted to shoot me on the spot, but he just kept that enraged look of a frustrated spoiled brat on his face all the way into town.

When we came down the main street into the business section, the townspeople came to doors and windows and storefronts to cheer us on. Up ahead, our boys struck up a stirring rendition of "Solidarity Forever," and soon all two hundred of us were singing it loud enough to make the wooden walls of the buildings shake.

They herded us into a big open space near the edge of town and posted sentinels. What in hell were they going to do with us? There still had been no mention by anyone of any arrest, of any warrant. After about an hour I called over to one of our guards: "Hey, pardner, what's the beef? What are they charging us with?"

"Stay where you are and keep your mouth shut if you don't want a face full of buckshot," he shot back.

We saw a few contingents of armed men going off down the various streets of the small town. Presently we learned their purpose: They were going from house to house in search of the Wobbly homeguards, and soon they began escorting them in small groups to join us, while a few wives came sobbing along behind, begging the deputies to leave their menfolk alone.

Eventually there were 225 of us under guard. We began singing more Wobbly songs, making the canyon walls ring. The strike captain began to circulate among us, cheering us up and cautioning us to keep cool.

"What are the charges?" I asked him.

"That's what I've been trying to find out," he answered. "Maybe they've passed a new law called interfering with profits."

We waited. Some of the boys asked if they could get their packs for needed clothing or a smoke or chewing tobacco, but they were turned down cold.

Around noon we saw several of the deputies race off toward the auto-trucks. Suddenly the big vehicles began roaring toward us. What were they going to do now—run us down like stray dogs? But the big trucks slammed to a stop near us and their drivers leaped down.

"All right, you men—in the trucks!" sheriff Conn barked, and his deputies and the company gunmen began moving in on us, prodding us with their guns.

An uproar went up from the men. Those who hesitated were poked and prodded roughly with muzzles and gunbutts. Off to one side I could see our strike captain carrying on a heated conversation with Conn now, and heard his angry words: "We'll be back!" Off beyond the gunmen, crowds of townspeople stood now, with a few women crying or screaming hysterically.

I followed Shorty up into one of the big trucks. The nearest deputy waving his rifle at us was one of the few who looked half human. "Hey pard," I yelled over at him as I got up into the truck, "where's this caravan goin'?"

He chomped on his cigar. "We're just takin' you boys for a nice little outing to the county line," he said.

The county line! "Hey, that's kidnapping!" I yelled back.

He gave a sadistic grin. "Now there's a 'bo with some book larnin'," he wisecracked back.

"Let me get my pack!" one fellow worker yelled, hesitating by the side of the truck. "Yeah—at least let me get my balloon!" yelled another.

"You'll get your balloon in hell," yelled back one of the deputies, prodding him in the stomach with the muzzle of his rifle.

We crowded into the trucks, cursing and grumbling. No arrest, but a trip to the county line! This must be the second biggest kidnapping in history, I suddenly realized. Second only to the notorious Bisbee deportation, when they had packed 1200 Wobbly miners into cattle cars and left them stranded in the scorching New Mexico desert back in 1917. Then they had the excuse there was a war on. What would their excuse be this time?

"It looks like we'll make the history books yet," I half-grinned at Shorty, trying to ease the tension a little.

The big trucks roared into life. Off in the distance we could see that our picket headquarters had been set on fire. People were rushing back and forth in the streets, yelling and screaming. A big plug-ugly sat next to our driver, the muzzle of his gun almost sticking in my belly. We sat grim-faced and angry as the trucks roared off, exchanging waves here and there with groups of our supporters along the streets. "We'll be back! We'll be back!" we yelled at them, and they cheered us on.

We rocked south through the mountains. It began to rain. Here and there a solitary motorist or pedestrian gaped at our strange procession goggle-eyed. We began to sing again, "Tramp Tramp Tramp, Keep on a-Tramping," "Hallelujah I'm a Bum" and "Workers of the World Awaken."

In the early afternoon we came to the county line. In spite of the fact sheriff Conn had advised the sheriff of adjoining

Snohomish County of our imminent arrival, not a single cop was there to greet us.

We hopped down from the trucks and lined up just across the line. As the big trucks began to turn around we began chanting in unison: "We'll be back! We'll be back!" The gun thugs on the trucks hurled a few epithets at us and roared off the way we had come.

We stood looking around us at the desolate snow-capped mountains. Drygulched. Kangarooed. It beat everything.

After a short meeting we began marching south toward the nearby town of McMurray. A few Wobs threatened to begin immediately hiking back the forty miles through the mountains to Concrete, but when it started raining again they thought better of it. Two or three dozen others announced they were heading south to help out our fellow workers in the big new strike at the Natron Cutoff in southern Oregon. But the vast majority decided to make the next stop the Wobbly hall in Seattle.

I pushed up ahead in the line of march until I found the chairman of the publicity committee. He already knew about my mission for Mortimer Downing. I told him how anxious Downing was to see me as soon as possible. "I think I'll hike ahead at double time," I told him, "and see if I can hop a ride in to Seattle. I'll see if I can find somebody in McMurray to come out for some of you guys."

The fellow worker wished me his best. I said goodbye to Fargo Shorty, figuring I'd have a better chance of getting a ride alone, and started off at a fast pace toward the head of the line.

I was in luck. Within fifteen minutes a hoosier came along and gave me a lift into McMurray. In McMurray I hitched for an hour in a driving rain, but I finally got a ride all the way to Seattle.

I found Mortimer Downing at the IWW printing plant out on Western Avenue. He looked worried and pale, almost as if he'd aged five or ten years since our last meeting. But the old Wobbly spirit still shone in his large intelligent eyes, and he held my hand between his two gnarled paws for a long moment in greeting.

"Hello, old hoss," he said. "You eat yet?"

"A few days ago," I said.

"Well let's rustle up some grub, and then we can settle all the problems of the world," he said.

We dodged into the first beanery we came to and went to a booth at the rear. While we waited for coffee Downing sat looking at me, shaking his head. "In the words of my mother, 'It bangs Bannaher,'" he said finally. "I'll be a suck-egg mule if I can make heads or tails of some of the things going on in the IWW nowadays, Joseph."

I told him I felt the same way—the Chinese puzzle at Chicago and now this new outrage at Concrete.

First I answered some of his questions about the deportation while he took out a notebook and scribbled notes. Then he filled me in on a few recent developments I was unaware of: My old Portland friend P. J. Welinder, the convention chairman, had been elected secretary-treasurer pro tem, and in its final days the convention had enacted a few of the decentralizing measures the Rowan faction had advocated; but Rowan and his group had begun issuing their own cards and dues stamps as the Emergency Program (EP) of the IWW. "It looks like the die is cast, Joe," he said with a deeply thoughtful look.

After we had finished eating he sat and listened patiently for the next hour-and-a-half, interrupting to ask a question from time to time, while I recounted my experiences in Chicago.

When I had finished, Downing gave a deep sigh. "It's got me completely bumfuzzled, Joe," he said. "I'm afraid the IWW has some rough days ahead. We'll just have to wait and see what happens. And fight like hell to keep the IWW—or both IWW's—going in the meantime. Rowan should be heading out this way soon, and then maybe we can get a better idea of what's going to happen and what the possibilities are."

It was almost midnight before our powwow wound down. Downing looked into my eyes earnestly. "And you, Joe?" he said. "What do you have in mind to do?"

I'd been thinking about that all the way in from McMurray. I was still mad as hell about what the cop stooges of the plutes had done to us, and I was itching to get back in the fight. "Well, it sounds like there's a hell of a scrap going on down in Oregon," I said. "I thought maybe I'd buy a new pack and head down to the fray."

Downing smiled. "Spoken like a true-blue Wobbly," he said. "And don't forget to send me frequent dispatches on the action there."

I spent the night at Downing's place and next day went down to the hall. November 11*th*, the Wobbly day of infamy, had always been a big day there, but now with many of the angry veterans of the Concrete deportation there already, it was almost bursting its seams with activity. There were speeches and singing and skits and impassioned vows to carry the fight to the enemy. And to make it more chaotic and confusing, on the sidelines there were frequent discussions and sometimes heated arguments over the split.

"Shut up! Shut up all of you!" one fiery little guy yelled, leaping up on a table. "When are you ignoramuses going to come to your senses? The IWW has had its big successes when it was centralized and when it was *dis*centralized. So what are we all yapping about? Let's stop this BS and all pull together. Solidarity, remember? Solidarity!" He jumped back down as a cheer went up.

"Well-meaning simpleton," I heard a big logger next to me growl.

I stayed in the Wobbly hall that night. My funds were running low. Next day after some coffee an', I went out and bought a secondhand pack and a couple of wool blankets and a water canteen. I wanted to wait around a couple of days to hear the latest news from Concrete.

That day the plute rags had screaming headlines about the deportation. They made it sound like a bunch of heroic cops had routed a dangerous invading army. But soon the truth began to filter in to the Wobbly hall. After our kidnapping, three of our men who had gone to try to recover our possessions had been beaten and jailed by sheriff Conn and his flunkies. They had rousted out the families of several of the strikers and chased the women and children down the railroad track and out of town.

Now Stone and Webster was threatening to open their own store in Concrete to undersell the local merchants and drive them out of business. And Conn was threatening to bring in the state militia. Roger Baldwin and the ACLU were already preparing a lawsuit over the mass kidnapping and the beatings.

Reading of these new developments, my blood boiled. Several of us discussed the possibility of going back to Concrete immediately. But the branch secretary pointed out to us that we would undoubtedly be jailed as soon as we hit town. It was a wiser idea to let our Natron strikers drift innocuously into Concrete to take our places, while we took up their struggle at Natron.

I stuck around the hall for a couple of days preparing for the new campaign at Natron. There was an ongoing dispute and uncertainty about the split. Like the lumber workers, many members of the construction workers union were followers of Rowan. But no one seemed to know when or where the new supplies of Rowan's faction could be had or what their plan of action was. So I stuffed my shirt and mackinaw with literature and supplies from the local Centralist group. Then I glommed a freight south with some other members to Oregon.

I spent the next several months organizing the workers at the Natron Cutoff. It was very rough work, slogging through the snow and ice, delivering IWW literature and signing up new members. We had a number of quickie strikes, and in some cases got better food and the pay raised a nickel an hour.

In the meantime all was chaos. Sometimes the Centralists and the EP'ers would work together, sometimes there was a frosty silence between them, and sometimes they were at each others' throats, making any effective job action impossible. And often members became so depressed or disgusted with both factions they stopped paying dues altogether.

We'd occasionally run into a few Communists, mostly Slavs, who also carried Wobbly cards and who backed the Centralist faction. All they would talk about was electing some sonofabitch who was never going to do us any good. They were strictly political, while the real Wobblies were industrial.

The greatest myth the working class can have is that they're going to elect somebody that's going to emancipate them. They can never be emancipated through electoral politics. Under our present system that allows so many parasites to vote, and sway the votes of others, the ballot box is just a rattle box for children to play with. Joe Hill said it all in his famous song "Mr. Block," about the deluded scissorbill who got taken in by the politicos:

Election day he shouted, 'A Socialist for mayor!'
The 'Comrade' got elected, he happy was for fair;
But after the election he got an awful shock:
A great big Socialistic bull did rap him on the block...

There was an aura of sadness now in the struggle. And for many years afterward there were many arguments around campfires all over the West where men sat discussing the controversy late into the night, reliving the arguments that had split the great IWW asunder, weeping and moaning and sometimes leaping at one another's throats. It was a bitter family quarrel that would not die.

I did a lot of heavy thinking on the split. It seemed almost inevitable there would be some disagreement over centralization versus decentralization in any large organization. Pure democracy was impossible—except maybe at a workplace of a few dozen workers. A perfectly fair and equal system was impossible, it seemed. There were valid arguments on both sides. You had to try to arrive at some kind of happy medium.

As far as I could figure out, the general rule should be that local groups should control purely local concerns, but that issues that concerned the workers and consumers as a whole should be decided by the whole organization. We needed some national and international cohesion, but undoubtedly the IWW had become too centralized.

Like Mortimer Downing, I was moving more to the EP side, which stressed more local autonomy and organization at the point of production. But perhaps the main reason I leaned toward the EP'ers was that they believed much more strongly than the Centralists in the traditional Wobbly struggle for a workers' world, a purely workers' government, completely removed from the political swamp.

In early January of 1925, still on the Natron Cut-off, I read in the *Industrial Worker* that there was an important message for me in Portland. I wrote to have the message forwarded. A few days later I got a letter notifying me that my father had died in Springfield on January 1st.

It was a shattering blow. I had known he was partially paralyzed after a stroke, but I hadn't known how serious his condition was. I spent several days just lying around moping, cursing myself for not having gone home more often, thinking of what a great person my dad had been—his idealism, his dedication to Debs and his American Railway Union, of what a good and devoted father he had been to us.

I wondered how my mother was and how she was taking it, and I had an aching desire to see her again. But I was almost broke and it would be almost suicide to try to ride the freights east through the freezing weather. I decided that the time had come for me to move on south where I wasn't known and try to get a steady job for a while until I could buy some decent clothes and ride the cushions back to Springfield.

One freezing March day I hefted my pack, said goodbye to my fellow workers and hit the high lonesome in the direction of

Klamath Falls. After a brief visit with some fellow workers there, I headed southwest to a big new construction job along the Klamath River not far south of the California line, building a dam and tunnel for the California and Oregon Power Company.

I soon rustled a job as a mucker in one of the camps. It was the usual story—low pay, bad chuck and long hours. Most of the construction workers union members had gone into the EP camp now, so now I was organizing for the Rowanites. Soon the EP began putting out its own fine newspaper in Portland, the *Industrial Unionist*, with Mortimer Downing on the staff. Although there weren't very many of us, we considered ourselves the real Wobblies, and our spirit was high. We pulled a number of small strikes on the Klamath, some successful, some not.

In my spare time I continued reading, jotting down things that impressed me in my notebooks. Some from this period are as follows:

> I never could believe that Providence had sent a few men into the world, ready booted and spurred to ride, and millions ready saddled and bridled to be ridden.
> —Richard Rumbold, 1685

> All men are equal before the Serene Majesty of the Law. Millionaires and muckers are not allowed to beg on the streets or sleep in boxcars.
> —Anatole France

> The workers can be crushed to any depth if it is done gradually enough.
> —Karl Marx

> I love my country but I hate my government.
> —Herbert Spencer

> The strongest bond of human sympathy outside the family relation should be one uniting all working people.
> —Abraham Lincoln

> We must some day, at last and forever, cross the line between nonsense and common sense. On that day we shall pass from class paternalism...to human brotherhood; from political government to industrial administration; from competition in individualism to individuality in cooperation; from war and despotism to peace and liberty.
> —Thomas Carlyle

By early April I had finally saved enough money for the trip back to Springfield to see my mother. Then I got the crushing news that she too had died. To lose them both in such a brief span of time! O why hadn't I made a greater effort to get back to see them? My mind was numb. I felt I had to get away, be by myself.

I hiked up to the top of a nearby peak, through slush and ice. I sat down in the cold wind and sank my head in my hands. Life was so complex...at times lately it felt like my head was about to burst. So many problems in life. As if the struggle against the greedy heartless capitalists was not hard enough, now my parents' death, and the disastrous split in the IWW. The tension of always wondering which side the next fellow worker you met was on. I was so worn down and despairing from the endless arguments. And now this—both of them gone. I felt I had to get away from it all for a while. Maybe I would go to sea again. In the small isolated world of a ship I could organize without the continual fear of running into someone from the opposing faction. And I wanted to see more of the world, to learn more, to have more adventures.

Perhaps I would gradually work my way closer to San Francisco and then ship out again. Maybe my experiences at sea hadn't been that bad after all—perhaps at the time I had exaggerated the rigors of the work. And the IWW had already brought about shorter hours and better conditions at sea. Perhaps I could get on as an oiler or fireman next time—the work would be easier and the pay better.

To top it off, I read that Eugene Debs was making a tour of California in July, starting in San Francisco. That clinched it—I longed to see my father's hero at last, I felt I owed it to him. Debs, one of the founders of the IWW. I knew I would never join a political party. But I had the feeling that Debs was perhaps one of the very few politicians with enough intelligence and ideals and enough of a working-class background that, if the opportunity arose, would step down, dismantle his political party and place the reins of power in the hands of the workers.

I worked my way south from construction camp to construction camp, organizing along the way. One night in late June I found myself in Sacramento. I went to flop late that night in the celebrated St. Nicholas Pool Hall on Fourth Street. It was owned by a humanitarian named Nicholas Matcovich, and every night he would let three or four hundred homeless people sleep there from midnight to four AM.

Before dawn I had some coffee an', then meandered down to the riverfront and stowed away on the deck of a paddlewheel steamer headed downstream to San Francisco.

31

DRIVING WITH DEBS

A ferment of activity greeted me next morning when I stepped ashore on the Embarcadero near the foot of Market Street. People were rushing to and fro in all directions, bells of streetcars clanged, ships from all parts of the world were being loaded or unloaded, and a feeling of excitement filled the air.

I grabbed a coffee an' at a dockside cafe, then made my way to the nearby Wobbly hall. I got the usual hearty back–slapping welcome from fellow workers. But as I sat around and shot the bull for a while with my fellow Wobs, the main topic of conversation was the split in the organization, and little effort seemed to be going into organizing the slaves. When I suggested that perhaps the two sides should try to get together it set off a storm of controversy.

When I brought up the subject of Eugene Debs' speech the following night there was a similar explosion. Most of those present lumped Debs with the other "political fakirs." But one or two ventured the opinion that the IWW stood a lot better chance with Debs as president than some Republican or Democrat—and that the election of a socialist like Debs might be a transition to a real workers' government.

Lollygagging around the city the rest of the day, a Wobbly named Clint and I fell to discussing Debs' remarkable career. A railroad fireman out of Terre Haute, Indiana in his teens, Debs had risen rapidly to become secretary of the local union. Later he formed the militant American Railway Union and brought the mighty Northern Pacific Railroad to its knees in the hard-fought strike of 1893. He had run for president on the Socialist Party ticket five times, once garnering almost a million votes and scaring the hell out of the plutocrats.

But the story about Debs that intrigued me the most was how he and Bill Haywood and Thomas Hagerty, a Catholic priest and labor editor, had ended up in a Denver hotel room one night with a bottle of good whisky and come up with the idea of the IWW. Although Debs had dropped out of the IWW after it disavowed electoral politics in 1908, he had frequently defended it in his speeches and writings. He had spoken out against the war in a Canton, Ohio speech in 1918 and spent two years in federal prison for his beliefs. Now he and his brother Theodore were attempting in their old age to rebuild some of the faltering Socialist Party locals on the West Coast.

We got to the small hall on Market Street the next evening a few minutes before the meeting began. There was a small crowd, most of them looking pretty bourgeois, but a few other Wobblies and others who looked like wage slaves too. How I wished my father could have been alive and present to see his hero.

Debs appeared right on time, wearing his usual jaunty bow tie. I couldn't believe I was only a few yards from the great man. Even at seventy his beaming, very alive face radiated love and high spirits. A burst of enthusiastic applause greeted him—applause he richly deserved and obviously enjoyed.

Debs began to speak. His deep musical voice seemed to pour forth like honey. It combined remarkable beauty of sound with a high intelligence that was offering some solutions to the greatest problems facing humanity. I had listened to many great Wobbly orators who spoke in a rougher, more direct and powerful way, but Debs had a poetic beauty to his speech that made it unique. He was certainly one of the three greatest speakers I had ever heard—right up there with Bill Haywood and Jim Thompson.

Swept away by his rhetoric, I had to remind myself that Wobblies weren't supposed to believe in hero worship ("We are *all* leaders"). But hell, I was only human, and even the most egalitarian Wobs had special places in their hearts for the Saint and Joe Hill and Frank Little and Wesley Everest. Listening to Debs, I decided that—although I would never join the Socialist Party—I would vote for him if he ran again, as many other Wobs had done, as by far the least of the political evils.

Some of Debs' phrases stirred me so much that I scribbled them down in one of the small notebooks I always carried with me:

"The handwriting is on all the billboards of the universe: The worst in socialism will be better than the best in capitalism... The working class must be enrolled in the cause; it must be made to hear the trumpet call of solidarity—economic solidarity and political solidarity. One great industrial union and one great all-embracing political party; two hearts with but a single soul..." Well, at least he put the union first, I thought.

"What is the socialist goal? To strike all fetters, to equalize burdens, to demand joy, to recognize all men as potential gods, to free them to rise to the sublimest heights of intellectual and moral and spiritual exaltation."

By the time Debs finished speaking I felt mesmerized by his energy and eloquence. A tremendous round of applause greeted the famous socialist, and dozens of people rushed up to shake his hand.

Clint and I were about to leave when a fellow who looked vaguely familiar came up to us. "Hey—fellow worker!" he said. "Aren't you Joe Murphy who worked with me in that lumber camp up at Sedro Woolley?"

It turned out it was a guy named Ingemar Eriksson who was now an official of the local Socialist Party. "Come on over here and meet Gene," he said.

I felt like the doors of heaven had opened. Clint and I followed the ex-Wobbly to the back of the hall where seven or eight people waited to shake hands with Debs. It's funny how charismatic public figures have a way of making you think you're extra special, that they are more struck by you than by hundreds of others. I could have sworn—or deluded myself into thinking—that a special light of joy and interest entered Debs' eyes when I stepped up to shake his hand.

"I can tell you're a socialist," he said, pressing my hand warmly. "You have stars for eyes."

I felt like I had just been selected as one of the disciples by Jerusalem Slim. No one could say for sure whether it was correct to call a revolutionary industrial unionist like myself a socialist, but I always took the term as a compliment.

"It's an honor to meet you," I managed to stammer out. "My father was in the ARU."

"It's an honor to meet *you*," shot back Debs.

Then, not wanting to monopolize the great man, I moved aside so he could meet Clint and the others at our backs.

Clint and I stood talking for a few minutes at one side of the auditorium. We ended up standing next to Eriksson and some other party functionaries. I overheard them talking in concerned tones about how the party member scheduled to drive Debs on his speaking tour had taken ill, and how they had been looking frantically for a replacement. I felt galvanized by the news. What if—? But that would be too much to hope for. And I wasn't even a member of the Socialist Party.

As if through mental telepathy, Eriksson turned toward me. He said something in undertones to the man beside him. Then: "Hey Joe—do you know how to drive?"

I felt thunderstruck. "I know how to drive a hard bargain," I said. "Sure, I know how to drive."

Several of us got in a huddle. They said they had the car, I said I had the time. "Well how about a practice drive around the block?"

I felt like a star. "Be right back, Clint," I said. "If I don't run into a streetcar."

They led me to a spiffy new sedan. I thought I could handle it. Traffic wasn't too thick, and I managed to tool the beautiful machine around the long block without incident.

Back in the hall, the next step was to be interviewed by Debs' brother Theodore. He was somewhat more stiff and formal than his famous brother, but he too had the love of humanity in his eyes. First Eriksson filled him in on some of my background in the labor movement, and I supplied more recent details. Theodore seemed sufficiently impressed.

Then he called me aside. When we were a few feet away from the others he told me in low tones something he made me promise to keep in strict secrecy. Gene was no alcoholic, he said, but friendly admirers were always pressing booze on him, and sometimes out of politeness Gene went too far. He made me promise to try to prevent such occurrences and to summon him immediately if things got out of hand. I agreed. After all, hadn't I been on the dehorn squad?

Theodore finally took me over to confer with his brother. Most of the others had left by now. I didn't see Clint anywhere. Debs looked a little tired by now, but he still had the look of a zestful

lover of life in his eyes. "Now it's really my turn to be honored,"
grinned Debs when his brother told him I was to be their
chauffeur. "I had hoped to have a union driver."

We were leaving next morning for Sacramento—back the way
I'd come on the riverboat as a stowaway. I would be returning
upstream in style. I was to spend the night in the small hotel
nearby where the Debses were staying. First someone drove me by
the Wobbly hall to get my gear. Then I was driven to the hotel
and assigned to a room next to theirs on the third floor.

As the Debs brothers prepared to enter their room I observed
a curious thing. Gene reached up and extracted a hairpin which
had been wedged in over the door. He winked at me. "I'm a
curious old codger," he grinned. "Always want to know if someone's been in my room."

"Good idea," I said. "I'll have to do the same after this."

I was so excited I could hardly sleep that night. Finally, drifting
off to sleep, listening dimly to the late night sounds of the city, I
was struck suddenly by the fact it was a Wobbly, and not a
Socialist, who would be chauffeuring Debs. Was it because they
really couldn't find one of their own members from among all
those present at the meeting? Or was it because the Debs people
trusted me, a Wobbly, more than their own members? What an
irony! It seemed to sum up in a nutshell what was obvious to me
and any really intelligent thinking person: Neither the masters of
industry nor the professional politicians could get along without
the workers.

We started out early next morning after a hearty breakfast.
A few party stalwarts saw us off. I felt a heady thrill tooling the
fine machine down Market Street to the Ferry Building, a smiling
and chipper Gene Debs beside me, his brother in the back seat,
wondering if anyone along the bustling sidewalk recognized my
famous passenger. Then there was the excitement of the ferry
edging out into the crisp saltwater smell of the bay, with Jack
London's Oakland up ahead and Debs filling me and Theodore in
on vignettes of London's life. From Oakland it was north to the
delta of the Sacramento River, across it on another ferry, and on
into the hot hinterlands to the state capital.

The Sacramento crowd that night was not so large, but it was
enthusiastic. In spite of the heat, Debs was in good form. He used
some of the same stirring phrases he had used in his Frisco speech
and they got the same rousing response:

"The socialist movement is as wide as the world. Its goal is to win the world from capitalism and capitalist inhumanity... What is the legacy of capitalism? Rushing roaring Niagaras of wealth, leaving the toilers in greater poverty, insecurity and anguish than before..."

As part of the tour, I was befriended and pampered by many of the people who milled about before and after the talks, although a couple of people, hearing I was a Wobbly, gave me rather shocked looks as though I might be dangerous to know. I filled up on some choice grub at a little get-together after the speech, and was able to head off a rather drunken comrade—or police infiltrator?—who was bent on offering some bootleg booze to Debs. When he offered me a preliminary taster's sip out of his hip flask, I quickly chugalugged the whole thing, then went and collapsed in my room in a nearby hotel.

Next day and the days that followed we headed south into the steaming Sacramento and San Joaquin Valleys, down through Stockton, Modesto, Merced, Fresno and Bakersfield. The crowds were small but enthusiastic, and at least a few new members signed up in the Socialist Party. But the best moments for me were out on the road, tooling that beautiful machine along through the bright sunlight, with the irrepressible Gene Debs beside me making bright and witty comments on an endless multitude of topics, from politics and economics to agriculture to the natural beauty of the vast valley we were passing through.

The more I saw of Debs the more I liked him. And yet, in spite of all his stunning speechifying, I could not accept his idea that the political party should be dominant. I kept remembering Helen Keller's words: "The Socialist Party is too slow." And the Wobbly maxim: "Direct action gets the goods." I loved Debs the way you would love a wonderful father who would never relinquish complete control over you.

The tour's finale was in Los Angeles, at the Hollywood Bowl. A huge crowd turned out, fifteen or twenty thousand people. Introducing Debs was Upton Sinclair, hero of the IWW free speech fight in nearby San Pedro, where he had been arrested on Liberty Hill for reading from the Bill of Rights. Near Debs on the stage was Norman Thomas, who was to succeed him as head of the Socialist Party.

Debs soon had the crowd spellbound. Along with a host of new observations, he recapitulated some of the high points of his life, and threw in some of the well-known phrases that had made him famous:

"While there is a lower class, I am in it; while there is a criminal element, I am of it; while there is a soul in prison, I am not free..."

And finally, announcing that his long career was nearing its close, he spoke of death, proclaiming:

"I shall welcome my new adventure with a smile on my lips. I shall take old Father Time by the arm—and make a socialist out of him..."

He finished with:

"Let the people take heart and hope everywhere, for the cross is bending, the midnight is passing, and joy cometh with the morning..."

I wandered out into the warm southern California night, feeling I had been conversing with the angels.

32

A GLIMMER OF HOPE

I felt I was a better, more confident and more serious person for having known Debs. Some of the remarkable people I had been fortunate enough to know had added much greater dimensions to my life and personality. It was the one undeniably positive reward for undergoing the dangers and difficulties of the radical movement. From Debs I had an increased determination to present a happy positive face to the world, to give people the benefit of the doubt unless I learned they were consciously evil, to try to make better people of them by being a cheerful, upbeat, idealistic person myself.

I wandered around Lost Angels for a couple of days taking in the sights. I still felt a sharp pang of grief now and then at the thought of my parents' death, but I usually was able to force these thoughts from my mind. In the *Industrial Unionist* I had seen an EP construction workers hall listed on South Spring Street, so I dropped by to shoot the bull with the fellow shirkers.

I was surprised to learn that Mortimer Downing had just given a series of lectures here, but to my disappointment he had already left town. But I did meet a couple of other EP'ers I had worked with on the Natron Cutoff. They told me enthusiastically of a number of IWW job actions they had been involved in at a big hydroelectric project in central California that had resulted in gains for the workers.

Thumbing through the *Industrial Unionist*, I was happy to learn the EP'ers were active in other areas too. We had a current farm worker drive going on in the Kansas wheat harvest, we had a railroad strike going on in British Columbia, and more and more seamen were lining up with us. Perhaps most heartening was a short piece about a brand-new strike at a railroad car icing plant at Pasco, Washington. The writer said it was not yet known if the strike had been started by the EP'ers or the Centralists, but the *Industrial Unionist* urged all members to support it REGARDLESS OF WHICH FACTION IS INVOLVED! I felt a new surge of hope in my heart.

Under the stack of *Industrial Unionists* I was a little surprised to find a copy of the *Industrial Worker*. I felt a little secret thrill at seeing it for the first time in weeks, followed by a faint pang of confused guilt. Coward! I thought—so what if some of my fellow EP'ers saw me reading it? I remembered what Mortimer Downing had said about the importance of freedom of speech. So what if its editors took a different view of things than ours—it still had a lot of damned good class-conscious stuff in it. You couldn't be in L.A. long without hearing of real estate promoters swindling thousands of people out of their life's savings, so I perked up when I came to the following poem:

SONG OF THE LANDLORD

Everything belongs to me,
On earth, in air and on the sea.
Mountain and valley, hill and plain
Are there to fill my purse with gain.
The very forests clasp their hands
To show they grow upon my lands.
I claim a share of every pound
Of coal that's brought above the ground.
To common men and when I please
A portion of the earth I lease,
At my own price and by my grace
I let them have a little place.
But after several years, why then
The place becomes my own again.
For why? I cannot answer thee,
But everything belongs to me.
—David McKenzie

That about summed up the way I felt about it myself.

The minute I put down the paper a Wobbly seaman walked into the hall. I remembered my plan to ship out before I met Debs. He said there was an opening on his ship so I decided to go down to the harbor and sign on.

For most of the next year I sailed the seas, sometimes working in the deck crew and sometimes in the engine room gang. I went to Europe and up and down the East Coast of the United States. We had several successful job actions and I continued to sign up workers in the union. And I continued to read voraciously.

In the summer of 1926 my ship put in to Seattle. I decided to swallow the anchor for a while so I could take some courses in night school. I worked at several construction jobs near Seattle while I took courses in English, literature, history and economics.

The halls of the two factions were all separated now. The split was discouraging as hell, but what could you do? If you really believed in something you had to fight on. They had a saying in those days: "Once a Wobbly, always a Wobbly: You can't make a capitalist out of him"—or even a Centralist. Still, thumbing through old copies of the *Industrial Worker* and *Industrial Unionist* and reading of a few "mixed meetings," I felt a glimmer of hope in my heart. Maybe there could be a compromise between the two groups yet.

In spite of the split we had considerable success in signing up new members, as well as deserters from the Centralist faction. So much so that the federal government now seemed determined to destroy James Rowan. Although he had lived in the U.S. since childhood, they now decided to revoke his citizenship.

In Spokane on February 13, 1927, federal judge Stanley Webster branded Rowan "the most dangerous man with whom I have ever come in contact. He has never stood when the national anthem was being played, never cast a vote and has never removed his hat in respect to the flag. He has denounced the Constitution as outgrown and the Government as 'growing rottener and rottener every day.'" The court proceedings revealed that Rowan was employed in a Portland sawmill—another true-blue Wob who practiced what he preached.

At one point I was working on a big railroad tunnel job east of Seattle. We had a strike. After a few days the company brought in a bunch of scabs from Ironwood, Michigan. We tried to figure out what to do about it. Way up above the tunnel on the mountain-side was a little lake, Skylight Lake. So I got an idea.

One day I climbed up there, caught a few fish and put them in a can of water to keep them alive. Then, because I was too well known by then, I got a friend to smuggle the can of fish into the tunnel. When nobody was looking he dumped the fish into the water on the floor of the tunnel and they started to thrash about. Then he called to the scabs: "Hey look! There's water coming in from the lake. You're even getting *fish!*" And those scabs took off on high and they never came back. They thought the lake was going to crash in on top of them. They were scared to death of those fish. So the company finally agreed to what we were asking for, and we went back to work.

I kept on at construction work on through the winter and into the summer of 1927, continuing to organize workers into the union, and trying to get the two factions together.

33

'ON TO COLORADO, WOBBLY REBELS!'

Birds and Wobblies go south for the winter. At least some of them do. Actually it was still early autumn of 1927 when I rolled south into the L.A. freight yards—as nice a day as a footloose bindle-stiff could ever hope to see. After playing a fancy game of hide-and-seek with the railroad bulls for a few minutes, I grabbed a cup of java and a sinker at a little dive near the tracks and then made my way to the Wobbly hall on South Spring Street in downtown L.A.

The EP hall was only a block or two from the Centralist hall—whether by accident or design I don't know. But the proximity did facilitate the sporadic but continuing efforts of myself and others to get the two factions together. In fact, sitting around the hall with some of my old buddies I learned that Wobs from both groups had cooperated recently in huge worldwide demonstrations on behalf of Sacco and Vanzetti, the Italian immigrant workers framed up on a murder charge in Massachusetts.

All summer long, parades and demonstrations had been going on to save the lives of the two men condemned to be executed in early August. On August 10th the IWW called for a general strike in all industries. Famous people from all over the world appealed for clemency: H. G. Wells, Arnold Bennett, John Galsworthy, Edna

St. Vincent Millay, Romain Rolland, Alfred Dreyfus, Heywood Broun, John Dos Passos—even Woodrow Wilson's daughter Margaret.

Fifteen thousand cigar workers struck in Tampa, Florida to free Sacco and Vanzetti. The IWW led a march of thousands through Manhattan. A hundred thousand marched in Berlin. The government of Uruguay and the city council of Buenos Aires sent protests. Denmark and Sweden threatened to boycott all U.S. products. There was a general strike in France, demonstrations in London, protests throughout the USSR, and even a Fascist newspaper in Rome protested.

In L.A. the two IWW factions had joined several other groups in a huge parade and motorcade to the main plaza near the Union Depot. But the plaza was walled off by over a thousand police, and the marchers were met by machine guns and tear gas. Nineteen were arrested and the demonstration was broken up.

But the most successful of the IWW protests was in the coalfields of eastern Colorado, where the IWW got over four thousand miners to stage a two-day strike. The widespread protests gained a twelve-day respite for the two prisoners, but they were finally executed on August 23rd.

Everyone was depressed by the execution of the two class-conscious workers. I sulked around the Wobbly hall for a few days, reading back issues of the IWW papers. One of the items that impressed me most was another of those unique gems found only in the Wobbly press. It was a poem by Jim Seymour, who had written the famous ballad of the dishwasher. This effort by the Wobbly bard was in the Shakespearean mode, but infinitely more socially advanced:

To a Fair Libertarian

Though moonbeams romp through softest shadows there,
I write no tuneful sonnets to your hair;
Nor pencil lyrics simply that your eyes
Recall the peaceful stars of tropic skies;
Nor shall your cheeks be subject of an ode
Because therein the roses make abode;
No verse about the goblet of your lip
Whence I, a god, the honeyed nectar sip;
To greater beauty far I write instead—
A paean to a gem of priceless worth;
To that which wakes the sleeper from his bed

Of matted thorns upon a blood-soaked earth:
I write but to the brilliance of your mind
That to the heights of freedom leads the blind.

I got a little short-term construction work and continued to hang around the hall. There was more and more in the Wob papers about the situation in Colorado. The August protest strike for Sacco and Vanzetti had been so successful that the Wobbly organizers were now talking of a massive strike among all of the state's twelve thousand coal miners to protest recent wage cuts and terrible conditions. One of the IWW's most successful organizers, A. S. Embree, was in charge of our organizing drive there.

Embree, a miner himself, had become general secretary-treasurer of the IWW for a year when Bill Haywood was jailed in the big trial in 1917-18. The rumor was that Embree was so charismatic and popular that, the year before, when he had finished a four-year criminal syndicalism term in an Idaho prison, IWW leaders in Chicago had feared his immense popularity so much they sent him to the most difficult spot to organize of all—the coal mines of Colorado—hoping he would fail and disgrace himself. Embree denied the rumor.

Embree and the chief Mexican-American Wobbly organizer, Conrado Avilar, had made rapid gains, quadrupling IWW membership in the past year. Now, as a result of the Sacco-Vanzetti strike, more and more miners were taking out red cards. When sentiment for a strike seemed overwhelming, the IWW held a vote, and the vote to strike was almost unanimous. It was decided to begin the strike on October 8th.

Both factions of the IWW began organizing support for the strike. From IWW headquarters in Chicago came a dedicated woman named Mary Gallagher to help organize strike support in L.A. In the meantime, back in Colorado, the mines, most of them owned by Rockefeller, had already begun evicting union miners and mobilizing an army of gun thugs.

In late September I picked up a copy of *Industrial Solidarity* and saw a blaring call to action:

ON TO COLORADO, REBELS OF THE IWW!

I felt my blood stir. It looked like it was to be a massive effort, the biggest thing to happen in the IWW in years. Better yet, both factions were involved and it looked like the best chance yet to get the two sides together. Another aspect that appealed to me was that it involved workers from dozens of lands and ethnic backgrounds—Anglos, Mexicans, Italians, Greeks, Slavs, Poles and many others—and as such would present to the world the Wobbly ideal of all workers and races working together for the common good.

A bunch of the boys and I sat around the Wobbly hall discussing it. Finally we got tired of rattling our teeth at each other and decided to act. By early October we had corralled three flivvers and a small mountain of supplies. A Wobbly support dance helped us with our expense money. We were off and cracking. Life had come to life again.

We bumped and rattled east, out into the great desert. There were eleven of us in the three vehicles, all seasoned Wobblies. Colorado: The word sounded almost as good as "Missouri." Colorado: brightly colored. And it was, too. And it had a colorful history, closely involved with the origins of the IWW.

We zipped east, rabble-rousing along the way, stopping at little working-class cafes for java, sleeping at night out on the desert. I began to feel like it was a sort of holy pilgrimage. And lying on the desert among the moonlit cactus, I saw the moon rising one night all aglow and reddish in the east and it seemed to be the Wobbly symbol, a giant round IWW membership pin with the globe and the letters "IWW" superimposed on it—it seemed like some miraculous talisman urging us on in our noble fight. Next day, as we passed through some mining areas, two more flivvers and six more fellow workers joined us as our caravan roared on east.

Rushing along, we exchanged bits of information about Colorado's tempestuous past. It was there that the most ferocious labor struggles in the nation's history had transpired as the Western Federation of Miners fought the mine owners tooth and nail at Leadville, at Cripple Creek, at Telluride. Gun battles had been rampant, mines and tipples and railroad stations had been blown up by the owners and blamed on the miners, the union had been suppressed ruthlessly. The Saint had been run out of Telluride in 1903 after a mine-owner proclaimed in the town's newspaper: "The main trouble is there is not enough money in the entire state of Colorado to buy off Vincent St. John." The Saint had gone west to organize Goldfield, Nevada and make it into the nearest thing to a classless society in America's history. At Cripple Creek governor Waite ordered the militia in to protect the miners from armies of company gunmen; it was the only time I knew of that a major politician had used the military on the side of labor, and it was undoubtedly because he had been a miner himself—which is why we Wobblies wanted a workers' government.

But that had all been *metal* mining. The history of the coalfields on the eastern slopes of the Rockies had followed a different, if equally bloody course. There were three main coalfields: one north of Denver, another stretching south from Walsenburg to Trinidad near the New Mexico border, and a smaller one near Canon City, west of Pueblo.

John D. Rockefeller owned a big steel mill in Pueblo. Steel needed coal for coke. So John D. had bought up most of the coal mines of eastern Colorado. And coal and steel needed transportation, so he bought up the railroads too. Soon he had a huge feudal barony, complete with company towns and the ownership of stores, homes, schools and even churches. And politicians.

In the early years of the century there had been some hard-fought strikes, chiefly by Welsh and English miners, all crushed by the companies. But the United Mine Workers began to grow and militancy increased. The fiery Mother Jones came to Colorado to organize, was kidnapped and deported into Utah, but smuggled herself back in disguise and continued her organizing and hell-raising. Seeking more docile workers, Rockefeller began importing miners from Greece and Italy and the Slavic nations and Mexico. But they too became quickly dissatisfied with the low pay, tyrannical treatment and terrible conditions.

In 1913 another huge strike broke out under the aegis of the United Mine Workers (UMWA). Gun thugs and a special force of state "Rangers" began brutalizing the strikers. In April of 1914 state militia machine guns opened fire on a tent colony of strikers and their families in the small settlement of Ludlow, north of Trinidad. The Greek leader of the colony was shot when he approached the gunmen with a white flag. The soldiers then doused the tents with kerosene and shot or bayonetted those who attempted to escape. Twenty were killed, among them eleven children and two women, burned to death in pits dug under the tents.

There followed a ten-day war between roving bands of militia and miners. A group of Greek miners marched north from New Mexico to aid their embattled brothers, and armed unionists came from all over Colorado. Over a hundred were killed. Finally president Wilson sent in federal troops to disarm both sides and the strike was lost. The Ludlow massacre of innocent women and children was among the most shameful episodes in American history.

By now John D. Rockefeller Jr. was head of the massive Rocke-feller interests. Professing shock at events in Colorado, he intro-duced a company union which was supposed to give a voice to his workers in improving their conditions, but which in reality was mainly a sham and a way of getting rid of the UMWA. Unrest began to grow again.

By now the UMWA had only a handful of locals left in Colorado. In the East it had achieved the so-called "Jacksonville scale" of $7.75 a day. But in Colorado the slaves went underground for $5.25 a day. To make matters worse, the UMWA had launched a massive new coal strike in the East but ordered its western branches to keep on working; the One Big Union of the IWW would never tolerate such an unfair and suicidal situation.

The workers became more and more angry. A particularly burning grievance was the companies' refusal to allow the men to have their own checkweighmen to end the widespread practice of short weighing. Also, Rockefeller's Colorado Fuel and Iron Company had begun installing coal loading machines at some of the mines, causing more unemployment and resentment.

A few months earlier the IWW had begun holding mass meet-ings, urging the miners not to scab on their brothers in the East and to protest the execution of Sacco and Vanzetti. Seasoned Wobbly orators, and the IWW girls' chorus singing revolutionary songs in both English and Spanish, had begun to whip up the sentiment for a strike. Finally in September the workers issued their demands: $7.75 a day, a six-hour day, checkweighmen elected by the workers, and the enforcement of Colorado mine safety laws.

Footloose Wobblies like ourselves began flocking into the state. The state militia and company gunmen began mobilizing. The owners began firing and evicting known union men. The IWW announced that every fired miner would become an organizer. The strike was set for October 18*th*. It was now October 17*th*.

Our rattletraps rumbled east. It got cold. Soon we were headed north into the Rockies, their peaks powdered with early snow. It was hard to believe those beautiful snow-covered mountains concealed such bleak horrors as the mines. With the strike beginning next morning, we decided to drive all night. I bundled up and held the wheel down from midnight to four AM, my fellow workers asleep beside me, feeling very alive in the cold bracing air, feeling the thrill and fear of impending battle, the heady feeling of total involvement in life.

A little after dawn we came to Trinidad, an old battered enclave tilted up against the high eastern slope of the Rockies, winding along the shores of the rushing Purgatoire River. The blood-red sun came up like a warning signal far out across the broad prairie that swept away to the east. Seeing some of the first shacks of the miners, I thought of Herrin, Illinois, and the downtrodden miners there and wondered if I could make as important a contribution here.

The town was in a ferment. Groups of men and women and children came and went along the streets in the gray light carrying picket signs. Some stood watchfully in front of crude wood or adobe shacks. About half were dark-skinned, Mexicans and a few Italians, some with grim looks, some flashing bright defiant smiles. Cute little Mexican kids waved at us. When they saw the IWW banner on the side of our car they began to cheer, and we exchanged waves and clenched fist salutes. We threw out handfuls of our red-and-black support leaflets and they fluttered in the cold morning breeze like flocks of red-winged blackbirds, then settled to earth as laughing miners' children clutched at them.

We roared on into the murmurous center of town. Knots of men along the street, some with badges and guns, looked at us suspiciously, or waved and cheered. People stared uneasily from upper-storey windows. The small town was filling with dusty light now. We saw an IWW banner in a second-storey window and pulled to a stop, the other four cars pulling up behind us. I got out and yelled back to the driver of the car behind, "Wait here. We'll see if the hall's around here somewhere."

The four of us got out and began to walk along past the storefronts. Just as we were nearing the building with the Wobbly banner in it, four large men wearing badges came out of what looked like a speakeasy and began walking toward us, four abreast. They looked mean. When they saw our red Wobbly buttons their eyes quickened. It was obvious they didn't intend to give us room to pass. And it was obvious, with other men watching along the street, that we didn't intend to bow and scrape to them.

The two groups came closer. I had prided myself on developing a talent for quick thinking in the clutch. But this one had me stumped and I felt panicky.

When we were about eight feet apart something came to me. I looked into the eyes of the biggest man, about six feet six. "Hey, ain't you my third cousin I met at that family get-together three or four years ago?" I beamed, and rushed up and shook his hand. He looked as befuddled as his three sidekicks.

It broke up the juggernaut, and the four of us slipped through. As I went past him I slapped the tall man on the back. "Nice to see you, Cuz," I said, and I affixed an IWW sticker to his back. It had a picture of a jackass on it and read: "HE BELONGS TO NO UNION, THE ASS." As the four gunmen walked on, the bystanders along the street burst out in laughter. The four men looked back, perplexed, and strutted on.

We found the Wobbly hall and went back to get the others. The hall was a ferment of activity. Our members were doling out supplies, planning their strategy, feeding early morning pickets. We were greeted with enthusiasm and set down to a warm breakfast. To my delight, one of the local strike leaders was a long-time Mexican Wobbly named Mendez who had led the Mexicans out at the Natron Cutoff in Oregon. After we had unloaded our supplies he filled us in on the situation.

The strike was about seventy percent successful here in the south, he said. And almost all of the strikers had joined the IWW. The United Mine Workers had declared themselves neutral. Three nights before, on the 15th, a mob of men led by members of the Ku Klux Klan, American Legion and Rockefeller's gunmen had stormed into the IWW hall at Walsenburg, forty miles to the north, and IWW publicist Byron Kitto had barely escaped with his life. They had burned IWW supplies and wrecked the hall—but now it had been reopened.

The city council voted to evict all IWWs from Walsenburg, and next day a mob ran ten Wobbly organizers out of town. The same day the hall at Lafayette in the northern fields had been raided, and yesterday the hall in Pueblo was raided. Under Colorado law a union had to announce a strike thirty days in advance, and the IWW had done this, but now the Colorado Industrial Commission was threatening to have the strike ruled illegal and ban all picketing on the phony grounds the IWW didn't represent the workers.

After chowing down, Mendez asked us to divide up our forces and take supplies and strike literature out to some of the camps and mines where some men were still working. He sent along with us as a guide an enthusiastic fourteen-year-old Mexican-American boy named Emilio Coolidge. "Presidente Coolidge" everyone called him.

We rumbled out into the countryside to the north. It was completely light now. Occasionally groups of miners came along, in old jalopies or on foot. We swept along the eastern slopes of the foothills, dotted with purple columbine and pines and quaking aspen, while off to the east was the great prairie stretching as far as the eye could see. Far up to the west towered the snow-clad Rockies.

After a few miles Presidente Coolidge directed us down a bumpy road that led off toward the Black Hills to the east. We were near Ludlow now. I could see round piles of reddish shale with rifle ports where the miners' army had fought off the militia in the ten-day war back in 1914.

Presently we saw a mine tipple with a U.S. flag over it loom above a low rise. Then we were over it, pulling up toward the mine entrance, where a stirring sight greeted us: dozens of pickets, about half of them Mexican-looking, pacing back and forth, accompanied by their wives with flying skirts, carrying on a spirited dialogue with a few soot-faced men gathered around the tipple.

We parked and began to walk toward the others with our songbooks and other supplies. I suddenly saw the three gunmen off to one side. The started toward us, their fingers twitching on their gun butts. They seemed a little bleary-eyed and unsteady, as if they'd just been lapping up jackass brandy in one of the company-owned saloons. One of them placed himself squarely in our path.

"You with this trash?" the potbellied gunman bellowed. "Well I don't want no dirty Bolshevik of a greaser to come and run a white man's mine!"

Presidente Coolidge, all of five feet tall, went up to him and spat on the ground near his feet. "You don't know a Bolshevik from your own asshole, *pendejo*," he sneered.

The gunman whipped his right hand out and sent our diminutive guide sprawling in the dust. My instinct was to deck the gunsel, but I knew the IWW policy was one of non-violence.

The brutality backfired on the three goons. One of the soot-faced miners who had been undecided suddenly sprang to his feet and turned to the others. "I say if we can't make a decent living in these dirty holes, let's call them deep enough!" he yelled. He crossed over to join us, followed by fifteen or twenty of the other miners, while a few more remained talking among themselves, still undecided.

Presidente Coolidge picked himself up, dusted himself off, and began distributing copies of a new IWW song that had been written especially for the strike. The goons stood glowering. The half-Mexican boy turned to the massed pickets and their new supporters. "All together!" he shouted, and the strikers began chanting in unison the new Wobbly rallying call while Emilio jumped up and down and cavorted in front of them:

> Rang–u–tang,
> Rang–u–tang,
> Siss boom ba,
> Who in the hell
> Do you think we are?
> Wobblies,
> Wobblies, Ha, ha, ha.
> We're rough,
> We're tough,
> We never take a bluff.
> Of free speech
> We never get enough.
> We're Wobblies,
> Wobblies,
> Wobblies!

A big cheer went up when the chant ended. Suddenly the remaining miners got up and came over to join us, to wild applause. The three gunmen looked disgusted and turned and began walking to their car. We welcomed the new recruits with pats on the back and invited them to partake of the coffee and snacks we had brought along in our flivver. Then we began signing them up in the One Big Union.

We went from camp to camp. Some were out solid. Some had a few men still working. Some came out in response to our pleas. Some stayed in. Some were deep in the earth beyond our beck and call. Some were held virtual slaves inside company compounds with barbed wire fences and guards at the gates.

We came to one of the latter after a couple of hours. "We haven't been able to get in to talk to the men," Presidente Emilio Coolidge said. "If only we could get some of our leaflets in to them. But you have to be a friend of someone in the camp before they'll let you in, and they recognize all of us around here."

"Know the name of anyone in there?" asked Mose, the Wobbly beside me in the front seat.

"Yeah, one guy—Sean Muldoon."

"You wait here," I said. "We'll try to get in—I'm a relative of Sean's."

We took the IWW banner off the car. Presidente Coolidge hid behind some rocks a couple of hundred yards outside the camp gate. I got behind the wheel. Mose and I motored up slowly. A big dumb-looking guard stopped us at the gate. "Cousin of Sean Muldoon," I said.

"See some identification?" the guard said.

Mose gave me a hopeless look. But again, some subconscious impulse sprang to my aid. Without batting an eye I pulled out my red card and flashed it at the guard officiously.

He looked at it with uncomprehending eyes. I wondered if he could read and write. "All right, go on in," he said with a little wave. "Last shack on the left."

We drove on into the camp. A few gloomy-looking women and children peered out at us from the rickety unpainted company shacks. We decided Muldoon's was as good as any to stop at. We pulled up in front and Mose and I went to the door. A worried-looking woman in her thirties answered our knock.

"Personal representatives of Mr. Rockefeller's," I said, trying to look serious. "We're making a survey of the camps."

The unhappy-looking woman invited us in, shooing two small children into a corner of the small dark living room. The uncarpeted floor was of splintery wood. Torn curtains hung at the windows. A few rickety chairs sat about.

"My husband—he's sick," the woman said unconvincingly. "Several of the men are sick—they really are." She motioned to us to sit down.

"How many men are working?" Mose asked.

"Oh I don't rightly know—maybe half o' them."

"Anything catching?" I smiled. "Like strike fever?"

A frightened look came into the woman's eyes. She began to protest, but just then a husky male voice came from the open door to the bedroom. "Molly—show those men in."

A burly man with a prematurely lined face sat up in bed. He began coughing as we entered. I handed him a copy of the Wobbly paper. "Maybe this will help your cough," I said.

He glanced at the paper and a grin spread across his face. "There's more than one way to go on strike," he said. "Have a seat, boys. Molly, heat up some coffee for these gentlemen."

We talked over the situation with the "sick" miner and his wife. Maybe for people in company housing this method was the best. Some were old enough to remember the 1914 strike, being evicted into tent colonies, then being burned out or run off by gunmen.

"Think this disease might spread to the other boys?" Mose asked.

"With the help of your little paper I think it might," Muldoon grinned. "Leave a few dozen copies and soon's it gets dark I'll sneak out and pass 'em around."

I looked at the two kids. Mose and I decided the best policy was to let the Wobbly literature do the work. The "sick" miners and their families would be evicted soon enough without our creating a ruckus. Later anyone who stayed on to scab could be picketed. We told the Muldoons where they could get help at IWW headquarters if they were evicted, and left as inconspicuously as we had arrived.

34

THE GIRL IN
THE RED DRESS

We picked up Presidente Emilio Coolidge and headed on north. We got to the little town of Walsenburg, where A. S. Embree had set up his strike headquarters, around noon just as a big open-air rally was taking place. I was dead tired after my almost sleepless night, but the exhilaration of events drove me on. Armed deputies eyed us warily as we approached the huge throng. There must have been at least a thousand people there, men, women and children, singing and chanting and waving picket signs and Wobbly banners.

A handsome young speaker in his mid-twenties named Byron Kitto was on the platform. He was the IWW publicist from Chicago who had been in the hall when it was raided three nights before. He had an infectious boyish charm, and almost every sentence of his rapid-fire oratory brought a cheer from the crowd.

Next came Kristen Svanum, the head of the IWW mine workers union who had come down from Butte, Montana. He told of black Wobbly leader Ben Fletcher's tour of the East in support of the strike, announced that the American Negro Labor Congress meeting in Philadelphia had urged all black miners in Colorado to join the IWW, and that every single one of the five hundred or so black miners in the northern fields had come out on strike. A roar of approval went up from the crowd.

Next a lively-looking seventeen-year-old girl named Millie Buzich was introduced. "I'm from Ludlow," she began. She pointed to her IWW button. "I've been a Wobbly since I was four years old — that's when Rockefeller and his gunmen burned my relatives to death in the tent colony. If there's a man in this crowd who's afraid to go out on the picket line, I'll trade you my skirt for your overalls." A wild cheer went up, mingled with laughter.

Later we all joined in singing Wobbly songs, and we made the sides of the distant hillsides ring.

After the rally, sitting around the reopened IWW hall sipping coffee, Mose and Presidente Emilio Coolidge and I picked up bits and pieces of news from other strike fronts. In the north they were out solid. Hundreds of special deputies were being sworn in and there had been more arrests and beatings. Wobblies were streaming in to the strike area from all over the country, by flivver, boxcar, thumb and on foot. Some of the plute newspapers had come out with reports that there was "no strike" and at the same time demanded that the governor call out the National Guard. I was reminded of the story about the farmer seeing his first elephant at the zoo and exclaiming: "There ain't no such animal!"

Suddenly Byron Kitto was standing beside us. When he learned we had a car, he asked us to take an urgent message to A. S. Embree, who was speaking at some meetings that night in the northern fields. It was already past two, and we had around two hundred miles to go, so Mose and I decided to gulp down one more cup of coffee and get cracking. We arranged for a ride back to Trinidad for Emilio, then piled into our old flivver and took off.

The whole countryside was in ferment. Racing along, our Wobbly banner flying, we waved at groups of miners along the road and at fellow workers in other cars. We swept along the eastern escarpment of the Rockies, the great snow peaks hovering off to the west, past Colorado Springs, east of Denver, and finally northwest to the big coalfields around Boulder.

It was just getting dark when we got to Wobbly headquarters at Lafayette. We were directed to the small mining town nearby where Embree was scheduled to speak. Hundreds of miners and their wives and children were streaming along the roads, singing and waving. We learned that the nearby hall was too small for the crowd, so they were going to have the meeting in an open field illuminated only by moonlight and the headlights of the cars.

We finally found Embree and gave him Kitto's letter. He was just going up to the speaker's platform on a flatbed truck. We maneuvered our flivver into a big semicircle with the others and turned our headlights on. I looked up at the moon—it was always a private joke with me now, imagining it was an IWW pin.

Embree began to speak. The crowd of thousands hushed. He spoke with firmness and yet with gentleness and compassion. I reflected on how strange it was that years in prison broke some people, and yet it seemed to make people like Rowan and Debs and Embree even more tough and dedicated. And even if he was a Centralist I couldn't help having an immense admiration for the man. When he sat down a thunderous ovation greeted his call for solidarity.

I noticed a few dozen black faces scattered through the crowd. And the next speaker was a handsome Negro named William Lofton, one of the IWW's top organizers and strike tacticians, who that morning had brought the miners out one hundred percent at Green Canyon. There seemed to be an abnormal hush as the black man spoke.

"My skin is black, my soul is white, and my card is red," he began in his deep resonant voice, and he held his Wobbly card high in the glare of the headlights. There was a second of silence, then a few scattered cheers and claps, as if most people didn't know quite how to react to such an unheard-of statement; and then, suddenly, came sustained applause. Lofton went on to describe the events of the day and his reasons for being a Wobbly. By the time he had finished I don't think there was a man or woman in the audience (except perhaps for a few stoolpigeons) who wouldn't have followed him to hell and back for the IWW.

I was out on my feet by the time the rally was over. The nearest Wobbly hall was jammed with evicted miners and the many volunteers who had begun flooding in, so Mose and I slept in the car in a big field where dozens of Wobs had spread out their blankets on the cold earth. I cast one look at the towering mountains to the west, heard the lonely howl of a coyote, and then I was asleep.

The next few days were a frenzy of activity. Four thousand miners were out in the area around Boulder. The mines were shut down so tight a cockroach couldn't crawl in. But we wanted to be sure they stayed closed, so there were big rallies daily to keep up the spirit of the troops.

The best thing about the whole shebang was that the Wobblies did everything democratically. There were no generals bossing people around. The miners elected committees of their own members to attend to everything, with us "outside agitators" merely acting as advisers and helpers, and all important decisions were voted on by the entire membership. And it was pure joy to see these people who had been virtual slaves all their lives suddenly asked their opinions about things and given the dignity to make decisions about the things that affected their lives. They luxuriated in it and they excelled at it—it was the magic that held the strike together.

Mose and I were kept busy from dawn till midnight: picketing, carrying pickets here and there in our flivver, helping feed the strikers at the various union halls, helping grind out strike leaflets, and at a multitude of other jobs. More and more veteran Wobblies came pouring into the area, tough veterans of the class struggle who knew what the score was and how to go about changing things.

One day I saw a familiar figure with a bindle on his back striding up to the speakers' platform. It was Jack London's friend George Speed, whom I had met at the '24 convention, who had just ridden the freights out from Chicago at age seventy-two. There was a hush of curiosity among the two or three thousand in the crowd as this strange and imposing old "hobo" rose to speak.

"Power is the thing that determines everything today," Speed's deep voice thundered. "...It stands to reason that the fellow that has got the big club swings it over the balance. That is life as it exists today. Learn the uses of power. Neither socialism nor politics will aid you. You must organize and help yourselves...

"Understandably some of you are a little surprised and unaccustomed to the universal nature of our One Big Union—whites and blacks and Mexicans and Greeks and Turks and Finns and Irish and Slavs all working together. But if all the different peoples can't learn to work together there will always be trouble in the world and it will hurt all of us. One man is as good as another to me. I don't care whether he is black, blue, green or yellow, as long as he acts the man and acts true to his economic interests as a worker..." Loud bursts of applause greeted the words of the old Wobbly warrior.

The committee in charge of the rallies was always looking for new speakers, and after a couple of days they asked me to speak. There were so many speakers now that we were limited to ten minutes each. I got up and gave it my best shot.

"Something is rotten in Denver," I began, referring to the decision of the Colorado Industrial Commission to outlaw the strike, and it got a few laughs from the more literary in the crowd. "But there are ten thousand of us on strike now and there aren't enough jails in Colorado to hold us all."

I held up a newspaper with a picture of president Calvin Coolidge smiling hypocritically when asked about the strike. "Look at our great leader," I said. "When he smiles it looks like a wrinkle on a pickle. When we're through it will be you the workers making the decisions in this world and not a bunch of clowns elected by Rockefeller and Wall Street." Then I went on to talk briefly of Centralia and the Portland longshore strike. When I had finished I got a good round of applause.

And then we began to hear of a remarkable thing: It sounded like in the south down around Walsenburg and Ludlow and Trinidad, the women had taken over the strike. On the 20th women pickets had convinced the scabs to leave at two mines, and fifteen women had been arrested. The next day sixteen more women were hauled in to jail. One woman had bested a mine guard in a fistfight. Idealistic young Joan of Arcs of the labor movement of sixteen and seventeen were leading lightning charges of hundreds of strikers up through the canyons to the camps and mines. We began to hear of seventeen-year-old "Flaming Milka" Sablich, "the girl in the red dress," who had already become a legend and stricken terror into the mine owners.

Now that the mines in the north were closed down almost completely, it was decided to form a huge car caravan of strikers to help our brothers and sisters in the south. On the 23rd at a big meeting in Lafayette attended by over three thousand strikers and their wives, plans were laid for the huge procession. We were to depart on the 26th.

Mose and I were assigned to go around getting people to volunteer their cars for the caravan. We went from store to store through Lafayette, Frederick, Erie, Louisville, Boulder. Many of the small businessmen depended on purchases of the miners for their livelihood and offered to help. Some agreed to loan their cars outright, others decided to come along as chauffeurs. By the time the 26th rolled around we had around 130 vehicles. It was the first huge motorized strikers' caravan in history.

The massive encampment awakened at three-thirty on the morning of the 26th. There were over five hundred of us, including many women. The caravan members had been carefully screened for booze and weapons. Local merchants had donated a mountain of food and tents and blankets and other supplies. Flags and banners flew from our cars and covered their sides: JOIN THE IWW AND BE A MAN; AN INJURY TO ONE IS AN INJURY TO ALL; MINERS OF COLORADO, DO NOT SCAB ON YOUR FELLOW WORKERS!

Since the mine owners were now flying American flags at all their camps and tipples, we flew U.S. flags too: This country was as much ours as theirs...or should be. We learned that the governor had ordered National Guard exercises that same day at nearby Golden, and three military planes, including a bomber equipped with machine guns and bombs, were being pressed into service.

The great caravan departed. Mose and I and two strikers and their wives were about thirty cars back from the front. The hundreds of headlights flashed on. The motors roared into life. We swept through Erie and Louisville in the chilly early dawn, singing and chanting, picking up more vehicles. We stopped at every little town we came to, holding early-morning rallies to raise support. As dawn came we looked back and saw the long caravan stretching to the horizon.

In many places crowds of people cheered us on or provided coffee and sandwiches for us. At each town of any size we halted the huge caravan while we took turns addressing the crowds through megaphones from flatbed trucks. We swept out past Denver toward Arvada and Colorado Springs. At night we stopped at parks or campgrounds and found rooms for the women in town, while the men slept in cars or tents or on the cold ground. We were up at 3:30 AM building campfires to cook our breakfast on, and by 4:30 we were on the road again.

When we got to the southern strike area the huge caravan went from camp to camp and mine to mine, pulling out those still working. In the late afternoons we went from house to house to turn out people for the big evening rallies.

One day we found ourselves part of a procession of over two hundred cars heading up a canyon south of Walsenburg toward one of the few large mines still working, the Ideal. Mose was at the wheel. As the long caravan slowed to a halt near a point where the canyon narrowed, I stood up in the car to look ahead. I saw a sight that made my heart skip a beat. Standing up in the lead car fifty yards ahead, her red hair streaming, was "Flaming Milka"!

The road had petered out into a rough trail paralleling the spur rail line. We got out of our cars and formed ourselves into a marching column half a mile long. We began marching up toward the mine, singing at the top of our lungs. I forged ahead, passing the ranks of the singing marchers. Finally I got to the head of the column. There she was, Milka Sablich, in her bright red dress, leading the column of fifteen hundred strikers.

Only seventeen, she was an arresting figure, the sort of person one would single out in a crowd of a hundred or a thousand people. As tall as most men and taller than some, her proud strong face seemed hewn out of granite, and with her large worker's hands she seemed a bit mannish, perhaps to transcend ordinary distinctions of sex. With her intensity and charisma and energy and gift for rhetoric she was a born leader, and perhaps the most intelligent of all the people I was to meet in the strike.

I seemed to catch her eye for one instant as she turned briefly, and I like to think there was some intense communion for that bare moment, but perhaps it was just wishful thinking. To one side of her was a Mexican boy carrying the American flag. On her other side was a somewhat older woman I later learned was named Unwin, wife of one of the strikers. I fell in line just behind the two women and the Mexican boy.

We marched along, chanting and singing. It must have been four or five miles up to the mine. At one point, where we were close to the rail line, a locomotive roared up ominously and chugged along beside us, blowing hot steam on us. Suddenly a gaggle of thugs appeared through the steam, hurling rocks and curses at us. I felt like charging up the bank at them, but we gritted our teeth and took it.

We finally reached the mining camp. Just before it was a bridge, and just beyond the bridge a post office, on whose steps we had been told we could have a meeting.

But when we reached the bridge it was blocked by gunmen and mounted state troopers. Our column came to a halt.

"Flaming Milka" Sablich speaking in Boston (1928).

"Where are your leaders?" a gunman shouted, apparently unprepared to believe a seventeen-year-old girl could lead an army of fifteen hundred.

"*That* is our leader," shouted back Mrs. Unwin, pointing to the flag held by the Mexican boy.

In response one of the gunmen threw a rock, cutting one of the hands of the Mexican boy who held the flag. He flinched but his small brown fingers remained clamped tightly on the flagpole.

Milka and the others led us closer, but when we reached the edge of the bridge one of the mounted troopers placed himself in our path and said, "You've gone far enough!" Reaching out, he ripped the flag from the hands of the Mexican boy and pushed him roughly out of the way.

Undaunted, Milka yelled out: "This way, fellow workers!"

Turning to one side, she began to lead us down under the bridge and up toward the steps of the post office on the other side. We streamed after her, hundreds of us, waving our banners and red cards. Meanwhile some of the gunmen took up stations on the steps of the small post office.

The Mexican flagboy was the first one to make it up the post office steps. "Here's what I got out of it, boys!" he shouted, raising his bleeding hand. Louis Scherf, the head of the state police, threw him to the ground and began beating him unmercifully. Mrs. Unwin started up the steps and was hurled back and knocked down, unconscious. I tried to protect her, but I was clubbed to the ground. Our forces began to scatter.

As I picked myself up, my ears ringing, I saw Milka, off to one side, being run down by one of the mounted cossacks. The militiaman suddenly reached for a coiled rope, swung it in the air and roped the young redhead around one arm like a steer and began dragging her along over the rough terrain. Dozens of us rushed after them, screaming for him to stop. The horseman finally reined in his horse, disentangled his rope and rode off, leaving Milka unconscious in a heap.

In the meantime dozens of our people were being arrested and beaten by the gunmen. Several of us ran over to Milka and tried to revive her. She slowly regained consciousness, crying out in pain. It was obvious her limp arm had been broken, and no doubt she suffered internal injuries as well. While the police were arresting others we spirited her away as gently as we could and back the way we had come.

The massive retreat began. Thirty or forty of our people had been arrested and scores were injured. We carried our wounded slowly back the four or five miles to our cars. I helped carry the valiant redhead part of the way myself, looking down into her eyes as she opened them from time to time in mute agony. God, I hoped she didn't die. I knew I was madly in love with her already.

We took our wounded to the closest hospitals that would take them, our long column proceeding with the solemnity of a funeral cortege now. Milka had a broken arm and four busted ribs. But by next day she was in good enough condition to be placed under arrest at the hospital.

The events at the "Ideal" mine had their repercussions. We received word from the north that A.S. Embree was leaving for Walsenburg immediately with a caravan of five hundred miners. Big relief caravans were being organized in Los Angeles, San Francisco, Chicago and the Northwest. For every Wobbly arrested, two more appeared in Colorado.

The shutting down of the Ideal Mine now became a holy crusade for us. A couple of days later a caravan twice as big as the one Milka had led besieged the mine, and this time we pulled out the scabs and closed it down completely.

Pressured by Rockefeller and the other desperate mine owners, the governor now reconstituted a group of desperadoes voted out of existence by the legislature only a few months before: the Colorado Rangers. Several of them had been among the brutal killers at Ludlow. Now the National Guard planes began swooping low and threateningly over the rallies of the workers. Yet it seemed obvious we would win—they couldn't jail ten thousand miners and another eight or ten thousand wives and children. Maybe John D. Rockefeller Jr. was so relentless because he just couldn't believe an organization like the IWW could beat him.

The more our success grew, the more viciously the owners fought back. Our prisoners were transferred from jail to jail in the freezing cold to prevent our attorneys from getting them released on writs of *habeas corpus*. Our chief publicist, Byron Kitto, was jailed on a picketing charge. The governor, finally forced to admit the IWW really did represent the miners, urged us to petition the Industrial Commission for a meeting with the owners; when ten of our delegates arrived to discuss the proposal they were all arrested and held incommunicado.

Just as we were having more success in the southern fields, a growing number of scabs began working the big Columbine mine near Boulder again. There was a weird setup there. The official U.S. post office was behind barbed wire, on company property. No doubt it was for this reason the growing army of Wobbly pickets had been allowed to go onto company property. There were spirited marches of hundreds of pickets every morning now in the below-freezing weather singing Wobbly songs, and an IWW band played. More armed guards appeared and National Guard planes began swooping low over the marching strikers.

On November 20th a contingent of the newly reconstituted Rangers arrived, armed with machine guns. That afternoon strikers saw them holding target practice nearby, killing two horses and a number of dogs and cats. They were heard carousing drunkenly all night long, boasting they were going to kill the strikers.

Next morning, the 21st, the marching column of Wobblies appeared as usual, but this time the gate was closed. The guards hurled taunts and threats at the strikers. Gas bombs were hurled and some of the strikers, demanding their right to go to the post office, were clubbed to the ground. Two miners were shot outside the gate and the crowd spread in all directions, some retreating, some pushing on into the compound. The machine guns opened fire. Soon five miners lay dead on the ground and twenty or thirty more were wounded. The gunmen refused to allow the strikers to carry away their dead and wounded.

Mose and I were in the union hall in Lafayette when the news came in. We jumped in our car and along with several other vehicles sped to the scene of the tragedy. It was a bloody mess. As we arrived the gunmen had finally allowed the strikers to gather up their dead and wounded. Silent and moaning bodies lay all about on the freezing ground. We gingerly picked up the living and carried them to our cars, then took them to the nearest hospitals.

We spent the day going back and forth from the field of slaughter to the hospitals, caring for the wounded and their families. We were all in a state of shock. The governor proclaimed martial law and sent in a National Guard unit of five hundred soldiers with tanks, cavalry and artillery.

The repercussions were immediate. There were nationwide protests. The IWW demanded the governor's impeachment. The miners still working in the biggest scab areas in the south now came out solid. Other holdout miners followed suit, and now almost all of the state's twelve thousand coal miners were on strike. In the south, amazingly, some of the hired gunmen dropped their guns and began coming to IWW meetings.

A coroner's jury whitewashed the murders, finding their perpetrators not guilty, though no weapon of any kind, not even a single pocket knife, was found on the demonstrators. This outrage increased the determination of the strikers. Huge fund-raisers all over the country rushed aid. Tom Connors, the brilliant former head of the California IWW defense, left L.A. for Denver, and Big Jim Thompson headed west from Chicago. Most of the mine owners now agreed to arbitration of the dispute, but the enraged miners stuck to their original demands.

The sad procession of funerals began. On November 23rd over three thousand marched to the grave of fellow worker John Eastenes. A miners' quartet sang "Some Day They Will Under-stand" and another fellow worker read some words of Helen Keller's from the IWW songbook. Next day four thousand attended the services for Nick Stanudakis and sang "The Workers Funeral Hymn."

The most memorable funeral was that of Mike Vidovitch, attended by six thousand. Vidovitch had been the first citizen of Colorado to enlist in the army in World War I, and I thought of Wesley Everest in his army uniform defending the Wobbly hall in Centralia, proclaiming: "I fought for democracy in France and I'm going to fight for it here!" This ceremony was unprecedented, the only time the IWW and its old enemy the American Legion ever conducted a joint funeral service or ceremony of any kind. Legionnaires fired a volley over the fallen Wobbly's grave (why did they do that for people who had heard too many bullets already?) and then played taps. The high lingering notes rang across the snowdrifts with an agonizing beauty.

As December wore on, public opinion began swinging more and more to the side of the strikers. But in spite of it some of the owners fought on desperately, suicidally, and there were still arrests and sporadic outbursts of violence. Strike leader A. S. Embree was in jail now, and Tom Connors, released only a few months before after years in San Quentin, took over the direction of the strike. Pressure mounted for a settlement.

Wobbly hall in Trinidad, Colorado, ransacked by police on December 27, 1927.

Our strike remained nearly solid and our spirits high. Silver-voiced Big Jim Thompson kept the ranks fired up at our daily rallies, along with dozens of other speakers. More and more caravans of support arrived. Students from the Iliff School of Theology in Denver toured the strike area, urging the owners to meet our terms, and Catholic bishop Henry Tihen of Denver spoke out on the side of the workers. Several caravans of students from Denver University arrived and spoke at our rallies.

Byron Kitto, transferred from jail to jail in the freezing cold without even a coat, came down with pneumonia. Recuperating, he left around mid-December for California to head a fund-raising tour there. A. S. Embree and Milka Sablich, also recently released, headed out for an extensive tour of the Midwest and East, where they appeared with Edwin Markham, author of "The Man with the Hoe."

The Colorado Industrial Commission, at last convinced that the IWW had the right and the mandate to represent the workers, began hearings to try to settle the strike. The battery of mine-owner lawyers could not produce a single miner witness to bolster their case. The evidence of terrible and dangerous conditions and fraud was overwhelming against the owners. The state inspector of mines gave devastating testimony against the companies. Tom Connors and blind IWW attorney Raymond Henderson argued brilliantly for the miners. But in spite of our progress at the hearings, violence continued in the south. More IWW halls were raided, and strikers beaten and jailed.

On January 12*th* another outrage occurred. During an IWW rally at Walsenburg, state police sprayed machine-gun fire into the crowd, killing striker Clement Chavez and a fourteen-year-old boy named Celestino Martinez, and wounding many others. It seemed like a last desperate attempt to disrupt the peaceful process of the Industrial Commission hearing. This time the evidence was overwhelmingly on the side of the strikers. An inquest found the troopers guilty of an unprovoked attack.

Mose and I drove down for the funeral of fellow worker Chavez a couple of days later. His favorite song, "Solidarity Forever," was sung, and a Catholic priest delivered the funeral oration in Spanish. Presidente Emilio Coolidge was there, in tears, standing beside me. "The padre gave the capitalists hell," the precocious Mexican-American boy told me afterward.

Front of IWW headquarters in Walsenburg,
after the state police attacked with machine-guns on January 12, 1928.

In Frederick, in the northern strike zone, two students were expelled because they refused to sit in class next to one of the children of a scab. In protest around two hundred of the students went on strike, picketing the school and marching two miles to pull the students out of another school as well. As an upshot of it all the Junior Wobblies was formed, with ten-cents-a-month dues. In no time at all five locals had been set up, each with fifty to two hundred members.

Going into February our ranks were stronger than ever. In the final session of the Industrial Commission hearings at Denver the Rockefeller company union was shown up as a sham and an instrument to keep the miners in servitude. On February 15th a federal district court branded the Colorado Rangers as "outlaws" and declared their arrests illegal.

A few days later the owners agreed to grant the strikers' demands for a dollar a day raise in pay, checkweighmen, pit committees and most of the other demands. On February 19th ninety percent of the strikers agreed to accept the settlement.

The great Colorado coal strike was at an end.

But not quite. Ironically, now that even the Colorado Industrial Commission wanted the owners to accept the IWW as the miners' bargaining agent, a conflict flared up among the Wobblies over the issue of whether to accept a written contract. The traditional view through the years had been that the IWW would sign no agreements limiting our right to struggle. As the generally more revolutionary faction of the IWW, most EP'ers had felt more strongly about this than the Centralists: "No truces in the class war." But now, paradoxically, it was strike organizer Embree of the Centralist faction who insisted on revolutionary purity, while Tom Connors of the EP favored the *realpolitik* of signing an agreement that would keep the miners in the IWW and guarantee some stability of job organization.

It was an agonizing dilemma. Mose and I and many other Wobblies sat around in the aftermath of the strike arguing it up one side of the Wobbly halls and down the other. If the thousands of new members did not care enough about the IWW to pay their dues voluntarily, what kind of revolutionaries would they be? On the other hand, if they were bound to the IWW by a written contract, at least they would be in continual touch with the organization and receiving its publications, and there was perhaps more of a chance for a militant vanguard to lead them into future revolutionary struggles.

I finally came to agree with Tom Connors. But convincing as his arguments were, Embree still had a larger following and his traditional views prevailed. It was the last big chance for the IWW to develop into a stable functioning union.

It had been the most successful strike in Colorado's history. But in spite of all our efforts, the IWW lost out again. Within a few months all but a few hundred Wobbly stalwarts had stopped paying dues. Josephine Roche, probably the most humane of the mine owners, secured a large loan for her troubled Rocky Mountain Fuel Company from the United Mine Workers and allowed that union to organize her workers. Under more humane union conditions her company became more efficient than Rockefeller's CF&I and began to outsell it. By the early thirties, virtually all of Colorado's coal miners were in the United Mine Workers. But soon the volume of coal mining began to decline due to inroads from oil and natural gas.

Milka Sablich entered Work People's College in Duluth.

Byron Kitto's pneumonia resulted in his coming down with TB, and he died a couple of years later at age thirty in Los Angeles.

Mose and I cranked up his old flivver and began the long trip back to California.

35

A PAIR OF SLIPPERS FOR THE SAINT

When I got back to L.A., I was delighted to discover that my old friend and mentor Mortimer Downing was in town, working on a new EP paper. He wanted to know all the minutest details of the Colorado strike, and we sat up all night in a little greasy spoon on South Spring Street while I filled him in. He looked older and was discouraged about the continuing split in the organization, but he was far from ready to throw in the towel.

Both factions had shown signs of increasing activity lately, and members of the opposing groups had even worked on some things together. As usual, one of the biggest problems was finances, both for organizing and the defense of class war prisoners. Downing persuaded me to go to work raising funds for the Centralia prisoners, still languishing in their stinking cells in Walla Walla. He arranged a few speaking engagements for me and I collected a few hundred dollars. Then one day he told me, to my amazement, that Charlie Chaplin had agreed to see me out at his studio in Hollywood. In spite of being a well-known radical, Mortimer had worked as a writer on the big L.A. dailies, and he had a lot of contacts.

I took the streetcar out to Hollywood, filled with conflicting feelings of excitement and contempt regarding the movie industry with its phony glitter and millionaires. But with Chaplin's reputation as a communist or at least some kind of radical, he certainly couldn't be blamed for the inhumanity of the studio heads. I was surprised that, if he was a communist, he would be willing to help the IWW. Perhaps like many people he was confused about the distinction and unaware of the bitter battles between the two groups. You shouldn't expect a great actor to be an expert in everything. Or perhaps—who knows?—he was a secret Wobbly. It certainly fit in with his hobo roles.

The studio guard was expecting me. When he asked for some identification I showed him my red card. He blinked, but let me in. I was directed to a cafeteria about half a block away. Chaplin, I was told, would be there shortly. I walked down the studio street, trying not to show my excitement too much. I recognized a couple of faces I had seen on the screen. Some of the people I passed had friendly honest faces, and some seemed as phony as a three-dollar bill.

I entered the big buzzing cafeteria and looked around at the ocean of faces. What if I couldn't recognize Chaplin? I thought. He obviously wouldn't be wearing his hobo outfit. Or would he? I grabbed a cup of coffee and went to an empty table. People were gabbing a mile a minute all around me. Then I saw a man at the next table nod at a group entering the room. One man among them seemed to glide rather than walk towards the counter, slipping ahead of the others. He looked round, as if looking for me. Then he ordered something at the counter, and he and a companion sat down at a table in one corner of the big room.

Trembling a little, I went over to them. I was surprised how different Chaplin looked off the screen. He looked perfectly serious and down-to-earth and normal and friendly—not a hint of his puckish screen image. He shot up like a rocket when I went up to him. "You must be fellow worker Murphy!" he said, grasping my hand warmly and introducing me to his friend.

They invited me to sit down and Chaplin immediately wanted to know about the condition of the Centralia prisoners. I filled them in and gave them some literature. Chaplin studied it assiduously.

"Come on, Joe!" he said suddenly, shooting up from the table. "Let's go shake down some of these rich *prima donnas!*" And slipping me a C-note, he led me off on a tour of the studio.

I was with the great comic genius for about an hour. To my embarrassment he kept introducing me as a "hero of the labor movement." He introduced me to directors, producers, two or three famous actors, cameramen, writers. Every single one shelled out. When we finished I had collected about five hundred smackers. I stuttered out my gratitude to Chaplin and he shook my hand warmly in parting. "When you have the time, fellow worker, come back and organize the studios," he said. "I'll help you."

"I'll keep that in mind," I said, and I thanked him again.

A week or so later Mortimer Downing asked me if I'd like to go along with him while he paid a visit to Upton Sinclair out in Pasadena. Naturally I jumped at the opportunity.

The Sinclairs lived in a beautiful but unpretentious home in an area filled with trees and flowers. Sinclair was quiet and friendly, and at times a boyish enthusiasm broke through his usually serious demeanor. He wanted to know all about my life and adventures in the IWW. After I had filled him in, feeling flattered by his interest, he surprised me by telling me he'd like to write a book based upon my life, and asked me to return in a few weeks to fill him in on more details. But I never did get back to see him.

Over the next few months I traveled up and down the West Coast, organizing and raising money for the Centralia defense, stopping here and there to work for a few days to pay my way. Along late in 1928, in Frisco, I ran into an older Wobbly construction worker I had known named John Graham. He was working on a pile-driving crew building a wharf down around Redwood City and told me they could use an extra hand. So I went to work down there with the pile-driving crew.

One Sunday when Graham and I were sitting around the Wobbly hall in Frisco I happened to hear the name of the Saint mentioned. I was suddenly all ears. I had almost forgotten he existed in the rush of events. "Poor old stiff," I heard one of the fellow workers say. "It's a damn shame more of the boys don't go out and visit him."

"Where is he?" I demanded.

"Why out at the county pill farm, right here in Frisco," came the answer.

Suddenly my blood felt like electricity in my veins. Here my favorite person in history was right here in San Francisco and I hadn't even known it!

John Graham seemed as excited as I was, and we decided then and there to knock off work next day, even at the risk of being fired, and go visit our hero. But our spirits sank a little when we were told what bad shape the Saint was in—slowly dying from complications from the bronchitis he had contracted in his twenties while rescuing workers from a smoke-filled mine.

We tried to decide what to take to St. John, and finally settled on some books and magazines and a box of candy. Next morning we headed out to the hospital. Hospitals had always depressed me, although most nurses did seem to come from some distinct species several notches above my own. It was a big old smelly building with the feel of death about it. But everyone who directed us toward the Saint had a gentle smile on his or her lips when we mentioned his name. Maybe he had the place organized, I thought wishfully.

We were finally ushered into the room he shared with some others. There was no mistaking which one was the Saint. The eyes in the sallow face resting on the pillow had a glow that seemed to fill the whole room. Looking into those eyes, I felt like I was looking into all of history. The Saint immediately spotted our IWW buttons. A smile lit up his face. "Come sit down, fellow workers!" he said in a faint raspy voice, lifting himself up with difficulty in the bed. Although he was only fifty-eight, it was obvious he was in very poor condition.

We introduced ourselves and presented our gifts, and he seemed almost on the verge of tears in his gratitude. In his raspy voice that made it so difficult to speak he asked us for the latest news of the organization and we filled him in as best we could.

"Don't worry about numbers," he told us haltingly. "Jerusalem Slim started with only a dozen and one of those turned out to be a scissorbill. It's the principle that counts."

We stayed with him about an hour. It pained us to see the difficulty he had in speaking, and we didn't want him to overexert himself. As we prepared to leave he grasped both our hands and again his eyes seemed near tears. "Promise me something boys," he said. "That you'll try to get the two sides together."

We promised and we kept our promise. Leaving him there, I felt that in a certain way my life was at last complete.

We discovered a week later that the Saint didn't even own a pair of slippers and had to shuffle along the cold hospital corridor barefoot, so we bought him a pair. And we went to visit the Saint once a week for the next few months we were living near San Francisco.

A few months later the Depression hit. Millionaires threw themselves out of skyscrapers rather than face the horror of honest work or the stigma of poverty they themselves had created. Everyone said it was due to buying on margins on the stock market. But we Wobblies knew it was the fault of the whole rotten irrational capitalist system, with the growing automation that had thrown millions out of work, when the obvious solution would have been to shorten the hours so everyone could work and benefit from modern technology and have the buying power to keep the economy going.

The pile-driving job ended and construction work took a nosedive. The IWW organized an unemployed union and I began to travel around organizing for it and giving speeches with a fellow worker called Unemployed Clark. We were trying to get food and clothing and shelter for the poor and to enlighten them so they wouldn't scab on strikers. And we formed teams that went around helping people reconnect their utilities that had been turned off, bypassing the meters.

In 1930 I was sitting with another Wobbly in a little greasy spoon in Yakima, Washington, when a waitress told us our IWW attorney, Elmer Smith, had died. Tears came to my eyes and I had to get up and leave. He was only in his late thirties or early forties, I thought. An ulcer had got him, no doubt due to his unceasing efforts to get the Centralia prisoners released. I remembered the night he had given me his only blanket in the Centralia jail.

My fellow Wobbly and I immediately hoofed it down to the railyards and glommed the first freight for Centralia. There were around five hundred people at the funeral. I never knew a better man than Elmer Smith. He, for one, deserved to be called something better than "shyster." He was a fellow worker.

The summer of 1930 found me back in L.A. There had been a couple of small meetings between the Centralists and the EP'ers to attempt to get the two sides together. I remembered my promise to the Saint and I wanted to do all I could to help. A member of the Centralist group, C. E. Setzer, and I co-authored an appeal to unity that appeared in the EP paper, *The New Unionist*:

2 MEMBERS PLEAD FOR UNITY TO BOTH FACTIONS OF I.W.W.

We, the undersigned members, attended the Los Angeles, Calif., General Membership meeting of the two factions of the I.W.W. on February 8, and wish to state our reasons for supporting the proposed merger plan as adopted by the members present at that meeting.

Considering the question from various angles together with what confronts both factions now, as well as what has transpired in the past six years, we find the following facts, which speak for themselves:

In 1924 the I.W.W. had approximately 30,000 members and was acknowledged as the vanguard of Revolutionary Labor activity in the United States. Today finds both factions with a combined membership of less than 3,000. In terms of simple arithmetic the organization has decreased at the rate of almost 5,000 per year. This decline in membership has been due almost wholly to the existence of two organizations with the same name and statement of fundamental principles as embodied in the I.W.W. Preamble.

To us the loss of this membership during the past six years is the important and vital matter to be considered and not the factional disputes and personal prejudices. It is obvious to anyone that if the same percentage of loss continues, the I.W.W. is doomed to an untimely end, just when the need of the working class for industrial unionism is greatest.

Referring to the proposals submitted by the joint meeting of Los Angeles, we believe that the plan complies with the idea of rank and file rule, which is accepted and practiced in both factions. If anyone can offer a plan whereby we can merge and have continuous solidarity in our ranks, without having to face the predominant factor of rank and file rule, we would appreciate the presentation of that plan. It is our opinion that any plan that does not recognize the rank and file rule is not feasible and cannot hope to accomplish the desired unity of the two factions.

On the one side we find those who maintain that a minority seceded and have no rights to consideration. On the other side we find some who maintain that they are right regardless of the majority. Both are wrong attitudes for reasons stated in previous paragraphs. Above all this is the fact that nothing can be accomplished by a continued division of the I.W.W.

In conclusion we wish to ask, who built the I.W.W.? Was it these small groups within the ranks of both factions today or those tens of thousands who made history, that are now not members? Who has rights? Is it the minority of both factions who are stifling industrial unionism by refusing to face the vital facts because of petty prejudices, or is it the working class that has all the rights and all the needs for the benefit of a fighting economic organization. Shall the last chapter of the I.W.W. be the story of its death due to factional disputes, or shall we reunite the two factions and make greater progress towards the emancipation of the working class?

The future of the I.W.W. is up to the membership. Shall we go forward facing the common enemy or shall we sink into ignoble oblivion?

Joe A. Murphy, X138,594, E.P.
C. E. Setzer, X13,068, Four Trey

I wanted to stay in L.A. and try to do more to promote the reconciliation effort. But times were rough and I needed work. And when I ran into some hoosier who was recruiting men to do construction work in Kingman, Arizona, I said goodbye to my fellow workers, hefted my pack and headed east into the desert.

36

BOULDER DAM

It was to be the biggest and highest dam in history—the largest structure ever built except for the great pyramid of Cheops. The IWW, in one of its silent agitators, billed itself as "The Greatest Thing on Earth." It seemed like manifest destiny that the two should come in contact.

The depression was deepening. Desperate homeless unemployed workers and their families could be seen everywhere now. When the job in Kingman, Arizona petered out, another Wobbly called Dirty Shirt Huey and I sat around trying to decide what to do. With summer coming on out on the desert it was hot as the hinges of hell. We had been reading in the Wobbly papers about the drive on the new Boulder Dam job near Las Vegas, so we decided to head up toward Vegas and see if we could lend a hand. It seemed like the best chance in a long time that the IWW had of making a comeback and pulling the two factions together.

The eighty–mile direct route to Vegas was little more than a donkey trail in those days, but we decided to get some water bags and grub and light out across the desert on foot. It was a little scary, but I always had liked trying something different. And it fired up my sagging spirits to be headed off once more on a great Wobbly crusade.

We plodded off through the cactus and mesquite. Soon we were out of sight of all signs of civilization, alone with ourselves and the vastness of nature.

We plodded through the burning sun, sweat pouring down our faces. At midday the desert looked like one huge griddle: You could fry an egg on a rock. Rattlesnakes were fanning each other with their tails to try to keep cool. Even at night it never really cooled down much, and Dirty Shirt and I would drift off to sleep in our skivvies, wondering if a scorpion or a sidewinder would nuzzle up to us in our sleep. The trek took us four days.

I'll never forget my first glimpse of Vegas as we came over a rise in the foothills to the east. We faced west into the sundown. It looked like someone had taken a huge orange and squashed it down against the earth, with its juice running out along the whole length of the horizon. There is nothing quite as beautiful as sunset on the desert. And as we got nearer, the glittering lights of the town began blinking on like a thousand fireflies just come to life, the clear air of the desert making each one sparkle like a diamond.

We managed to hitch a ride the last few miles over the washboard road into town. It was a burg of only four or five thousand in those days, in '31, but there was a wild west liveliness to it from the minute we jolted in out of the sagebrush. Cars full of chattering people, workers and tourists and townspeople, raced this way and that. The streets were full of pedestrians, some well-dressed, some in work clothes, some in rags. The very air seemed supercharged with energy.

Our driver let us off on the main drag, and we began walking toward the center of town. First we stopped for a burger at a little greasy spoon. Then we got directions to a place where we could shower, shave and stow our gear. Then, feeling refreshed even in the cloying evening heat, we set out to explore the main stem.

It was a bizarre circus of high spirits and despair. We came to the first casino and peered in. Gambling had been legalized in Nevada only a few months before. Only ten or twelve casinos had opened up so far, but they were crammed with sweating humanity. We pushed our way in through the jostling crowd. All kinds of people were there—dam workers, well-dressed tourists, the recently or about-to-be divorced or married, pimps, whores, pickpockets, real estate sharks, gangsters, bootleggers, card sharps, down-and-outers, drunks, the optimistic, the desperate and the despairing.

Like a fool I put one of my last dollars on the number seven (for my birthday, November 7th) at a roulette table—and lost. Now I knew why some folks already called the town "Lost Wages." So much more reason to organize it. We elbowed our way on past the blackjack tables, the poker games, the chuckaluck, the keno and back out into the steamy night.

We turned a corner and began to pass a series of doorways and open windows where scantily clad women sat. A couple of them beckoned to us in low voices and I felt my blood stirring, but I knew I might need the few coins I had left for food. We went on through the neon-lit streets, peering in one club or casino after another.

Finally we came to the Union Pacific depot at the end of the main stem. Here life took on a different aspect. Hundreds of shabbily clad men sat or lay sprawled out on the grass. I had seldom seen such a sad-looking scene. With the millions thrown out of work by the depression, thousands had flocked to Vegas in search of work—by boxcar, flivver, on horseback or on foot like ourselves.

We edged up to a couple of stiffs with bedrolls who were sitting at the edge of the grass taking turns puffing on a single home-made cigarette. They invited us to join them.

"What's the job situation?" I asked.

"Hell, we been waitin' here three weeks an' not a job turned up yet," said one. "The vets gits first choice on the dam, y'know. Some o' these boys been waitin' here fer two, three months. 'Bout the on'y time a job opens up is when some stiff passes out from the heat an' has to be hauled off t' the hospital or the boneyard."

Dirty Shirt had some Bull Durham so he rolled a couple of smokes and handed them to the boys. They were both boomers who had been all over the West working on various construction projects. They knew their biscuits when it came to the local situation, and little by little they filled us in on things.

The dam was being built by the federal government. It was such a big job that no one construction company was big enough to handle it. So some of the biggest companies in the country had combined—Henry Kaiser, Bechtel, Utah Construction and three others. They called themselves the Six Companies.

There had been a little confusion about the name of the project. Originally it had been planned to build the dam in Boulder Canyon, on the Colorado River about thirty-five miles southeast of Vegas. But then the Bureau of Reclamation had decided a better location was in nearby Black Canyon. But they had kept the misnomer "Boulder Dam." To make things more confusing, when the Secretary of the Interior had arrived a few months before for a big ceremony to launch the project, he had renamed it "Hoover Dam." But most people still called it Boulder Dam—especially those who weren't fans of the sponsor of the biggest depression in history.

To add to the dubious beginnings, president Hoover had made a disastrous last-minute change of plans. The original plan had three main provisions: that job preference be given to veterans; that no "Mongolians" (Asian immigrants) be hired; and that six months be spent building a "model city" to house the workers at Boulder City, seven miles from the dam site, before work on the dam began.

But to give work to three to four thousand men out of the millions without jobs, Hoover had decided to start the work immediately in the blistering heat of summer, with no place for most of the workers to live—to get a little cheap publicity for his efforts to help the unemployed. As a result even many of those who had jobs on the dam were living in shacks, tents, cars or wherever they could throw down a bindle without benefit of sanitation, bathing facilities, electric lights or any of the other amenities of so-called civilization. And already it was the hottest summer in memory, and getting hotter every day.

It was one of the worst highball jobs in history. The government had saddled the Big Six with a daily penalty for every day the dam's completion was delayed beyond a certain date. As a result the bosses were driving the slaves like maniacs. One foreman had fired a worker for taking off his gloves to wipe sweat from his brow. There was a seven-day work week with two days a year off —Christmas and the Fourth of July. Pay was only around five dollars a day for most common laborers. And the violations of Nevada and Arizona safety regulations were already notorious, with a death around every three days and hundreds of injuries.

We thanked our two fellow workers and began to circulate among the other unfortunate men—and a few women and children—sprawled out across the lawn. Everywhere we heard stories of woe—people who had lost jobs and homes and cars and businesses and farms, people who had seen their children go hungry, people who had come hundreds and even thousands of miles in search of work, only to end up begging for food and seeing their hopes shattered.

At ten o'clock it was still over 105 degrees. A few people had newspapers spread over them—California blankets, they were called—but most lay stifling and sleepless without a scrap of cover. Dirty Shirt and I finally found an unoccupied corner and plopped ourselves down. After the long day's trek across the mountains and desert I was dead tired. I started to take off my shoes to ease my blistered feet.

"Oh no, don't take off your kicks, pardner," a stiff nearby told me. "They'll be stole by dawn sure as frogs love flies."

So my first night in Las Vegas I slept with my shoes on.

We were awakened next morning by the roar of a train clanking into the railyards. We could see several stiffs with bindles jump down, and they registered disbelief and consternation when they saw the hundreds of down-and-outers camped about. At a little past dawn it was already 95 degrees, and the ball of fire rising across the mountains to the east looked like it was going to scorch us all to cinders. Dirty Shirt and I got up and brushed ourselves off and went in search of a cheap greasy spoon.

By the time we got through breakfast it was already 110°. Jesus, I thought—how are men expected to do hard physical labor all day long in this? They said the local bakers didn't need ovens—they just left their dough out in the sun. If you drank alcohol, some 'bo told us, you had to guzzle your booze quick before it boiled away. If you were outdoors and put an ice cube in a glass it would shatter—that was really true.

We ambled along the street looking for some of our fellow workers, sweat dripping down our faces. It wasn't long before we ran into a familiar face—it was C. E. Setzer, the Centralist I had collaborated on the unity appeal with for the *New Unionist*. He was standing selling Wobbly papers in front of one of the blind pigs. We grinned at each other and gave each other a little hug. I introduced Dirty Shirt. We went into a little dive for some coffee an' while he filled us in on the situation.

Setzer was full of optimism. There were somewhere between two and three hundred Wobs in the area, he said, and most of them had managed to get some kind of work on the dam. The Centralists and EP'ers seemed to be getting along pretty good together. The chief organizer was a guy named Frank Anderson, only about thirty years old, but everybody seemed to have confidence in him. He had gotten on as a truck driver out on the dam.

At first most of the Wobs had trouble getting hired because of the preference for vets, Setzer said. But they had written to IWW locals all over the country for discharge papers of members who had been in the service, and an expert Wobbly forger named Ryan had done the rest. The men on the dam were getting more and more dissatisfied. When we had a few more signed up, we'd be ready to pull the pin.

We finished our coffee and sinkers. Setzer said that in a little while a few of them were going out to deliver Wob literature at the dam and we could go along. In the meantime Dirty Shirt and I helped him sell papers along the main stem.

A little before noon we walked to a drab little house near the edge of town. Going into the place was like a great Wobbly homecoming. In one glance I recognized half a dozen good buddies from former struggles through the years and we all shook hands eagerly. There was Ryan the forger, Frenchie Moreau the hardrock miner, Joe Jarvis the seaman, and my boon companion John Graham the construction worker, who had joined me to visit the Saint. We sat and had a rousing reunion while the sweat rolled off us in buckets.

"Joe, this job should be duck soup," grinned Graham. "The Saint organized Goldfield only a couple hundred miles north of here back in 1907 and '08, and a lot of local folks still remember that. We can count on a lot of local support."

"Yeah—and a lot of local *non*-support from the bulls and all those vets and Legionnaires on the dam and all those potential scabs down at the Union Pacific station," someone else put in.

"Well, how can Dirty Shirt and I help out?" I asked.

"Just help us get out the literature and line up members for the time being," said Graham. "In the meantime fellow worker Ryan can fix you up some papers so you can try to get on at the dam."

About one o'clock we all piled into two old flivvers and headed out for the dam. Everything looked different in the blazing light of day. A hot wind blew through town and most people were indoors. As we neared the outskirts of town we passed a few auto camps full of broken-down cars and trailers. Beyond these were a few tar-paper shacks and hovels, and beyond that the scorching open desert. John Graham, sitting beside me in the back seat, told me the highway we were on was called "The Widow-maker" because of all the accidents involving dam workers racing hell-bent to the casinos and whorehouses of Vegas.

After ten or fifteen miles we came to a couple of shantytowns called Texas Acres and Oklahoma City. They were nothing but cardboard shacks and lean-to's, with a few ragged tents and people living out of broken-down jalopies. We stopped and gave out Wobbly papers and leaflets. Hollow-eyed men and women and children stared out from inside tentflaps or from under cars where they had taken refuge from the sun. A few showed a mild interest, but most looked too starved or listless to express much reaction.

We got back in our flivvers and went on down toward the river. The farther we went the more desolate the terrain became. Here in the broiling heat nothing lived but a few Joshua trees and a little sagebrush and cactus and greasewood. The closer we got to the river the hotter it got. Even the rattlesnakes avoided this part of the country, somebody said. Now hot winds began blowing alkali and gypsum dust across the road and I felt myself begin to choke.

We turned off the main highway to the left and rattled down a rough road through what was called Hemenway Wash. It was like going down into a steaming oven. I had sweated in the wheat fields of the Midwest and sweltered in the pitching engine rooms of ships, but that was only purgatory; this was hell. The heat was an implacable enemy from which there was no escape. Why did Wobblies always pick the most difficult places of all to organize? I wondered. Because nobody else would do it. Because nobody else was tough enough to do it.

"I ain't 'fraid o' dyin'," the Wobbly on one side of me broke into my thoughts. "After this, hell will seem like paradise."

We finally came to Hell's Hole, or Ragtown as it was more commonly called, an enclave of several hundred desperate people on the banks of the Colorado. Beyond, in the sunbleached hills, were the stills of Bootleg Canyon. To the east flowed the mighty Colorado, a coffee-colored torrent of whirling eddies and treacherous currents — "too thick to drink and too thin to plow."

Compared to Ragtown, Texas Acres and Oklahoma City had been like Park Avenue. This was the bottom of the pit. The only vegetation was a few scraggly tamarisk trees down by the river-bank. Back among the blazing sand and rocks were dozens of wretched lean-to's and ragged tents. Half-starved-looking children peered out from under cars and through doors of tar-paper shanties. Down at the river's edge a few women and children stood waist-deep in water trying to keep cool. A few old jalopies were parked hubcap deep in water so the wooden wheel spokes wouldn't shatter on the washboard road to Vegas. Off to one side in the scanty shade of a tamarisk tree four men sat playing cards at a rickety table, their feet in a single washtub of water to keep them cool. At the river's edge stood a small general store and a boat landing. Downstream rose the beetling walls of Black Canyon, shutting off the view of the river where it rushed around a bend and down toward the dam site.

At one side of the campground, beyond the trenches of slaked lime that were used as latrines, we came upon some sweating men digging a pit. Nearby lay the freshly slaughtered carcass of a large animal. John Graham told me that in their desperation some people had turned to hunting wild burros in the desert. We watched as the sweating men wrapped the burro meat in wet gunny sacks, put it on hot coals, then covered it with dirt to steam until nightfall.

When we had given out all our literature we yelled goodbye to everyone and piled in the flivvers. We headed over the rough road to what was called the River Camp, around the bend at Cape Horn, under the towering cliffs of the canyon. We came presently to a few two-storey barracks of raw lumber perched precariously on a steep slope above the river in the blazing sun. The only vegetation was a few withered creosote bushes. This was the home of some four hundred single workers, the only quarters thus far built by the Six Companies pending the completion of Boulder City. John Graham told me we had several dozen members living there.

We parked our flivvers and looked around while we were waiting for the day shift to come off duty. Inside, the hastily built barracks was like an oven. Graveyard shift workers lay on their bunks like men in a coma, tossing this way and that, occasionally brushing off the strange species of small jumping mice that scurried across their bodies and faces. There was no electricity, no fans, no water coolers, no showers, nothing in the way of comfort. Outside, the sandy water from the river was stored in open tanks for drinking purposes, and several men had died of amebic dysentery.

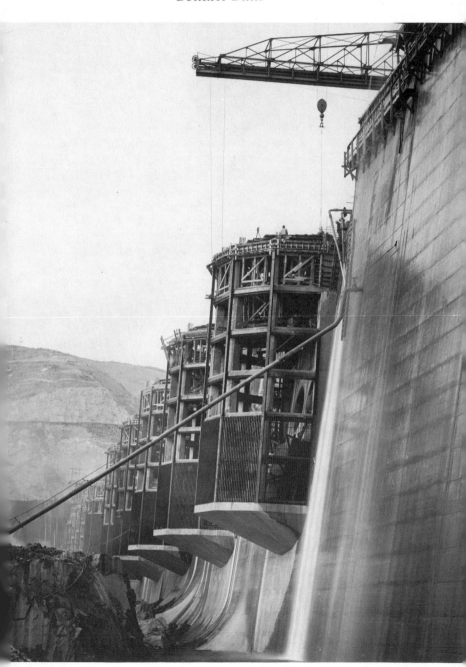

The day shift men arrived, covered with sweat and grime, many so exhausted they threw themselves down on their bunks immediately. Some went down to wash themselves off in the river. A few covert winks were exchanged between the exhausted workers and ourselves as we gave out our literature, but there were no open conversations in the barracks about the IWW because of the ever-present stoolpigeons.

When we had given out the latest IWW papers, John Graham decided to take me and Dirty Shirt on a tour of the dam. We soon began to climb to the top of the sheer rock walls of Black Canyon, fifteen hundred feet above the red-brown ribbon of the Colorado far below. Here there was no vegetation whatsoever, only immense slabs of black lava rock mixed with red and purple porphyry, with the deep slit of the canyon slicing through it like an immense wound.

We pulled to a halt and walked as close as we dared to the edge of the precipitous drop-off. I was dizzy already. Far below, tiny men and machines scurried back and forth near the river's edge in a fury of activity. Graham pointed out to us where four huge three-quarter-mile-long diversion tunnels, fifty-six feet in diameter, were in the process of being drilled, two on each side of the river, to carry the water around the dam site while the 727-foot-high structure was being built.

As I watched I was amazed to see a large truck far below drive into one of the tunnels and disappear from view. When the immense tunnels were completed, earthen cofferdams would be built upriver and downstream from the dam site to force the water into the tunnels and dry out the river bed for the foundation of the dam.

The most astounding thing of all was watching the "high-scalers." They were daredevils armed with crowbars who were scaling off loose rock and shale so the sides of the dam could be anchored in solid rock. They were lowered over the canyon rim on long cables, sitting precariously on small swaying wooden seats. Across on the Arizona side they looked like dozens of strange spiders spinning webs down into the depths of the canyon. Many were former circus trapeze artists or steeplejacks. As we watched we saw a couple of them perform zany dangerous stunts, bouncing themselves far out from the canyon wall and dangling in precarious positions. There were no minor injuries among high-scalers.

We drove on. Finally we took a brief gander at the dusty steaming plateau of Boulder City seven miles away where workers were rushing the construction of hundreds of cheap houses and a few luxury dwellings for the big shots. Then, after grabbing some chuck at a place called the Hunger Cure Cafe we headed back on the long dusty highway for Vegas.

That evening we had a meeting at the dilapidated house we had been at earlier in the day. It was still well over 110° at seven in the evening and most of us sat around shirtless. Presently the chief organizer arrived, a short compact no-nonsense guy named Frank Anderson. He was only twenty-eight, but the first few sentences he uttered told me he was as savvy about the IWW as any of us.

As usual I decided to lie back and let the others do most of the talking in a new situation. For the benefit of me and Dirty Shirt and a couple of other footloose Wobs who had just blown into town, there was a brief discussion of our general approach. Because this was a government job and because of all the veterans and Legionnaires employed, it had been decided to downplay the IWW's ultimate revolutionary goals and concentrate on improvements on the job. If we could get something concrete for the workers like improved safety conditions and shorter hours and better pay and grub, then we could begin the process of revolutionary education.

Anderson spoke optimistically of lining up thirty or forty new members in the past couple of weeks, and of new successes we had had in organizing in the coalfields of Harlan County, Kentucky. Then the meeting got around to the new arrivals.

"Joe," Anderson turned to me with an earnest look, "your reputation has preceded you. Fellow worker Graham and some of the other boys have filled me in on what a good speaker and organizer you are. If it's okay with you, we'd like you to hold off applying for a job at the dam for a while and help us with a little speechifying and lining up the slaves here in town."

I told the group I was anxious to help in any way I could.

The next part of the meeting was given over to reports by various members working on the dam about the current state of affairs on the job and possible approaches to lining up certain workers, which men were suspected as stoolpigeons, and what grievances Wobs should talk up at various job locations. Everyone was in agreement that the vast majority of the workers were afraid to join the IWW ("**I**daho **W**ild **W**omen" our enemies had labeled us locally), but that if the IWW called a walkout over legitimate grievances, most would support it. The tricky question was, which of the many grievances to seize upon, and when to strike.

After the meeting a few of us sat around fanning ourselves and shooting the bull. The fellow workers seemed more deadly earnest about this campaign than any I had ever been in. It was a desperate proposition. With the IWW down to almost nothing, we were like the three hundred Spartans defending Greece against the invading hordes. With the tremendous amount of public attention focused on this biggest of all construction projects in modern times we had a chance to grab nationwide publicity and revitalize our beloved IWW. If we lost—disaster.

"This is it the big test, Joe," John Graham said to me as the meeting broke up. "We've got to win it."

We went out into the cloying heat. There was no escape from it, even at night. The past few days the average high had been 119° and the average low, just before dawn, 95°. A couple of our fellow workers led us out to the edge of town where fifty or sixty of our members had erected a number of lean-to's among the mesquite and sagebrush. I lay until what must have been one or two in the morning looking up at the stars, unable to sleep, thinking of how important it was for us to win this crucial struggle, and of ways we might do it.

Next day I began my soapboxing. First we gave out leaflets and Wobbly papers all over the area near the railroad depot. Then about eight, before the blazing sun drove everyone to seek shelter, I got up on the box—actually an empty bootleg booze box—and made my pitch. We knew that most of the poor wretches sitting or lying about probably would never even get a chance to work on the dam. But of those few who did at least we might prick their consciences enough that they wouldn't scab in case of a strike.

I started out by asking the simple question: "Why are you here?" Then pointing out that it was because something was not right in society. I told how the IWW was trying to provide decent jobs at decent pay for all workers, and gave a few examples of where and how we'd done it. I gave a few facts and figures about the deaths and injuries on the dam. I appealed to those present to be men and not slaves. Swallowing hard, I told them of the pride of carrying an IWW card and that it sometimes was worth missing a meal over.

By the time I had finished, twenty-five or thirty men had come close to listen. Of those, four or five stayed to talk after I had finished my spiel. One wanted to join. It was progress.

We kept waiting for the right moment to strike. Now my efforts were divided between speaking, selling papers, and soliciting contributions from businessmen and others. A few remembered the Saint and Goldfield and gave generously, mostly food and clothing. Now I was also helping to prepare meals at our sage-brush jungle out near the edge of town.

June melted into scalding July. I was getting to know a lot of people. One day, feeling my oats, I decided to hit up some of the madams on whorehouse row for contributions. To my surprise a couple of them, and some of the whores too, kicked in with a few badly needed shekels. Some of them seemed like quite nice gals, victims of the system just like the poor 'bos sleeping on the courthouse lawn and down at the train depot.

A couple of times as I was on my way to soapbox or pick up the mail I saw a whore being carried along the street in a basket, her legs dangling over the side, on the way to the cemetery. It seemed like at least once a week one would commit suicide— usually from an overdose of sleeping pills. The suicide rate of the whores was about the same as the death rate on the dam.

Once as I was passing a whorehouse the madam was standing in the entrance with tears running down her cheeks, lamenting the fact that no preacher, priest or rabbi would say a few words over the dead whores at the cemetery. She asked me if I couldn't do anything.

I went to the local priest. I said, "Why don't you go out, you sonofabitch, and say a few words over the whores' graves?"

He said: "Why should I? They are the riffraff of the world."

And so I began going out to say a few words over the whores' graves. And I would recite a little poem that began: "Sweatshops don't grow angel wings..."

The whores were very grateful, and I could have had a free ride any time I wanted. But we didn't need the whores because there were the divorcees. Sometimes we would meet them around the cafes and clubs. And some of them would practically pay you to take them out swimming with you, and one thing would lead to another. So there were a few good times in spite of the heat and the poverty and the difficult struggle we had to endure.

37

A QUIET JOY

The heat increased, unbelievably, nightmarishly. And with it the accidents and deaths. It was the hottest July in recent history. Dozens collapsed from heat prostration, but company doctors listed all such deaths as due to pneumonia so the Six Companies would not be blamed. In the case of certifiable job–related deaths, the workers immediately dragged the corpses over to the Arizona side of the river, because the state compensation payments were higher there than in Nevada. As the heat and the accidents and the deaths increased, the discontent of the workers increased. We knew something had to break soon.

On July 10th about nine at night I was down at the train depot soapboxing when Dirty Shirt came running up with the news that Frank Anderson had been arrested. Frank had been selling Wobbly papers on the main stem in front of the Boulder Club, one of the first casinos. A deputy sheriff named Eddie Johnson, moonlighting as a bouncer at the club, had arrested him on a charge of "vagrancy"—just for selling the IWW paper. He had been marched off to jail. Dirty Shirt had seen the whole thing.

We rushed off to the jail. We had been selling the Wobbly papers for months. Why had they picked this particular time to clamp down? I wondered.

We got to the tiny jail. Ten or fifteen other Wobs were already there. At one point I caught a brief glimpse of Frank, jammed into the small cell with a dozen or so others. We exchanged clenched-fist salutes. Then a door slammed and my view was cut off. A couple of my fellow workers were engaged in an earnest discussion with the jailer but after a few minutes it was apparent it was useless—Anderson was in for the night and that was it and the Bill of Rights be damned.

We had an emergency meeting in the ramshackle house out near the edge of town. First a committee to win Anderson's release was elected and they set off immediately in search of a lawyer. Next, two members were chosen to wire headquarters in Chicago about the arrest. Others were chosen to get up a leaflet on the arrest for immediate distribution. The rest of us were to step up the soapboxing and sale of Wobbly papers. It was like the old fighting days again.

I hardly slept that night in our sweltering enclave at the edge of the desert. I lay for hours looking up at the glittering stars, building my resolve for the struggle ahead, praying in my non-believer's way that the Wobblies would come through.

Dirty Shirt and I were up at dawn next morning giving out the new leaflets announcing Anderson's arrest. Then I began my soapboxing down at the train depot, keeping a wary eye out for the bulls. I could see immediately there was more interest than usual in my spiel in the motley crowd gathered about. When would the plutes learn that phony arrests almost always backfired against them?

Then about nine-thirty two Wobs came rushing down the street to tell us there had been two more arrests. C. E. Setzer and a fellow worker named Gracey had been grabbed by the bulls at the Western Union office just after sending a wire to Chicago requesting emergency defense funds. Again the charge was vagrancy.

Now we were really fired up. Several dozen of us rushed to the police station demanding our members' release. The sheriff, a former miner, was said to be a decent sort of guy, but the chief of police was a real louse. He refused to discuss the matter with us, and made a public statement implying the Wobblies might not be fed while in his custody.

We stepped up our propaganda campaign. Within an hour there were several dozen of us selling the Wobbly papers and giving out literature at the casinos, the train station and at the various camps and job sites near the dam. Around noon we got the good news that a local shyster named T. Alonzo Wells had agreed to represent our arrested members.

Adding excitement and insult to the situation, the *Las Vegas Age* came out with screaming headlines: I.W.W. GROUP AT DAM REVEALED. There followed a long inflammatory article full of lies implying the IWW was hell-bent on spreading havoc and shutting down the project completely. But another paper, the *Evening Review Journal*, criticized the *Age* for its inflammatory prose and downplayed any threat from the IWW. We issued a statement that our "primary purpose is not to call a Boulder Dam strike but to organize for better pay and hours. If a strike is necessary the men will have the power of unity to fight it to successful issue."

That evening as a couple dozen of us were spread out selling the Wobbly papers in front of the Boulder Club and other cafes and casinos, a small phalanx of harness bulls came swaggering toward us down the sidewalk. They went up to the fellow worker nearest the entrance to the Boulder Club and put him under arrest. One bull knocked the IWW papers out of his hands.

"Arrest—arrest for what?" the fellow worker asked.

"Vagrancy, that's what."

"But I've got eighteen smackers on me. Here's my wallet—see for yourself."

"Tell it to the judge," said the bull. And he began to march him off down the street.

Another fellow worker immediately sprang to his position near the door and began hawking our papers. He too was arrested. Then a third, and a fourth and a fifth. It was just like the days of the old Wobbly free speech fights all over again. I knew by the time this night was over the call would go out for footloose Wobblies all over the U.S. to flock to Lost Wages to fill the jails.

They trooped off down the street, five brave dedicated Wobblies —King, McFarland, Savilonis, Burroughs and Mather. A couple of our members followed after them to see if they could help out, while the rest of us plunged into the fray, hawking our papers with renewed determination.

To our surprise, they did not arrest the sixth man who took up the station by the Boulder Club door—perhaps because their rinky-dink jail was already filled beyond capacity.

Quite a crowd had gathered. I stepped up beside our member selling the papers and began to speak. First I protested the unconstitutionality of the arrests. Then I commented on the increasing deaths and accidents and the untenable conditions at the dam. Then I told the growing crowd what the IWW was asking for: a six-hour day (or eight hours portal-to-portal) to ease the misery in the intolerable heat and provide more jobs; better pay; the enforcement of state safety laws; and living improvements such as air conditioning, water coolers, flush toilets and decent food. To my surprise, I got a good round of applause after my impassioned spiel.

Next day we stepped up our agitating and soapboxing and got bigger and bigger crowds. More footloose Wobblies were starting to flock in from all directions. We signed up more workers on the dam. But our eight fellow workers still languished in the over-crowded oven of the jail and the sadistic police chief would neither let us visit them nor send food in to them.

On July 15th they appeared in court. The small courtroom was jammed. Our shyster, Alonzo Wells, proved he knew his biscuits. Frank Anderson's case came up first. The only witness the prosecution could produce was Eddie Johnson, the deputy sheriff who had made the vag arrest.

"Do you know what vagrancy is?" Wells asked.

"Yes." Johnson thought it meant lack of funds.

"Did you have knowledge of the defendant's financial situation on the night of the arrest?"

"No, I didn't."

"Did you know the defendant was paid twenty-eight dollars a month by the IWW?"

"No, I didn't."

"Have you ever read one of the papers the defendant was selling?"

"No, I haven't."

"Why, then, did you make the arrest?"

Because, said Johnson, chief deputy sheriff Bodell, owner of the Boulder Club, had told him to.

It was an open-and-shut case. The judge had no alternative but to dismiss the vagrancy charge against Anderson. The charges against the other Wobblies were dropped as well.

It was an exhilarating victory. We got favorable publicity for it throughout the country. "Much fine sentiment among the local people has come to light as a result of the affair," one of our imprisoned members wrote in *Industrial Solidarity.* "Nevadans have not forgotten the workers' condition in the unparalleled Goldfield which was controlled by the IWW."

Unfortunately the local bulls didn't forget the affair either. The small Vegas police force stepped up its efforts to harass us and down-and-outers in general. One night they rousted us out of our lean-to's and bindles just inside the city limits and forced us out onto the open desert. For a few days it was a struggle trying to find a place to sleep unmolested—if the desert heat would let you sleep.

The owners of the Six Companies became a little more sophisticated. No doubt in response to our court victory and our increasing numbers, they instituted a few grudging improvements: In place of the hot sandy Colorado River drinking water at the River Camp, water from the artesian wells of Vegas was hauled in; one inadequate water cooler was installed; dynamite stored a few yards from the machine shop was moved a safe distance away; and gasoline, which had exploded several times and burned several workers, was banned as a cleaning fluid.

Even a few of the rich and powerful liked the Wobblies, and late in July a movie director who owned a big spread just beyond the city limits agreed to let us live there in return for our digging a well and stringing some fence. So after that we had a legal place to sleep and could thumb our noses at the sadistic bulls in Vegas.

The first thing we did was build a bunch of lean-to's, many of them supported by giant saguaro cactus, to shelter us from the hot wind and scorching sun. Then we took turns digging the well and stringing fence. While some were doing that, others were gathering food for big mulligans or speaking and giving out literature in town or out at the dam. At one point we acquired a five-gallon ice cream maker, and some of us would go down to the icing plant for the refrigerator cars in the Union Pacific yards and get ice to make the ice cream with.

Once we were so low on food that some of us went on a hunting expedition out on the desert for wild burros, and we hauled back two of the unfortunate beasts and barbecued them all night in deep pits the way the men at Hell's Hole had done.

One night as I was walking back to the ranch from a stint of soapboxing, a gang of pistol petes jumped me at the edge of the desert and beat me unconscious. The last thing I heard was these American Legionnaires yelling: "Give it to 'im! Give it to 'im!"

The heat got even worse, some days reaching 128° in the open and up to 140° in the diversion tunnels on the dam. Worker dissatisfaction continued to grow. One day five workers collapsed from heat prostration, and a fifteen–year–old girl at Ragtown died.

That night at our meeting Anderson said that in his opinion it was now or never. The majority decided that within a week we should pull the pin. Now was the time for as many as possible of us to get work at the dam so we would be on the scene to help pull the other workers out.

Fellow worker Ryan provided me with forged army discharge papers. I went to the dam employment office with trepidation, knowing that I looked too young to have been in the war and that a lot of people would recognize me from my soapboxing. But the slave behind the desk hardly looked up past my chest and biceps, and to my amazement I was told to report for work the following Monday as a mucker in the diversion tunnels.

Riding out to the dam a couple of days later, I had conflicting feelings. I had seen the corpses of the workers who had died there. I had heard of the 140° heat in the tunnels. Yet the thought of going down into that immense slit in the earth and working on the biggest engineering project in modern history excited me. And of course I wanted to help in the coming fight.

A little after dawn we passed workers coming off the night shift, their faces grimy and drawn and exhausted. Several dozen of us went into the immense tunnel. Fifty–six feet across, it was big enough to hold a small house. Huge trucks came and went inside the giant shaft, carrying out the shattered rock that had been dynamited loose, their tailpipes belching carbon monoxide fumes. It was illegal for internal combustion engines to operate inside a tunnel, but the authorities refused to enforce the law. I looked around at the faces of the other workers as we walked deeper into the long jagged opening, looking for a face I knew, but I didn't recognize any fellow Wobblies.

The miners in our group leaped in to take the places of the graveyard shift workers, with hardly a motion lost in the drilling process. The dozens of long drills bit deep into the rock, grinding out holes for the dynamite. We, the muckers, were put to work immediately, shoveling up the fragments from former blasts.

The heat alone was enough to make you feel you were about to collapse. Each thrust and lift of the shovel sent an agonizing pain through me. Scowling foremen stood nearby, almost daring you to cease moving for a second. The noise of the drills was deafening, as if they were grinding right into my brain. And the fumes from the trucks that continually came and went seemed to be choking me to death.

How could anything human work under such conditions? And yet they were all around me, my fellow human beings, choking and coughing and shoveling for all they were worth. The only respite came every so often when they would set off the dynamite charges, and we would retreat a ways toward the mouth of the tunnel. Then we were driven back into the depths again before the gas and dust had a chance to disperse. It was a waking nightmare.

I thought the lunch break would never come. When it did, it was one big blur. I was so sick at my stomach from the fumes I could hardly eat. After choking and almost vomiting for several minutes, I turned to the man sitting beside me against the wall of the tunnel.

"How long you been doin' this?" I asked.

"'Bout two weeks."

"I can't take these fumes," I said. "How do you stand it?"

"Better than starvin'," he said.

"Anybody killed in this tunnel?"

"One or two from a rock slide. Three or four from the heat," he said matter-of-factly.

"If we'd all refuse to work in these conditions, they might ventilate the tunnel better," I said.

He just shrugged.

We went back to work. It got hotter. After an hour or so I felt my knees begin to weaken. I had had a slight headache from the fumes since the first hour or so on the job, but now it began to turn into sharp shooting pains. I ached all over, I felt nauseous and dizzy, I was beginning to get chills and my vision was blurring.

But I forced myself to labor on. We had to win the impending strike. How was I going to get any of the other workers out if I looked like a softie? I was big and strong, I had kayoed men even bigger than me in the ring, and yet I had to admit to myself that these work beasts beside me were apparently tougher than I was. Maybe it was because I had a better developed nervous system than they did, I told myself in desperation—that the fumes and heat affected me more because there was more to affect. Then I noticed that one of the men who had been working with us in the morning was no longer there.

"What happened to Shorty?" I looked at the man working beside me through my blurred vision.

"Had to lay off. Some men can't take it."

"I don't see how anyone can take it. We're murdering ourselves," I said. "In my opinion we should all throw down our mucksticks and tell the bosses to go to hell until conditions are better in this hellhole."

The man beside me said nothing. Well at least I wasn't the only one that was suffering, I thought.

After another hour I could hardly stand. My head was splitting and chills racked my body in waves. All of a sudden my vision seemed to fail me completely. I felt a cramp in my stomach and bent over and threw up. A foreman seemed to be leering at me contemptuously. So this was what it was like to die of carbon monoxide poisoning or heat prostration, I thought. Well they could take this job and shove it. This wasn't work, it was suicide. I wouldn't be any good to the IWW or anyone else if I cashed in my chips here in this bloody tunnel.

I turned to the men beside me. "You're fools," I coughed out. "If you continue at this kind of suicide you're fools." I dropped my shovel and began to stagger toward the entrance. It was the first time in my life that I hadn't been able to handle a job, but I was convinced that if I didn't get out of that gas-filled tunnel I'd be a dead man.

I threw myself down just outside the entrance and lay gasping. Somebody came up to me and gave me a drink of the dirty brown river water, and I felt sand in my teeth. After a few minutes I began to feel better.

I went back to the camp and got my gear, feeling shamefaced but lucky to be alive. I dreaded going back to the Wobbly jungle to explain what had happened. But after experiencing the untenable conditions in the tunnels I was more determined that we organize the job than ever.

The fellow workers at the camp that night were sympathetic and told me I had done the right thing. One of them had had a brother who had died of heat prostration in the tunnels. Later we sat around singing songs from the *Little Red Songbook* and my spirits revived somewhat. So it was back to soapboxing and selling the Wobbly papers.

August was even hotter than July. Still, hundreds of desperate job-seekers kept pouring into town. The big muckamucks of the Six Companies knew they had ten potential replacements for every worker who might be killed in an accident or go out on strike. The Depression meant more unrest, but it also meant more scabs.

Around three-thirty on August 7th three or four other Wobs and I were down at the dam site giving out literature when the swing shift arrived to work on the diversion tunnels. We were down at the boat landing where barges waited to take the day shift upstream to the River Camp barracks. The sun was blazing down like a thousand cannons. Somebody suddenly saw a notice proclaiming a pay reduction: Muckers were to be reduced from $5 a day to $4, cable-tenders from $5.60 to $4, and brakemen from $5.60 to $5.

A roar of angry protest went up from the group. The other Wobblies and I rushed over to look at the notice. Now, we knew, was the time to strike.

Fortunately all of us were seasoned Wobs. While the men milled about grouchily the older Wobbly beside me, a tough hard-rock miner who had been through the works, leaped up on a piling and shouted for silence. The very rapidity of his movement seemed to galvanize the milling men about us.

"Fellow workers!" he shouted. "My brother died in that tunnel over there! All of you are taking your lives in your hands every day to enrich the greedy s.o.b.s who own the Big Six. Is this how they show their appreciation for your work and sweat, by cutting you down below what men get for safe jobs in town? Let's show the s.o.b.s that we're men, not slaves!"

Cheers and shouts of approval went up. Then a few more men sounded off. I got up at one point and went over our list of grievances and urged the men to wait for the day shift crew to come off and ask them to join in our protest. When the day shift men began arriving a few minutes later we rushed up to them with the bad news, and these exhausted laborers joined in the outrage of the swing shift. The first Wobbly speaker got up again and urged both groups of workers to come to a meeting at the River Camp mess hall at five o'clock to discuss the situation. In the meantime we dispatched a fast car to Vegas to summon our veteran organizers.

Some four hundred disgruntled slaves jammed into the River Camp mess hall at five. I felt the fire of old Wobbly struggles being rekindled in my veins. Now we had our best speakers there, including Frank Anderson, John Graham and several others. If I had ever seen a group of workers chomping at the bit to strike it was this one. Worker after worker, their earnest faces dripping with sweat, got up and sounded off about the terrible conditions on the dam. Finally, when feeling was running at its highest, one of our speakers called for a strike vote. It was unanimous to go out. A huge cheer of jubilation and determination went up from the throng.

Then, when things had died down a little, one of our members suggested we elect a committee to draw up a list of demands to take to the Big Six. Nominations began. I realized this was a tricky, crucial time for us. The next few moments would decide whether this was a full-blown Wobbly strike, with all the publicity it would gain for our floundering movement, or only a *Wobbly-fomented* strike, which would be less impressive.

Several of our members were nominated, along with about twice as many who weren't Wobs. We held our breath as the voting began. When the voting ended my heart sank. We were outnumbered on the committee. But what the hell, I thought—we had always been the unappreciated shock troops of the labor movement, but we had always struggled just as hard to help the benighted work ox anyway—why should we stop now? So it would not be an official IWW strike.

Next a committee was chosen to go to the newly completed camp at Boulder City to try to get the men out there too. The men were in high spirits as they streamed out of the steaming hall, determined to show the big muckamucks of the Six Companies that they couldn't be pushed around.

The men at Boulder City were responsive. A meeting was called for seven o'clock in the new mess hall there, and over six hundred angry workers poured in to vent their grievances. Again speaker after speaker, including many Wobblies, got up and blistered the owners with their rhetoric. Again they voted overwhelmingly to strike. Even the higher-paid mechanics and carpenters joined in. Now almost fifteen hundred workers were on strike. But again, when an expanded strike committee was elected, we Wobblies were in the minority.

In jubilation the workers vowed to stay in the camps, and we felt there was still a chance we might emerge as leaders of the strike. We stayed up half the night distributing our literature to all the camps and urging individual workers to come out for the IWW, then plopped down exhausted beside our flivvers by the edge of the river at Ragtown to see what the next day would bring.

By the following day the committee had formulated its list of demands:

Cancel the pay cut.
Rehire all striking workers.
A portal-to-portal eight-hour day.
Cool, pure water and flush toilets.
Changing rooms at the tunnel exits.
A man in each tunnel to provide first aid to injured workers.
Compliance with all mine safety laws.

And a couple of others.

We were all jubilant and confident of success. Sure of victory, many workers raced off to Vegas to celebrate and have their first day off in weeks or months. Meanwhile our committee presented its list of demands to the Big Six. The head foreman, "Hurry Up" Crowe, answered that they would need twenty-four hours to consider a reply.

The *New York Times* and other papers all over the country carried front page stories about the strike. Interviewed by phone, foreman Crowe was quoted as saying the "protest" would have little effect, that it was "largely the effect of IWW agitation, and the company would be glad to get rid of such."

Due to our not having a majority on the strike committee, this body issued a statement to the press that the walkout was a spontaneous reaction to the wage cut and did not result from IWW agitation. But we were used to such disavowals, which we knew were in some cases needed to gain public support, and we vowed to fight on for the workers as hard as ever. In addition to continuing our propaganda among the workers we sent out committees to solicit support in Las Vegas and elsewhere, and many local merchants began to contribute "care packages" for the striking workers.

Next day came the answer from the Big Six. To everybody's shock and dismay, it was a flat NO. Big Six president William Wattis announced bluntly: "We will not discuss the matter with them. They will have to work under our conditions or not at all." "Hurry Up" Crowe announced that the project was being closed down entirely. The company refused to make concessions on a single point, and ordered the striking workers to leave the federal reservation the dam site and camps were on.

To drive their case home, Crowe boasted that the Six Companies were six months ahead of schedule "and we can afford to refuse concessions." It suddenly struck me: Herbert Hoover was an engineer. He had started the project six months early, before housing and sanitation were available, not so much to give jobs to a handful of unemployed, with the attendant good publicity, but to help the engineer-owners beat their deadline.

We were shocked, dismayed, angry, incredulous. Jubilant and determined a few hours before, many of the strikers now walked around like whipped dogs, their heads hanging sheepishly. Many got their paychecks and left for Vegas; some even hopped freight trains out of the area.

Reports circulated that federal troops might be called in, striking terror into the hearts of some of the less battle-scarred slaves. The strike suddenly seemed on the verge of falling apart. But the Wobblies and other members of the strike committee urged as many workers as possible to remain in the company camps, pointing out that we were on a U.S. government reservation and that it was up to the Bureau of Reclamation, not the Six Companies, to order us out of the area. And the U.S. government, thus far, had remained neutral.

Around two hundred men, many of them Wobs, decided to stay in at the River Camp and force the owners' hand. Some of the rest of us joined them, while other Wobs went back to Vegas to work on strike support. At the stifling River Camp we sat up half the night debating what to do if troops came.

Next morning our lookouts rushed into the sweltering barracks and announced that a caravan of trucks was approaching. We rushed to the windows just in time to see dozens of armed men leaping down from the big vehicles, surrounding the barracks.

The armed men came in after us. It was all I could do to refrain from slugging one of the gun-thugs, but it would have been suicidal to resist. As they swarmed into the barracks Fred Fuglevik, one of our main organizers, yelled out: "Keep cool, boys—remember that we're Wobblies." And so we bit our lips and swallowed our pride and let the pistol petes herd us into the waiting trucks.

But to everyone's astonishment, just as the trucks we were in were about to pull out, a U.S. marshal's car suddenly roared up in a swirl of dust. A deputy marshal leaped out and arrested the first gunman in sight. He ordered the other strikebreakers to hand over their guns, and told us to get out of the trucks. To our surprise and delight, he announced that the Big Six had no authority to evict anyone from a federal reservation. The strike was still alive.

Now it was the gunmen's turn to look cowed and sheepish. Scowling, they reluctantly climbed back into their trucks and drove away.

We thanked the deputy marshal and celebrated our at least temporary victory. By god maybe governments and bureaucracies weren't always so bad after all. We had won the case of Frank Anderson and the other jailed Wobs, and now this. Maybe a little justice and rationality was beginning to seep into civilization. To raise our spirits higher, a long caravan of Wobbly cars later arrived from Vegas, bringing us coffee, food and other supplies.

To raise our spirits even higher, that evening a group of writers and journalists, including the left-wing author and critic Edmund Wilson, came to visit the strikers. With such sympathetic high-level attention we began to feel we were invincible again.

But our euphoria was not to last for long. The news soon followed that the Bureau of Reclamation had come to a decision: Next morning federal officials were coming to order us off the reservation.

Our spirits plummeted. The federal government had pledged, months before, to try to maintain decent wage levels, and the Six Companies had pledged to do the same—and now this. Some of us argued for resistance and were willing to die if necessary for the cause, but the non-Wobblies were not of such mettle. A miasma of gloom settled over the stifling camp. And I remembered how, in some of his early writings, Eugene Debs had speculated that if the government owned all the industries under socialism, it might be even harder for the workers to remedy, through strike action, any injustices that might arise.

Even the weather seemed to be in collusion in the melodrama. A blanket of thick clouds, almost unheard of in summer, began to obscure the moon and stars.

Next morning we sat awaiting our fate. To some of us it seemed like the death knell of the IWW. Twelve years of almost incessant struggle, I thought, to end like this. It seemed an unbearable fate.

The sultry air was charged with moisture and smelling of rain. It was as if the river was going to rise and engulf us and drown us all. Around eight the government vehicles approached—several sedans, some trucks, and a bus. Several U.S. marshals, accompanied by the chief Bureau of Reclamation official on the dam, Walker R. Young, entered the big mess hall we were waiting in. It was a humiliating moment. As if the eternal grandeur of nature sympathized with the IWW and our plight, raindrops began to fall —the first in months of unbroken sunshine—just as the government men entered the building.

Young was a typical mealy-mouthed bureaucrat and apologist for the big money men. He mounted a bench and thanked us for the orderly non-violent way we had conducted the strike. Then he asked us to be good little boys and leave the reservation, as he was sure we would.

At that very instant, as if the gods were furious, a small landslide of boulders loosened up by the rain shot down the steep hillside just outside the building and plummeted into the river.

We saw it was useless to resist. But we could not go without some protest. I shot up and in no uncertain language told Young and the others that they were spineless pawns, pimps and puppets in the pockets of the Big Six. A number of other Wobblies did the same. Then Red Williams, chairman of the strike committee, got up and affirmed that leaving the reservation was not the end of the strike, because we could still picket at the entrance to the reservation.

The rain came down harder now. We trooped angry but undefeated out to the trucks. I had seldom felt more despondent. During the long run into Vegas most of us sat unspeaking, nursing our private thoughts of despair, anger, defiance, uncertainty.

We got as many of the workers together as we could in Vegas. They were an angry, desperate bunch. Some had already blown what money they had on booze, broads or blackjack, and hunger pangs were beginning to get the upper hand over their power of reason, their sense of justice. Of the nearly fifteen hundred who had gone out on strike, only three to four hundred seemed interested in lifting a finger to continue the struggle.

Of those who remained true-blue, most of them Wobblies, it was decided in a last desperate effort to establish a strikers' tent city, which came to be called Camp Stand, a ways outside the reservation on Boulder Highway. We would station pickets all along the roadway and hope we could dissuade workers from returning to the job until our demands were met. It might just work. If not, we would go down fighting.

The Big Six were quick to get moving again as soon as they got the government to evict us. They announced that they were beginning to hire replacement workers. But the employment office was to be moved from Vegas to the reservation boundary, agitators were to be screened out, and no one could henceforth enter the reservation without a government pass.

The walkout had not been completely unsuccessful, however. Though the reduced wage scale would stay in effect, the company guaranteed no more reductions for the duration of the project. They promised to begin installing electric lights and water coolers, to install changing rooms at the tunnel entrances, and to step up completion of the housing at Boulder City. We could take some consolation in achieving at least part of our demands.

Next day the hiring began and the two hundred or so of us who were sticking to our guns took up our lonely picket stations, strung out along the highway leading to the reservation. Could we keep the strike alive? It wasn't long before we got our answer: Hundreds of desperate workers raced by, choking us with dust in their hell-bent race to feed their bellies. It was the longest and most dismal day of my life.

We picketed for two days more, but by that time a full complement of workers had been hired again at the dam. In despair, we voted to "return the strike to the job"—under the circumstances, a hollow meaningless phrase.

Little by little, unable to get rehired, our members drifted off. I stuck around and worked on the Wobbly ranch for a while, and helped sell our papers, but we all knew in our inmost hearts that the cause was lost. Our great Wobbly dream was floundering, burnt out by the scalding summer heat, frozen out by the cold hearts of greedy men.

In September the heat began to ease a little, and late one evening a few of us sat around a campfire out at the edge of the desert, me and John Graham and Neil Logan and a couple of others. We all seemed to look into one another's eyes with a questioning look at the same time.

"Well, it's going down the tubes, boys." Neil said what we were all thinking. "Goodbye IWW."

"Well, we fought the good fight, boys," John Graham said. "We're the lucky ones. We had some vision. We tried to do something. The others are just lackeys or mindless work oxes."

"I remember what A.S. Embree told some reporter when we were in jail in the Colorado coal strike," I said: "'The end in view is well worth striving for, but in the struggle itself lies the happiness of the fighter.'"

"Maybe some day, hundreds of years from now, people will think of the IWW as America's Camelot," John Graham said. "And a hell of a lot more democratic and human one."

"Jesus, ain't we some high-blown philosopher 'bos," another Wobbly said.

"Don't put us down too bad," John Graham said. "Them in-te-lek-you-alls have to eat before they can philosophize. We Wobs have been helpin' folks to eat."

"Maybe we were just too far ahead of our time," another Wobbly said. "Maybe the world isn't ready for real democracy yet."

"There's never been anything like the IWW," Neil Logan said. "There never will be again."

A few days later I felt a strange need to take one last look at the dam. I hitched a ride out near the entrance gate to the reservation, sneaked around it out through the desert, and hiked a long ways down to the shoulder of Black Canyon. There it was all spread out below me, the vast immensity of it, and I sat there for hours as the sun went down and the hundreds of lights of the project flashed on below me. Boulder Dam—the biggest physical object in America's history...the vanquisher of the biggest idea in America's history.

Looking down into that immense beehive of relentless activity, I suddenly had an overpowering sense of the ceaseless flowing of history, moving like the ribbon of the river far below, all about me, endlessly, immersing me in its unending tide, ancient Egypt, Greece, the bitter class wars of Rome, the French and Russian revolutions, the struggles of the Wobblies, the endless struggle of human consciousness to make some sense of it all, the gropings upward into the light and the descents back into darkness, the ceaseless ebb and flow of good and evil, charity and greed, love and hate.

In the failing light a sudden compelling thought came to me, and I decided to pen one of my own aphorisms in one of the small notebooks I always kept with me:

Sanity consists of trying to do those things which produce the most happiness in proportion to unhappiness in all of the consciousness that exists and that will exist.

It's hard to see a dream die. Especially when it's the most beautiful and glowing dream that has ever existed. The IWW might be destroyed. But sooner or later another movement would take its place. Perhaps a movement more extreme — even as extreme as capitalism — or perhaps one making certain compromises with the beast that was trying to devour it. And perhaps after hundreds of years, and endless struggles and experiments and new combinations, a world would finally emerge in which people were no longer trying to take advantage of one another, but trying to help one another create the greatest common good.

The world above the great dam was now in blackness. What next? I wondered. I thought back to that day long ago when I had lain in a lumber camp north of Seattle trying to plot out the future course of my life. When I had decided to spend my life working partly for myself and partly to improve the world. Of getting a decent stable job and doing some part-time organizing. It still sounded like a good plan.

I thought of San Francisco, the city of my birth. It was cool there. It was a union town. Perhaps I could latch onto something decent there, put down roots, help both myself and others...

And I thought of how fortunate I was to have lived in these times, in the days of the IWW, to have taken part in the struggle for a better world. Yes, I was one of the lucky ones — I hadn't gone through my youth half-asleep, I had stood up like a stiff with some guts and brains, my life had been worthwhile. And I knew that though the IWW might die as an organization, its ideas of a good life for all would live on, they never could be crushed.

Night came down. I stretched out in the darkness and rested my head on my arms. The earth and the dark sky wrapped their arms about me and enveloped me in sleep. And that night I had a dream. It was all kind of jumbled up, but it had a kind of luminous quality through it all too. I was somewhere in a high mountain meadow. Huge peaks rose on all sides and a few miners' cabins stood here and there. I realized it must be Telluride.

Suddenly a familiar face appeared before me: It was the Saint. Looking into his eyes I felt filled with a quiet joy. I remember just a few words of the conversation we had. I remember saying "Hi, Saint..." and then he said something and I said "Sure my dues are paid up, I'm paid up way in advance, Vint." And I had a struggle to say the next words but I finally said, "Remember those times I visited you in the hospital in Frisco, Vint? Well I always wanted to tell you: You're my favorite Wobbly of all..."

And then suddenly my mom and dad were there. "Hi Ma. Hi Pop. Vint, this is my dad and mom. Best damned cook in all Missouri." And then I was talking to just my mom for a minute. "I did my best to be good, Ma, to try to figure it all out... Just because we call him Jerusalem Slim doesn't mean we don't have respect for him..."

And then I was with only the Saint again. And he was pointing way up in the sky and there was a switchback trail going back and forth and back and forth for what seemed miles almost straight up to this gaping hole in the mountaintop towering over us. "Where?" I said. "Oh, I see it now, Vint. So that's the Smuggler–Union up there. It's sure a long way up. You sure did a good job organizing there, Vint. Jesus, that mine is damn near up in the sky." And he said something and I said, "Sure I'll go up there with you, Vint, I'd go anywhere with you... You say Bill's up there too? And Gurley and Wesley and Joe and Frank Little and Gene and Father Hagerty? You say all of the fellow workers are up there? We got it totally organized, huh? You say there's a Wobbly utopian colony up there? The real Cooperative Commonwealth, huh? By god I knew we'd get it someday. Let's start climbin', Vint."

But when I turned my head the Saint was gone and I couldn't see him anywhere. I wondered if those dishes were still on the roof of that greasy spoon in Seattle...

SOLIDARITY!

AFTERWORD

After his years in the IWW, Joseph Murphy went on to become a major figure in West Coast labor. He made a motion for a general strike in the 1934 waterfront strike that became the most dramatic and significant labor struggle in the western United States, and later won for his union the first six-hour day and the first employer-financed medical plan.

INDEX

*Eugene Nelson with his
daughter, Tamar Juana Nelson*

'SONG OF MYSELF'

I was born in Modesto, California, which perhaps accounts for my seeming modesty. I don't give my date of birth, because I am seeking a female companion and want to be judged by more important things than my age. My two childhood homes and my garden, on farms, were taken by gangs of bankers who probably wouldn't work the land if their children were starving. Anyone working in a profession which involves taking homes away from children could not have much in the way of brains or morals. I lived in towns all over California where my mother worked as a waitress.

I was motivated to do my first serious thinking about the desirability of economic and political improvement at age twelve, from reading the Boy Scout manual with its message of being considerate to others. I was also made aware of the need for social change by reading *Citizen Tom Paine* by Howard Fast, and the poems and essays of Percy Shelley. I became aware of the connection between racism and capitalism through high–school friendships with Mexican American and Chinese American boys who lived in the slums. I won first place in the Lions Club speaking contest with a speech on world peace; the high–school poetry contest with a poem on Thomas Paine; and the high–school essay contest with an essay on the home.

At age sixteen I read the poems of Walt Whitman and began writing poetry. I decided to spend my life as a wandering poet, but I discovered that it is too cold in the U.S. much of the year to be able to sleep outdoors.

After high-school I worked for a while with Mexican immigrants thinning sugar beets near Stockton with a short-handled hoe. It was hard low-paid work, and made me sharply aware of the falsity of the myth that Mexicans are lazy. They were the warmest, friendliest and highest-spirited people I have ever known, and fueled my interest in things Mexican. Later I worked as a wage slave at forty or fifty different jobs, trying to get different and new perspectives on the world so hopefully I could write effectively about aspects of life not covered by other writers, thereby increasing human awareness.

I married a Mexican American nurse. We planned to raise an international family to show that different peoples can live together in harmony. Alas, we didn't have sufficient dedication or wherewithal to carry through on this, but other couples have done it with great success. We had a successful marriage for several years, partly because we each made the decisions on alternate days.

In 1966 I was Texas director of the first grape boycott by César Chávez's farmworker union. Later, in south Texas, I founded a union called the Independent Workers Association, which later affiliated with Chávez's United Farm Workers. A long strike and march to Austin resulted in improved pay and conditions for workers in south Texas. I was arrested on various phony or exaggerated charges, including inciting a riot and threatening the lives of Texas Rangers.

The best argument I can think of for unionism is Sweden, which has consistently had one of the highest standards of living in the world, with over 90% of its workforce unionized. (However, what we really need is a standard of *happiness*, since economic indicators alone do not tell the whole story; often people with fewer material goods live happier lives.) The best argument for syndicalism (a workers' government) or anarcho-syndicalism is the Spanish revolution in 1936 when workers took over the farms and factories in Catalonia and ran them more efficiently than the former capitalist owners.

I received my Ph.D. in Reality Studies in 1984 while sitting in a new Mercedes convertible outside a grocery store near Guerneville, California. Two women—in separate incidents—came out of the store and made overtures toward me. (Unfortunately a probably even higher percentage of men are also shameless suckers for wealth and opulence.) Since then I have been more devoted to the ideal of a classless society in which people are freed from the tyranny of money and choose friends and lovers for far more important reasons.

I think the chief priorities today are: preventing nuclear explosions; feeding the starving; lessening pollution and the exhaustion of the earth's resources; achieving a much lower birth rate; homes for all; industrial democracy; and cooperative and participatory democracy (with compassion) in all aspects of life. We are in a terrible crisis. If things are not turned around soon, I predict a rapid growth in organized religion in which millions of people will begin worship services in banks, many of which are already taller than cathedrals.

I have written fourteen books. I have two daughters, Tamar and Shelley.

Currently I am the coordinator of Homes for All, an organization whose aim is ending the landlord system and seeing that all the people of the world own a home or the land on which to build one.